D1248585

EVERYMAN'S LIBRARY

278

ESSAYS
&
BELLES-LETTRES

Everyman, I will go with thee, and be thy guide,
In thy most need to go by thy side

THOMAS CARLYLE, born 4th December 1795 at Ecclefechan in Dumfries-shire, the son of a stonemason. Educated there, at Annan Academy, and at Edinburgh University. Schoolmaster for a short time (1814–18), but decided on a literary career, visiting Paris and London. Married Jane Baillie Welsh, 17th October 1826. Settled in Edinburgh, and finally at No. 5 Cheyne Row, Chelsea, where he died on 4th February 1881.

THOMAS CARLYLE

SARTOR RESARTUS

—

ON HEROES
AND HERO WORSHIP

INTRODUCTION BY
W. H. HUDSON

LONDON J. M. DENT & SONS LTD
NEW YORK E. P. DUTTON & CO INC

INTRODUCTION

ONE of the most vital and pregnant books in our modern
literature, " Sartor Resartus " is also, in structure and
form, one of the most daringly original. It defies exact
classification. It is not a philosophic treatise. It is not
an autobiography. It is not a romance. Yet in a sense
it is all these combined. Its underlying purpose is to
expound in broad outline certain ideas which lay at the
root of Carlyle's whole reading of life. But he does not
elect to set these forth in regular methodic fashion, after
the manner of one writing a systematic essay. He presents
his philosophy in dramatic form and in a picturesque human
setting. He invents a certain Herr Diogenes Teufelsdröckh,
an erudite German professor of " Allerley-Wissenschaft,'' or
Things in General, in the University of Weissnichtwo, of
whose colossal work, " Die Kleider, Ihr Werden und
Wirken " (On Clothes : Their Origin and Influence), he
represents himself as being only the student and interpreter. With infinite humour he explains how this prodigious volume came into his hands; how he was struck
with amazement by its encyclopædic learning, and the depth
and suggestiveness of its thought; and how he determined
that it was his special mission to introduce its ideas to the
British public. But how was this to be done? As a mere
bald abstract of the original would never do, the would-be
apostle was for a time in despair. But at length the happy
thought occurred to him of combining a condensed statement of the main principles of the new philosophy with some
account of the philosopher's life and character. Thus the
work took the form of a " Life and Opinions of Herr
Teufelsdröckh," and as such it was offered to the world.
Here, of course, we reach the explanation of its fantastic
title—" Sartor Resartus," or the Tailor Patched : the tailor
being the great German " Clothes-philosopher," and the
patching being done by Carlyle as his English editor.

As a piece of literary mystification, Teufelsdröckh and

his treatise enjoyed a measure of the success which nearly twenty years before had been scored by Dietrich Knickerbocker and his " History of New York." The question of the professor's existence was solemnly discussed in at least one important review; Carlyle was gravely taken to task for attempting to mislead the public; a certain interested reader actually wrote to inquire where the original German work was to be obtained. All this seems to us surprising; the more so as we are now able to understand the purposes which Carlyle had in view in devising his dramatic scheme. In the first place, by associating the clothes-philosophy with the personality of its alleged author (himself one of Carlyle's splendidly living pieces of characterisation), and by presenting it as the product and expression of his spiritual experiences, he made the mystical creed intensely human. Stated in the abstract, it would have been a mere blank -*ism*; developed in its intimate relations with Teufelsdröckh's character and career, it is filled with the hot life-blood of natural thought and feeling. Secondly, by fathering his own philosophy upon a German professor Carlyle indicates his own indebtedness to German idealism, the ultimate source of much of his own teaching. Yet, deep as that indebtedness was, and anxious as he might be to acknowledge it, he was as a humourist keenly alive to certain glaring defects of the great German writers; to their frequent tendency to lose themselves among the mere minutiæ of erudition, and thus to confuse the unimportant and the important; to their habit of rising at times into the clouds rather than above the clouds, and of there disporting themselves in regions " close-bordering on the impalpable inane;" to their too conspicuous want of order, system, perspective. The dramatic machinery of " Sartor Resartus " is therefore turned to a third service. It is made the vehicle of much good-humoured satire upon these and similar characteristics of Teutonic scholarship and speculation; as in the many amusing criticisms which are passed upon Teufelsdröckh's volume as a sort of " mad banquet wherein all courses have been confounded;" in the burlesque parade of the professor's " omniverous reading " (*e. g.*, Book I, Chap. V); and in the whole amazing episode of the " six considerable paper bags," out of the chaotic contents of which the distracted editor in search of " biographic documents " has to make what he can. Nor is this quite all. Teufelsdröckh is further utilised as the mouthpiece of some of Carlyle's more extravagant speculations and of such ideas as he wished to throw out as it were tentatively, and without himself being necessarily held responsible for them. There is thus much point as well as humour in those sudden turns of the argument, when, after some exceptionally wild outburst on his *eidolon's* part, Carlyle sedately reproves him for the fantastic character or dangerous tendency of his opinions.

It is in connection with the dramatic scheme of the book that the third element, that of autobiography, enters into its texture, for the story of Teufelsdröckh is very largely a transfigured version of the story of Carlyle himself. In saying this, I am not of course thinking mainly of Carlyle's outer life. This, indeed, is in places freely drawn upon, as the outer lives of Dickens, George Eliot, Tolstoi are drawn upon in " David Copperfield," " The Mill on the Floss," " Anna Karénina." Entepfuhl is only another name for Ecclefechan; the picture of little Diogenes eating his supper out-of-doors on fine summer evenings, and meanwhile watching the sun sink behind the western hills, is clearly a loving transcript from memory; even the idyllic episode of Blumine may be safely traced back to a romance of Carlyle's youth. But to investigate the connection at these and other points between the mere externals of the two careers is a matter of little more than curious interest. It is because it incorporates and reproduces so much of Carlyle's inner history that the story of Teufelsdröckh is really important. Spiritually considered, the whole narrative is, in fact, a " symbolic myth," in which the writer's personal trials and conflicts are depicted with little change save in setting and accessories. Like Teufelsdröckh, Carlyle while still a young man had broken away from the old religious creed in which he had been bred; like Teufelsdröckh, he had thereupon passed into the " howling desert of infidelity;" like Teufelsdröckh, he had known all the agonies and anguish of a long period of blank scepticism and insurgent despair, during which, turn whither he would, life responded with nothing but negations to every question and appeal. And as to Teufelsdröckh in the Rue Saint-Thomas de l'Enfer in Paris, so to Carlyle in Leith

Walk, Edinburgh, there had come a moment of sudden and marvellous illumination, a mystical crisis from which he had emerged a different man. The paralellism is so obvious and so close as to leave no room for doubt that the story of Teufelsdröckh is substantially a piece of spiritual auto-biography.

This admitted, the question arises whether Carlyle had any purpose, beyond that of self-expression, in thus utilising his own experiences for the human setting of his philosophy. It seems evident that he had. As he conceived them, these experiences possessed far more than a merely personal interest and meaning. He wrote of himself because he saw in himself a type of his restless and much-troubled epoch; because he knew that in a broad sense his history was the history of thousands of other young men in the generation to which he belonged. The age which followed upon the vast upheaval of the Revolution was one of widespread turmoil and perplexity. Men felt themselves to be wandering aimlessly " between two worlds, one dead, the other powerless to be born." The old order had collapsed in shapeless ruin; but the promised Utopia had not been realised to take its place. In many directions the forces of reaction were at work. Religion, striving to maintain itself upon the dogmatic creeds of the past, was rapidly petrifying into a mere " dead Letter of Religion," from which all the living spirit had fled; and those who could not nourish themselves on hearsay and inherited formula knew not where to look for the renewal of faith and hope. The generous ardour and the splendid humanitarian enthusiasms which had been stirred by the opening phases of the revolutionary movement, had now ebbed away; revulsion had followed, and with it the mood of disillusion and despair. The spirit of doubt and denial was felt as a paralysing power in every department of life and thought, and the shadow of unbelief lay heavy on many hearts.

It was for the men of this " sad time " that Carlyle wrote Teufelsdröckh's story; and he wrote it not merely to depict the far-reaching consequences of their pessimism but also to make plain to them their true path out of it. He desired to exhibit to his age the real nature of the strange malady from which it was suffering in order that he might thereupon proclaim the remedy.

What, then, is the moral significance of Carlyle's "symbolic myth"? What are the supreme lessons which he uses it to convey?

We must begin by understanding his diagnosis. For him, all the evils of the time could ultimately be traced back to their common source in what may be briefly described as its want of real religion. Of churches and creeds there were plenty; of living faith little or nothing was left. Men had lost all vital sense of God in the world; and because of this, they had taken up a fatally wrong attitude to life. They looked at it wholly from the mechanical point of view, and judged it by merely utilitarian standards. The " body-politic " was no longer inspired by any " soul-politic." Men, individually and in the mass, cared only for material prosperity, sought only outward success, made the pursuit of happiness the end and aim of their being. The divine meaning of virtue, the infinite nature of duty, had been forgotten, and morality had been turned into a sort of ledger-philosophy, based upon calculations of profit and loss.

It was thus that Carlyle read the signs of the times. In such circumstances what was needed? Nothing less than a spiritual rebirth. Men must abandon their wrong attitude to life, and take up the right attitude. Everything hinged on that. And that they might take up this right attitude it was necesary first that they should be convinced of life's essential spirituality, and cease in consequence to seek its meaning and test its value on the plane of merely material things.

Carlyle thus throws passionate emphasis upon religion as the only saving power. But it must be noted that he does not suggest a return to any of the dogmatic creeds of the past. Though once the expression of a living faith, these were now for him mere lifeless formulas. Nor has he any new dogmatic creed to offer in their place. That mystical crisis which had broken the spell of the Everlasting No was in a strict sense—he uses the word himself—a conversion. But it was not a conversion in the theological sense, for it did not involve the acceptance of any specific articles of faith. It was simply a complete change of front; the protest of his whole nature, in a suddenly aroused mood of indignation and defiance, against the " spirit which denies;" the assertion of his manhood against the cowardice which had so long kept him trembling and whimpering before the facts of existence. But from that change of front came presently the vivid apprehension of certain great truths which his former mood had thus far concealed from him; and in these truths he found the secret of that right attitude to life in the discovery of which lay men's only hope of salvation from the unrest and melancholy of their time.

From this point of view the burden of Carlyle's message to his generation will be readily understood. Men were going wrong because they started with the thought of self, and made satisfaction of self the law of their lives; because, in consequence, they regarded happiness as the chief object of pursuit and the one thing worth striving for; because, under the influence of the current rationalism, they tried to escape from their spiritual perplexities through logic and speculation. They had, therefore, to set themselves right upon all these matters. They had to learn that not self-satisfaction but self-renunciation is the key to life and its true law; that we have no prescriptive claim to happiness and no business to quarrel with the universe if it withholds it from us; that the way out of pessimism lies, not through reason, but through honest work, steady adherence to the simple duty which each day brings, fidelity to the right as we know it. Such, in broad statement, is the substance of Carlyle's religious convictions and moral teaching. Like Kant he takes his stand on the principles of ethical idealism. God is to be sought, not through speculation, or syllogism, or the learning of the schools, but through the moral nature. It is the soul in action that alone finds God. And the finding of God means, not happiness as the world conceives it, but blessedness, or the inward peace which passes understanding.

The connection between the transfigured autobiography which serves to introduce the directly didactic element of the book and that element itself, will now be clear. Stripped of its whimsicalities of phraseology and its humorous extravagances, Carlyle's philosophy stands revealed as essentially idealistic in character. Spirit is the only reality. Visible things are but the manifestations, emblems, or clothings of spirit. The material universe itself is only the vesture or symbol of God; man is a spirit, though he wears the

wrappings of the flesh; and in everything that man creates
for himself he merely attempts to give body or expression to
thought. The science of Carlyle's time was busy proclaiming that, since the universe is governed by natural laws,
miracles are impossible and the supernatural is a myth.
Carlyle replies that the natural laws are themselves only the
manifestation of Spiritual Force, and that thus miracle is
everywhere and all nature supernatural. We, who are the
creatures of time and space, can indeed apprehend the
Absolute only when He weaves about Him the visible
garments of time and space. Thus God reveals Himself to
sense through symbols. But it is as we regard these symbols
in one or other of two possible ways that we class ourselves
with the foolish man or with the wise. The foolish man
sees only the symbol, thinks it exists for itself, takes it for
the ultimate fact, and therefore rests in it. The wise man
sees the symbol, knows that it is only a symbol, and pene-
trates into it for the ultimate fact or spiritual reality which
it symbolises.

Remote as such a doctrine may at first sight seem to be
from the questions with which men are commonly concerned,
it has none the less many important practical bearings.
Since " all Forms whereby Spirit manifests itself to sense,
whether outwardly or in the imagination, are Clothes,"
civilisation and everything belonging to it—our languages,
literatures and arts, our governments, social machinery and
institutions, our philosophies, creeds and rituals—are but so
many vestments woven for itself by the shaping spirit of
man. Indispensable these vestments are; for without them
society would collapse in anarchy, and humanity sink to the
level of the brute. Yet here again we must emphasise the
difference, already noted, between the foolish man and the
wise. The foolish man once more assumes that the vestments exist for themselves, as ultimate facts, and that they
have a value of their own. He, therefore, confuses the life
with its clothing; is even willing to sacrifice the life for the
sake of the clothing. The wise man, while he, too, recognises the necessity of the vestments, and indeed insists upon
it, knows that they have no independent importance, that
they derive all their potency and value from the inner reality
which they were fashioned to represent and embody, but
which they often misrepresent and obscure. He therefore

never confuses the life with the clothing, and well understands how often the clothing has to be sacrificed for the sake of the life. Thus, while the utility of clothes has to be recognised to the full, it is still of the essence of wisdom to press hard upon the vital distinction between the outer wrappings of man's life and that inner reality which they more or less adequately enfold.

The use which Carlyle makes of this doctrine in his interpretation of the religious history of the world and of the crisis in thought of his own day, will be anticipated. All dogmas, forms and ceremonials, he teaches, are but religious vestments—symbols expressing man's deepest sense of the divine mystery of the universe and the hunger and thirst of his soul for God. It is in response to the imperative necessities of his nature that he moulds for himself these outward emblems of his ideas and aspirations. Yet they are only emblems; and since, like all other human things, they partake of the ignorance and weakness of the times in which they were framed, it is inevitable that with the growth of knowledge and the expansion of thought they must presently be outgrown. When this happens, there follows what Carlyle calls the " superannuation of symbols." Men wake to the fact that the creeds and formulas which have come down to them from the past are no longer living for them, no longer what they need for the embodiment of their spiritual life. Two mistakes are now possible, and these are, indeed, commonly made together. On the one hand, men may try to ignore the growth of knowledge and the expansion of thought, and to cling to the outgrown symbols as things having in themselves some mysterious sanctity and power. On the other hand, they may recklessly endeavour to cast aside the reality symbolised along with the discredited symbol itself. Given such a condition of things, and we shall find religion degenerating into formalism and the worship of the dead letter, and, side by side with this, the impatient rejection of all religion, and the spread of a crude and debasing materialism. Religious symbols, then, must be renewed. But their renewal can come only from within. Form, to have any real value, must grow out of life and be fed by it.

The revolutionary quality in the philosophy of " Sartor Resartus " cannot, of course, be overlooked. Everything

that man has woven for himself must in time become merely
" old clothes "; the work of his thought, like that of his
hands, is perishable; his very highest symbols have no
permanence or finality. Carlyle cuts down to the essential
reality beneath all shows and forms and emblems : witness
his amazing vision of a naked House of Lords. Under his
penetrating gaze the " earthly hulls and garnitures " of
existence melt away. Men's habit is to rest in symbols.
But to rest in symbols is fatal, since they are at best but
the " adventitious wrappages " of life. Clothes " have
made men of us "—true; but now, so great has their influence become that " they are threatening to make clothes-
screens of us." Hence " the beginning of all wisdom is
to look fixedly on clothes . . . till they become transparent."
The logical tendency of such teaching may seem to be
towards utter nihilism. But that tendency is checked and
qualified by the strong conservative element which is everywhere prominent in Carlyle's thought. Upon the absolute
need of " clothes " the stress is again and again thrown.
They " have made men of us." By symbols alone man
lives and works. By symbols alone can he make life and
work effective. Thus even the world's " old clothes "—its
discarded forms and creeds—should be treated with the
reverence due to whatever has once played a part in human
development. Thus, moreover, we must be on our guard
against the impetuosity of the revolutionary spirit and all
rash rupture with the past. To cast old clothes aside before
new clothes are ready—this does not mean progress, but
sansculottism, or a lapse into nakedness and anarchy.

The lectures " On Heroes and Hero-Worship," here
printed with " Sartor Resartus," contain little more than
an amplication, through a series of brilliant character-
studies, of those fundamental ideas of history which had
already figured among Teufelsdröckh's social speculations.
Simple in statement and clear in doctrine, this second work
needs no formal introduction. It may, however, be of
service just to indicate one or two points at which, apart
from its set theses, it expresses or implies certain underlying principles of all Carlyle's thought.

In the first place, his philosophy of history rests entirely
on " the great man theory." " Universal History, the

history of what man has accomplished in the world," is for him "at bottom the History of the Great Men who have worked here." This conception, of course, brings him into sharp conflict with that scientific view of history which was already gaining ground when "Heroes and Hero-Worship" was written, and which since then has become even more popular under the powerful influence of the modern doctrine of evolution. A scientific historian, like Buckle or Taine, seeks to explain all changes in thought, all movements in politics and society, in terms of general laws; his habit is, therefore, to subordinate, if not quite to eliminate, the individual; the greatest man is treated as in a large measure the product and expression of the "spirit of the time." For Carlyle, individuality is everything. While, as he is bound to admit, "no one works save under conditions," external circumstances and influences count little. The Great Man is supreme. He is not the creature of his age, but its creator; not its servant, but its master. "The History of the World is but the Biography of Great Men."

Anti-scientific in his reading of history, Carlyle is also anti-democratic in the practical lessons he deduces from it. He teaches that our right relations with the Hero are discipular relations; that we should honestly acknowledge his superiority, look up to him, reverence him. Thus on the personal side he challenges that tendency to "level down" which he believed to be one alarming result of the fast-spreading spirit of the new democracy. But more than this. He insists that the one hope for our distracted world of to-day lies in the strength and wisdom of the few, not in the organised unwisdom of the many. The masses of the people can never be safely trusted to solve for themselves the intricate problems of their own welfare. They need to be guided, disciplined, at times even driven, by those great leaders of men, who see more deeply than they see into the reality of things, and know much better than they can ever know what is good for them, and how that good is to be attained. Political machinery, in which the modern world had come to put so much faith, is only another delusion of a mechanical age. The burden of history is for him always the need of the Able Man. "I say, Find me the true *Könning*, King, Able Man, and he *has* a divine right over me." Carlyle thus throws down the gauntlet at once to the scientific and to the democratic movements of his time. His pronounced antagonism to the modern spirit in these two most important manifestations must be kept steadily in mind in our study of him.

Finally, we have to remember that in the whole tone and temper of his teaching Carlyle is fundamentally the Puritan. The dogmas of Puritanism he had indeed outgrown; but he never outgrew its ethics. His thought was dominated and pervaded to the end, as Froude rightly says, by the spirit of the creed he had dismissed. By reference to this one fact we may account for much of his strength, and also for most of his limitations in outlook and sympathy. Those limitations the reader will not fail to notice for himself. But whatever allowance has to be made for them, the strength remains. It is, perhaps, the secret of Carlyle's imperishable greatness as a stimulating and uplifting power that, beyond any other modern writer, he makes us feel with him the supreme claims of the moral life, the meaning of our own responsibilities, the essential spirituality of things, the indestructible reality of religion. If he had thus a special message for his own generation, that message has surely not lost any of its value for ours. " Put Carlyle in your pocket," says Dr. Hal to Paul Kelver on his starting out in life. " He is not all the voices, but he is the best maker of men I know." And as a maker of men, Carlyle's appeal to us is as great as ever.

WILLIAM HENRY HUDSON.

SELECT BIBLIOGAPHY

COLLECTED WORKS. The most complete edition is that of H. D. Traill, 30 vols., 1896-9.

SEPARATE WORKS. *Elements of Geometry and Trigonometry* (from the French of A. M. Legendre), 1824; *Wilhelm Meister's Apprenticeship*, 3 vols., 1824; *The Life of Schiller* (*London Magazine*, 1823-4), 1825, 1845; *German Romance*, 4 vols., 1827; *Sartor Resartus* (*Fraser's Magazine*, 1833-4), 1836; latest English ed., P. C. Parr, 1913; *The French Revolution*, 3 vols., 1837; latest English ed., J. H. Rose, 3 vols., 1902; *Lectures on the History of Literature*, 1838; ed. F. R. Greene, 1892; *Critical and Miscellaneous Essays*, 4 vols., 1838; *Chartism*, 1840; *On Heroes, Hero-Worship, and the Heroic in History*, 1841; latest ed., H. M. Buller, 2 vols., 1926; Preface to R. W. Emerson's *Essays*, 1841, 1844, 1853; *Past and Present*, 1843; ed. A. M. D. Hughes, 1921; *Oliver Cromwell's Letters and Speeches*, 2 vols., 1845; *Latter-Day Pamphlets*, 1850;

Life of John Sterling, 1851, 1852; ed. W. H. White, 1907; *The History of Friedrich II of Prussia*, 6 vols., 1858–65; *On the Choice of Books*, 1866, 1869; *The Early Kings of Norway : also an Essay on the Portraits of John Knox* (*Fraser's Magazine*, 1875), 1875; *Reminiscences*, ed. J. A. Froude, 2 vols., 1881; ed. C. E. Norton, 2 vols., 1887; *Reminiscences of my Irish Journey in 1849*, 1882; *Last Words of Thomas Carlyle on Trades-Unions, Promoterism, and the Signs of the Times*, ed. J. C. Aitken, 1882; *Letters and Memorials of Jane Welsh Carlyle*, ed. J. A. Froude, 3 vols., 1883; *Last Words of Thomas Carlyle. Wotton Reinfred : A Romance. Excursion . . . to Paris. Letters*, 1892; *New Letters and Memorials of Jane Welsh Carlyle*, ed. A. Carlyle and Sir J. Crichton-Browne, 2 vols., 1903; *Historical Sketches of Notable Persons and Events in the Reigns of James I and Charles I*, ed. A. Carlyle, 1898 (written 1842–3); *Two Note-books of Thomas Carlyle*, ed. C. E. Norton, 1898; *Journey to Germany, 1858*, ed. R. A. E. Brooks, 1940.

LETTERS. *Letters to Mrs. B. Montagu and B. W. Procter*, 1881; *Correspondence of Carlyle and Emerson*, ed. C. E. Norton, 2 vols., 1883; *Early Letters of Carlyle*, ed. C. E. Norton, 2 vols., 1886; *Correspondence between Goethe and Carlyle*, ed. C. E. Norton, 1887; *Letters of Thomas Carlyle, 1826–36*, ed. C. E. Norton, 2 vols., 1888; *Letters of Carlyle to his Youngest Sister*, 1899; *New Letters of Thomas Carlyle*, ed. A. Carlyle, 2 vols., 1904; *Love Letters of Carlyle and Jane Welsh*, ed. A. Carlyle, 2 vols., 1909; *Letters of Thomas Carlyle to John Stuart Mill, John Sterling, and Robert Browning*, ed. A. Carlyle, 1923; *New Letters of Carlyle to Eckermann*, ed. W. A. Speck (*Yale Review*, xv), 1926; *Letters to W. Graham*, ed. J. Graham, 1950; *Letters to his Wife*, ed. Bliss, 1953.

PERIODICALS TO WHICH CARLYLE CONTRIBUTED. Brewster's *Edinburgh Encyclopaedia*, vols. xiv, xv, xvi; *Edinburgh Review*, 1827–32; *New Edinburgh Review*, 1821, 1822; *Fraser's Magazine*, 1830–5, 1837, 1839, 1844, 1847, 1849, 1875; *Westminster Review*, 1831, 1837, 1838, 1842, 1855; *Foreign Review*, 1828, 1829; *Foreign Quarterly Review*, 1831–3, 1843; *New Monthly Magazine*, 1832; *Nation* (Dublin), 1849; *Examiner*, 1839, 1848; *Spectator*, 1848; *Leigh Hunt's Journal*, 1850, 1851; *Keepsake*, 1852; *Proceedings of the Society of Antiquaries of Scotland*, 1855; *Macmillan's Magazine*, 1863, 1867; *The Times*, 19th June 1844; 28th November 1876; 5th May 1877.

BIOGRAPHY AND CRITICISM (Select List). W. S. Johnson: *Thomas Carlyle : a Study of his Literary Apprenticeship, 1814–31*, 1911; D. A. Wilson and D. W. MacArthur: *Life of Thomas Carlyle*, 6 vols., 1923–34; M. A. Hamilton: *Thomas Carlyle*, 1926; N. Young: *Carlyle, his Rise and Fall*, 1927; L. Cazamian: *Carlyle* (translation), 1932; H. J. Grierson: *Thomas Carlyle*, 1941; J. Symons: *Thomas Carlyle*, 1952.

CONTENTS

SARTOR RESARTUS

Contents

ON HEROES, HERO-WORSHIP, AND THE HEROIC IN HISTORY

LECTURE I

LECTURE II

LECTURE III

LECTURE IV

LECTURE V

LECTURE VI

SARTOR RESARTUS

BOOK FIRST

CHAPTER I

PRELIMINARY

CONSIDERING our present advanced state of culture
and how the Torch of Science has now been brandished
and borne about, with more or less effect, for five-thou-
sand years and upwards; how, in these times especially,
not only the Torch still burns, and perhaps more fiercely
than ever, but innumerable Rush-lights, and Sulphur-
matches, kindled thereat, are also glancing in every
direction, so that not the smallest cranny or doghole in
Nature or Art can remain unilluminated,—it might strike
the reflective mind with some surprise that hitherto
little or nothing of a fundamental character, whether
in the way of Philosophy or History, has been written
on the subject of Clothes.

Our Theory of Gravitation is as good as perfect:
Lagrange, it is well known, has proved that the Planet-
ary System, on this scheme, will endure forever; Laplace, still more cunningly, even guesses that it could
not have been made on any other scheme. Whereby,
at least, our nautical Logbooks can be better kept; and
water-transport of all kinds has grown more commodious. Of Geology and Geognosy we know enough:
what with the labours of our Werners and Huttons,
what with the ardent genius of their disciples, it has
come about that now, to many a Royal Society, the
Creation of a World is little more mysterious than the
cooking of a dumpling; concerning which last, indeed,
there have been minds to whom the question, *How the
apples were got in,* presented difficulties. Why mention
our disquisitions on the Social Contract, on the Standard

of Taste, on the Migrations of the Herring? Then, have we not a Doctrine of Rent, a Theory of Value; Philosophies of Language, of History, of Pottery, of Apparitions, of Intoxicating Liquors? Man's whole life and environment have been laid open and elucidated; scarcely a fragment or fibre of his Soul, Body, and Possessions, but has been probed, dissected, distilled, desiccated, and scientifically decomposed: our spiritual Faculties, of which it appears there are not a few, have their Stewarts, Cousins, Royer Collards: every cellular, vascular, muscular Tissue glories in its Lawrences, Majendies, Bichâts.

How, then, comes it, may the reflective mind repeat, that the grand Tissue of all Tissues, the only real Tissue, should have been quite overlooked by Science, —the vestural Tissue, namely, of woollen or other cloth; which Man's Soul wears as its outmost wrappage and overall; wherein his whole other Tissues are included and screened, his whole Faculties work, his whole Self lives, moves, and has its being? For if, now and then, some straggling, broken-winged thinker has cast an owl's-glance into this obscure region, the most have soared over it altogether heedless; regarding Clothes as a property, not an accident, as quite natural and spontaneous, like the leaves of trees, like the plumage of birds. In all speculations they have tacitly figured man as a *Clothed Animal;* whereas he is by nature a *Naked Animal;* and only in certain circumstances, by purpose and device, masks himself in Clothes. Shakespeare says, we are creatures that look before and after: the more surprising that we do not look round a little, and see what is passing under our very eyes.

But here, as in so many other cases, Germany, learned, indefatigable, deep-thinking Germany comes to our aid. It is, after all, a blessing that, in these revolutionary times, there should be one country where abstract Thought can still take shelter; that while the din and frenzy of Catholic Emancipations, and Rotten Boroughs, and Revolts of Paris, deafen every French and every English ear, the German can stand peaceful on his scientific watch-tower; and, to the raging, struggling multitude here and elsewhere, solemnly, from hour to hour, with preparatory blast of cowhorn, emit his *Höret ihr Herren und lasset's Euch sagen;* in other words, tell the Universe, which so often forgets that fact, what o'clock it really is. Not unfrequently the Germans have been blamed for an unprofitable diligence; as if they struck into devious courses, where nothing was to be had but the toil of a rough journey; as if, forsaking the gold-mines of finance and that political slaughter of fat oxen whereby a man himself grows fat, they were apt to run goose-hunting into regions of bilberries and crowberries, and be swallowed up at last in remote peat-bogs. Of that unwise science, which, as our Humorist expresses it,—

'By geometric scale
Doth take the size of pots of ale ;

still more, of that altogether misdirected industry, which is seen vigorously thrashing mere straw, there can nothing defensive be said. In so far as the Germans are chargeable with such, let them take the consequence. Nevertheless, be it remarked, that even a Russian steppe has tumuli and gold ornaments; also many a scene that looks desert and rock-bound from the distance, will unfold itself, when visited, into rare valleys. Nay, in any case, would Criticism erect not only finger-posts and turnpikes, but spiked gates and impassable barriers, for the mind of man? It is written, ' Many shall run to and fro, and knowledge shall be increased.' Surely the plain rule is, Let each considerate person have his way, and see what it will lead to. For not this man and that man, but all men make up mankind, and their united tasks the task of mankind. How often have we seen some such adventurous, and perhaps much-censured wanderer light on some out-lying, neglected, yet vitally-momentous province; the hidden treasures of which he first discovered, and kept proclaiming till the general eye and effort were directed thither, and the conquest was completed;—thereby, in these his seemingly so aim-less rambles, planting new standards, founding new habitable colonies, in the immeasurable circumambient realm of Nothingness and Night ! Wise man was he who counselled that Speculation should have free course, and look fearlessly towards all the thirty-two points of the compass, whithersoever and howsoever it listed.

Perhaps it is proof of the stunted condition in which pure Science, especially pure moral Science, languishes among us English; and how our mercantile greatness, and invaluable Constitution, impressing a political or other immediately practical tendency on all English culture and endeavour, cramps the free flight of Thought, —that this, not Philosophy of Clothes, but recognition even that we have no such Philosophy, stands here for the first time published in our language. What English intellect could have chosen such a topic, or by chance stumbled on it? But for that same unshackled, and even sequestered condition of the German Learned, which permits and induces them to fish in all manner of waters, with all manner of nets, it seems probable enough, this abstruse Inquiry might, in spite of the results it leads to, have continued dormant for indefinite periods. The Editor of these sheets, though otherwise boasting himself a man of confirmed speculative habits, and perhaps discursive enough, is free to confess, that never, till these last months, did the above very plain considerations, on our total want of a Philosophy of Clothes, occur to him; and then, by quite foreign suggestion. By the arrival, namely, of a new Book from Professor Teufelsdröckh of Weissnichtwo; treating expressly of this subject, and in a style which, whether understood or not, could not even by the blindest be overlooked. In the present Editor's way of thought, this remarkable Treatise, with its Doctrines, whether as judicially acceded to, or judicially denied, has not remained without effect.

' *Die Kleider, ihr Werden und Wirken* (Clothes, their Origin and Influence): *von Diog. Teufelsdröckh, J.U.D. etc. Stillschweigen und Co^{gnie}. Weissnichtwo,* 1831.

' Here,' says the *Weissnichtwo'sche Anzeiger,* ' comes a Volume of that extensive, close-printed, close-meditated sort, which, be it spoken with pride, is seen only in Germany, perhaps only in Weissnichtwo. Issuing from the hitherto irreproachable Firm of Stillschweigen and Company, with every external furtherance, it is of such internal quality as to set Neglect at defiance.' * * * * 'A work,' concludes the wellnigh enthusiastic Reviewer, 'interesting alike to the antiquary, the historian, and the philosophic thinker; a masterpiece of boldness, lynx-eyed acuteness, and rugged independent Germanism and Philanthropy (*derber Kerndeutschheit und Menschenliebe*); which will not, assuredly, pass current without opposition in high places; but must and will exalt the almost new name of Teufelsdröckh to the first ranks of Philosophy, in our German Temple of Honour.'

Mindful of old friendship, the distinguished Professor, in this the first blaze of his fame, which however does not dazzle him, sends hither a Presentation-copy of his Book; with compliments and encomiums which modesty forbids the present Editor to rehearse; yet without indicated wish or hope of any kind, except what may be implied in the concluding phrase: *Möchte es* (this remarkable Treatise) *auch im Brittischen Boden gedeihen!*

CHAPTER II

EDITORIAL DIFFICULTIES

IF for a speculative man, 'whose seedfield,' in the sublime words of the Poet, 'is Time,' no conquest is important but that of new ideas, then might the arrival of Professor Teufelsdröckh's Book be marked with chalk in the Editor's calendar. It is indeed an 'extensive Volume,' of boundless, almost formless contents, a very Sea of Thought; neither calm nor clear, if you will; yet wherein the toughest pearl-diver may dive to his utmost depth, and return not only with sea-wreck but with true orients.

Directly on the first perusal, almost on the first deliberate inspection, it became apparent that here a quite new Branch of Philosophy, leading to as yet undescried ulterior results, was disclosed; farther, what seemed scarcely less interesting, a quite new human Individuality, an almost unexampled personal character, that, namely, of Professor Teufelsdröckh the Discloser. Of both which novelties, as far as might be possible, we resolved to master the significance. But as man is emphatically a proselytising creature, no sooner was such mastery even fairly attempted, than the new question arose : How might this acquired good be imparted to others, perhaps in equal need thereof : how could the Philosophy of Clothes, and the Author of such Philosophy, be brought home, in any measure, to the business and bosoms of our own English Nation? For if new-got gold is said to burn the pockets till it be cast forth into circulation, much more may new truth.

Here, however, difficulties occurred. The first thought naturally was to publish Article after Article on this remarkable Volume, in such widely-circulating Critical Journals as the Editor might stand connected with, or by money or love procure access to. But, on the other hand, was it not clear that such matter as must here be revealed, and treated of, might endanger the circulation of any Journal extant? If, indeed, all party-divisions in the State could have been abolished, Whig, Tory, and Radical, embracing in discrepant union; and all the Journals of the Nation could have been jumbled into one Journal, and the Philosophy of Clothes poured forth in incessant torrents therefrom, the attempt had seemed possible. But, alas, what vehicle of that sort have we, except *Fraser's Magazine?* A vehicle all strewed (figuratively speaking) with the maddest Waterloo-Crackers, exploding distractively and destructively, wheresoever the mystified passenger stands or sits; nay, in any case, understood to be, of late years, a vehicle full to overflowing, and inexorably shut ! Besides, to state the Philosophy of Clothes without the Philosopher, the ideas of Teufelsdröckh without something of his personality, was it not to insure both of entire misapprehension? Now for Biography, had it been otherwise admissible, there were no adequate documents, no hope of obtaining such, but rather, owing to circumstances, a special despair. Thus did the Editor see himself, for the while, shut out from all public utterance of these extraordinary Doctrines, and constrained to revolve them, not without disquietude, in the dark depths of his own mind.

So had it lasted for some months; and now the Volume on Clothes, read and again read, was in several points becoming lucid and lucent; the personality of its Author more and more surprising, but, in spite of all that memory and conjecture could do, more and more enigmatic; whereby the old disquietude seemed fast settling into fixed discontent,—when altogether unexpectedly arrives a Letter from Herr Hofrath Heuschrecke, our Professor's chief friend and associate in Weissnichtwo, with whom we had not previously corresponded. The Hofrath, after much quite extraneous matter, began dilating largely on the ' agitation and attention ' which the Philosophy of Clothes was exciting in its own German Republic of Letters; on the deep significance and tendency of his Friend's Volume; and then, at length, with great circumlocution, hinted at the practicability of conveying ' some knowledge of it, and of him, to England, and through England to the distant West ': a work on Professor Teufelsdröckh ' were undoubtedly welcome to the *Family,* the *National,* or any other of those patriotic *Libraries,* at present the glory of British Literature '; might work revolutions in Thought; and so forth;—in conclusion, intimating not obscurely, that should the present Editor feel disposed to undertake a Biography of Teufelsdröckh, he, Hofrath Heuschrecke, had it in his power to furnish the requisite Documents.

As in some chemical mixture, that has stood long evaporating, but would not crystallise, instantly when the wire or other fixed substance is introduced, crystallisation commences, and rapidly proceeds till the whole is finished, so was it with the Editor's mind and this offer of Heuschrecke's. Form rose out of void solution and discontinuity; like united itself with like in definite arrangement: and soon either in actual vision and possession, or in fixed reasonable hope, the image of the whole Enterprise had shaped itself, so to speak, into a solid mass. Cautiously yet courageously, through the twopenny post, application to the famed redoubtable OLIVER YORKE was now made: an interview, interviews

with that singular man have taken place; with more
of assurance on our side, with less of satire (at least of
open satire) on his, than we anticipated;—for the rest,
with such issue as is now visible. As to those same
' patriotic *Libraries*,' the Hofrath's counsel could only
be viewed with silent amazement; but with his offer
of Documents we joyfully and almost instantaneously
closed. Thus, too, in the sure expectation of these,
we already see our task begun; and this our *Sartor
Resartus*, which is properly a ' Life and Opinions of
Herr Teufelsdröckh,' hourly advancing.

Of our fitness for the Enterprise, to which we have
such title and vocation, it were perhaps uninteresting
to say more. Let the British reader study and enjoy,
in simplicity of heart, what is here presented him, and
with whatever metaphysical acumen and talent for
meditation he is possessed of. Let him strive to keep
a free, open sense; cleared from the mists of prejudice,
above all from the paralysis of cant; and directed rather
to the Book itself than to the Editor of the Book. Who
or what such Editor may be, must remain conjec-
tural, and even insignificant :[1] it is a voice publishing
tidings of the Philosophy of Clothes; undoubtedly
a Spirit addressing Spirits : whoso hath ears, let him
hear.

On one other point the Editor thinks it needful to
give warning : namely, that he is animated with a true
though perhaps a feeble attachment to the Institutions
of our Ancestors; and minded to defend these, according to ability, at all hazards; nay, it was partly with
a view to such defence that he engaged in this under-
taking. To stem, or if that be impossible, profitably to
divert the current of Innovation, such a Volume as
Teufelsdröckh's, if cunningly planted down, were no
despicable pile, or floodgate, in the logical wear.

For the rest, be it nowise apprehended, that any
personal connexion of ours with Teufelsdröckh, Heuschrecke, or this Philosophy of Clothes can pervert our

[1] With us even he still communicates in some sort of mask,
or muffler : and, we have reason to think, under a feigned
name !—O. Y.

judgment, or sway us to extenuate or exaggerate. Powerless, we venture to promise, are those private Compliments themselves. Grateful they may well be; as generous illusions of friendship; as fair mementos of bygone unions, of those nights and suppers of the gods, when, lapped in the symphonies and harmonies of Philosophic Eloquence, though with baser accompaniments, the present Editor revelled in that feast of reason, never since vouchsafed him in so full measure! But what then? *Amicus Plato, magis amica veritas;* Teufelsdröckh is our friend, Truth is our divinity. In our historical and critical capacity, we hope we are strangers to all the world; have feud or favour with no one,—save indeed the Devil, with whom, as with the Prince of Lies and Darkness, we do at all times wage internecine war. This assurance, at an epoch when puffery and quackery have reached a height unexampled in the annals of mankind, and even English Editors, like Chinese Shopkeepers, must write on their door-lintels *No cheating here,*—we thought it good to premise.

CHAPTER III

REMINISCENCES

To the Author's private circle the appearance of this singular Work on Clothes must have occasioned little less surprise than it has to the rest of the world. For ourselves, at least, few things have been more unexpected. Professor Teufelsdröckh, at the period of our acquaintance with him, seemed to lead a quite still and self-contained life : a man devoted to the higher Philosophies, indeed; yet more likely, if he published at all, to publish a refutation of Hegel and Bardili, both of whom, strangely enough, he included under a common ban; than to descend, as he has here done, into the angry noisy Forum, with an Argument that cannot but exasperate and divide. Not, that we can remember, was the Philosophy of Clothes once touched upon be-

tween us. If through the high, silent, meditative
Transcendentalism of our Friend we detected any
practical tendency whatever, it was at most Political,
and towards a certain prospective, and for the present
quite speculative, Radicalism; as indeed some correspondence, on his part, with Herr Oken of Jena was
now and then suspected; though his special contribution
to the *Isis* could never be more than surmised at. But,
at all events, nothing Moral, still less anything Didactico-
Religious, was looked for from him.

Well do we recollect the last words he spoke in our
hearing; which indeed, with the Night they were
uttered in, are to be forever remembered. Lifting his
huge tumbler of *Gukguk*,[1] and for a moment lowering
his tobacco-pipe, he stood up in full Coffee-house (it was
Zur Grünen Gans, the largest in Weissnichtwo, where
all the Virtuosity, and nearly all the Intellect of the
place assembled of an evening); and there, with low,
soul-stirring tone, and the look truly of an angel, though
whether of a white or of a black one might be dubious,
proposed this toast: *Die Sache der Armen in Gottes
und Teufels Namen* (The Cause of the Poor, in Heaven's
name and ——'s)! One full shout, breaking the leaden
silence; then a gurgle of innumerable emptying
bumpers, again followed by universal cheering, returned
him loud acclaim. It was the finale of the night:
resuming their pipes; in the highest enthusiasm, amid
volumes of tobacco-smoke; triumphant, cloud-capt
without and within, the assembly broke up, each to his
thoughtful pillow. *Bleibt doch ein echter Spass- und
Galgen-vogel,* said several; meaning thereby that, one
day, he would probably be hanged for his democratic
sentiments. *Wo steckt doch der Schalk?* added they,
looking round: but Teufelsdröckh had retired by private
alleys, and the Compiler of these pages beheld him no
more.

In such scenes has it been our lot to live with this
Philosopher, such estimate to form of his purposes and
powers. And yet, thou brave Teufelsdröckh, who could
tell what lurked in thee? Under those thick locks of
thine, so long and lank, overlapping roof-wise the

[1] Gukguk is unhappily only an academical—beer.

gravest face we ever in this world saw, there dwelt a most busy brain. In thy eyes too, deep under their shaggy brows, and looking out so still and dreamy, have we not noticed gleams of an ethereal or else a diabolic fire, and half-fancied that their stillness was but the rest of infinite motion, the *sleep* of a spinning-top? Thy little figure, there as, in loose, ill-brushed thread-bare habiliments, thou sattest, amid litter and lumber, whole days, to ' think and smoke tobacco,' held in it a mighty heart. The secrets of man's Life were laid open to thee; thou sawest into the mystery of the Universe, farther than another; thou hadst *in petto* thy remarkable Volume on Clothes. Nay, was there not in that clear logically-founded Transcendentalism of thine; still more, in thy meek, silent, deep-seated Sanscullottism, combined with a true princely Courtesy of inward nature, the visible rudiments of such specula-tion? But great men are too often unknown, or what is worse, misknown. Already, when we dreamed not of it, the warp of thy remarkable Volume lay on the loom; and silently, mysterious shuttles were putting-in the woof !

How the Hofrath Heuschrecke is to furnish biogra-phical data, in this case, may be a curious question; the answer of which, however, is happily not our con-cern, but his. To us it appeared, after repeated trial, that in Weissnichtwo, from the archives or memories of the best-informed classes, no Biography of Teufels-dröckh was to be gathered; not so much as a false one. He was a stranger there, wafted thither by what is called the course of circumstances; concerning whose parent-age, birthplace, prospects, or pursuits, curiosity had indeed made inquiries, but satisfied herself with the most indistinct replies. For himself, he was a man so still and altogether unparticipating, that to question him even afar off on such particulars was a thing of more than usual delicacy : besides, in his sly way, he had ever some quaint turn, not without its satirical edge, wherewith to divert such intrusions, and deter you from the like. Wits spoke of him secretly as if he were a kind of Melchizedek, without father or mother of any kind; sometimes, with reference to his great historic and statistic knowledge, and the vivid way he had of expressing himself like an eye-witness of distant transactions and scenes, they called him the *Ewige Jude*, Everlasting, or as we say, Wandering Jew.

To the most, indeed, he had become not so much a Man as a Thing; which Thing doubtless they were accustomed to see, and with satisfaction; but no more thought of accounting for than for the fabrication of their daily *Allgemeine Zeitung,* or the domestic habits of the Sun. Both were there and welcome; the world enjoyed what good was in them, and thought no more of the matter. The man Teufelsdröckh passed and repassed, in his little circle, as one of those originals and nondescripts, more frequent in German Universities than elsewhere; of whom, though you see them alive, and feel certain enough that they must have a History, no History seems to be discoverable; or only such as men give of mountain rocks and antediluvian ruins : That they may have been created by unknown agencies, are in a state of gradual decay, and for the present reflect light and resist pressure; that is, are visible and tangible objects in this phantasm world, where so much other mystery is.

It was to be remarked that though, by title and diploma, *Professor der Allerley-Wissenschaft,* or as we should say in English, ' Professor of Things in General,' he had never delivered any Course; perhaps never been incited thereto by any public furtherance or requisition. To all appearance, the enlightened Government of Weissnichtwo, in founding their New University, imagined they had done enough, if ' in times like ours,' as the half-official Program expressed it, ' when all things are, rapidly or slowly, resolving themselves into Chaos, a Professorship of this kind had been established; whereby, as occasion called, the task of bodying somewhat forth again from such Chaos might be, even slightly, facilitated.' That actual Lectures should be held, and Public Classes for the ' Science of Things in General,' they doubtless considered premature; on which ground too they had only established the Professorship, nowise endowed it; so that Teufelsdröckh,

' recommended by the highest Names,' had been promoted thereby to a Name merely.

Great, among the more enlightened classes, was the
admiration of this new Professorship : how an enlightened Government had seen into the Want of
the Age (*Zeitbedürfniss*); how at length, instead
of Denial and Destruction, we were to have a science
of Affirmation and Reconstruction ; and Germany and
Weissnichtwo were where they should be, in the
vanguard of the world. Considerable also was the
wonder at the new Professor, dropt opportunely enough
into the nascent University ; so able to lecture,
should occasion call ; so ready to hold his peace for
indefinite periods, should an enlightened Government
consider that occasion did not call. But such admiration and such wonder, being followed by no act to keep
them living, could last only nine days ; and, long before
our visit to that scene, had quite died away. The
more cunning heads thought it was all an expiring
clutch at popularity, on the part of a Minister, whom
domestic embarrassments, court intrigues, old age,
and dropsy soon afterwards finally drove from the
helm.

As for Teufelsdröckh, except by his nightly appearances at the *Grüne Gans,* Weissnichtwo saw little of
him, felt little of him. Here, over his tumbler of Gukguk, he sat reading Journals ; sometimes contempla-
tively looking into the clouds of his tobacco-pipe, without other visible employment : always, from his mild
ways, an agreeable phenomenon there ; more especially
when he opened his lips for speech ; on which occasions
the whole Coffee-house would hush itself into silence,
as if sure to hear something noteworthy. Nay, perhaps to hear a whole series and river of the most
memorable utterances ; such as, when once thawed, he
would for hours indulge in, with fit audience : and the
more memorable, as issuing from a head apparently not
more interested in them, not more conscious of them,
than is the sculptured stone head of some public fountain, which through its brass mouth-tube emits water
to the worthy and the unworthy ; careless whether it
be for cooking victuals or quenching conflagrations ;

indeed, maintains the same earnest assiduous look, whether any water be flowing or not.

To the Editor of these sheets, as to a young enthusiastic Englishman, however unworthy, Teufelsdröckh opened himself perhaps more than to the most. Pity only that we could not then half guess his importance, and scrutinise him with due power of vision! We enjoyed, what not three men in Weissnichtwo could boast of, a certain degree of access to the Professor's private domicile. It was the attic floor of the highest house in the Wahngasse; and might truly be called the pinnacle of Weissnichtwo, for it rose sheer up above the contiguous roofs, themselves rising from elevated ground. Moreover, with its windows it looked towards all the four *Orte,* or as the Scotch say, and we ought to say, *Airts :* the sitting-room itself commanded three; another came to view in the *Schlafgemach* (bedroom) at the opposite end; to say nothing of the kitchen, which offered two, as it were, *duplicates*, and showing nothing new. So that it was in fact the speculum or watch-tower of Teufelsdröckh; wherefrom, sitting at ease, he might see the whole life-circulation of that considerable City; the streets and lanes of which, with all their doing and driving (*Thun und Treiben*), were for the most part visible there.

" I look down into all that wasp-nest or bee-hive," have we heard him say, " and witness their wax-laying and honey-making, and poison-brewing, and choking by sulphur. From the Palace esplanade, where music plays while Serene Highness is pleased to eat his victuals, down to the low lane, where in her door-sill the aged widow, knitting for a thin livelihood, sits to feel the afternoon sun, I see it all; for, except the Schlosskirche weathercock, no biped stands so high. Couriers arrive bestrapped and bebooted, bearing Joy and Sorrow bagged-up in pouches of leather : there, top-laden, and with four swift horses, rolls-in the country Baron and his household; here, on timber-leg, the lamed Soldier hops painfully along, begging alms : a thousand carriages, and wains, and cars, come tumbling-in with Food, with young Rusticity, and other Raw Produce, inanimate or animate, and go tumbling out again with Produce manufactured. That living flood, pouring through these streets, of all qualities and ages, knowest thou whence it is coming, whither it is going? *Aus der Ewigkeit, zu der Ewigkeit hin:* From Eternity, onwards to Eternity! These are Apparitions : what else? Are they not Souls rendered visible : in Bodies, that took shape and will lose it, melting into air? Their solid Pavement is a Picture of the Sense; they walk on the bosom of Nothing, blank Time is behind them and before them. Or fanciest thou, the red and yellow Clothes-screen yonder, with spurs on its heels and feather in its crown, is but of Today, without a Yesterday or a Tomorrow; and had not rather its Ancestor alive when Hengst and Horsa overran thy Island? Friend, thou seest here a living link in that Tissue of History, which inweaves all Being : watch well, or it will be past thee, and seen no more."

"*Ach, mein Lieber!*" said he once, at midnight, when we had returned from the Coffee-house in rather earnest talk, " it is a true sublimity to dwell here. These fringes of lamplight, struggling up through smoke and thousandfold exhalation, some fathoms into the ancient reign of Night, what thinks Boötes of them, as he leads his Hunting-Dogs over the Zenith in their leash of sidereal fire? That stifled hum of Midnight, when Traffic has lain down to rest; and the chariot-wheels of Vanity, still rolling here and there through distant streets, are bearing her to Halls roofed-in, and lighted to the due pitch for her; and only Vice and Misery, to prowl or to moan like nightbirds, are abroad : that hum, I say, like the stertorous, unquiet slumber of sick Life, is heard in Heaven! Oh, under that hideous covelet of vapours, and putrefactions, and unimaginable gases, what a Fermenting-vat lies simmering and hid! The joyful and the sorrowful are there; men are dying there, men are being born; men are praying,—on the other side of a brick partition, men are cursing; and around them all is the vast, void Night. The proud Grandee still lingers in his perfumed saloons, or reposes within damask curtains; Wretchedness cowers into truckle-beds, or shivers hunger-stricken into

its lair of straw: in obscure cellars, *Rouge-et-Noir*
languidly emits its voice-of-destiny to haggard hungry
Villains; while Councillors of State sit plotting, and
playing their high chess-game, whereof the pawns are
Men. The Lover whispers his mistress that the coach
is ready; and she, full of hope and fear, glides down,
to fly with him over the borders: the Thief, still more
silently, sets-to his picklocks and crowbars, or lurks
in wait till the watchmen first snore in their boxes.
Gay mansions, with supper-rooms and dancing-rooms,
are full of light and music and high-swelling hearts;
but, in the Condemned Cells, the pulse of life beats
tremulous and faint, and bloodshot eyes look-out through
the darkness, which is around and within, for the light
of a stern last morning. Six men are to be hanged
on the morrow: comes no hammering from the *Raben-
stein?*—their gallows must even now be o' building.
Upwards of five-hundred-thousand two-legged animals
without feathers lie round us, in horizontal positions;
their heads all in nightcaps, and full of the foolishest
dreams. Riot cries aloud, and staggers and swaggers
in his rank dens of shame; and the Mother, with
streaming hair, kneels over her pallid dying infant,
whose cracked lips only her tears now moisten.—All
these heaped and huddled together, with nothing but
a little carpentry and masonry between them;—crammed
in, like salted fish in their barrel;—or weltering, shall
I say, like an Egyptian pitcher of tamed vipers, each
struggling to get its *head above* the others: *such* work
goes on under that smoke-counterpane!—But I, *mein
Werther,* sit above it all; I am alone with the Stars.''

We looked in his face to see whether, in the utterance of such extraordinary Night-thoughts, no feeling
might be traced there; but with the light we had, which
indeed was only a single tallow-light, and far enough
from the window, nothing save that old calmness and
fixedness was visible.

These were the Professor's talking seasons: most
commonly he spoke in mere monosyllables, or sat altogether silent, and smoked; while the visitor had liberty
either to say what he listed, receiving for answer an
occasional grunt; or to look round for a space, and

then take himself away. It was a strange apartment; full of books and tattered papers, and miscellaneous shreds of all conceivable substances, 'united in a common element of dust.' Books lay on tables, and below tables; here fluttered a sheet of manuscript, there a torn handkerchief, or nightcap hastily thrown aside; ink-bottles alternated with bread-crusts, coffee-pots, tobacco-boxes, Periodical Literature, and Blücher Boots. Old Lieschen (Lisekin, 'Liza), who was his bed-maker and stove-lighter, his washer and wringer, cook, errand-maid, and general lion's-provider, and for the rest a very orderly creature, had no sovereign authority in this last citadel of Teufelsdröckh; only some once in the month she half-forcibly made her may thither, with broom and duster, and (Teufelsdröckh hastily saving his manuscripts) effected a partial clearance, a jail-delivery of such lumber as was not literary. These were her *Erdbeben* (earthquakes), which Teufelsdröckh dreaded worse than the pestilence; nevertheless, to such length he had been forced to comply. Glad would he have been to sit here philosophising forever, or till the litter, by accumulation, drove him out of doors : but Lieschen was his right-arm, and spoon, and necessary of life, and would not be flatly gainsayed. We can still remember the ancient woman; so silent that some thought her dumb; deaf also you would often have supposed her; for Teufelsdröckh, and Teufelsdröckh only, would she serve or give heed to; and with him she seemed to communicate chiefly by signs; if it were not rather by some secret divination that she guessed all his wants, and supplied them. Assiduous old dame ! she scoured, and sorted, and swept, in her kitchen, with the least possible violence to the ear; yet all was tight and right there : hot and black came the coffee ever at the due moment; and the speechless Lieschen herself looked out on you, from under her clean white coif with its lappets, through her clean withered face and wrinkles, with a look of helpful intelligence, almost of benevolence.

Few strangers, as above hinted, had admittance hither : the only one we ever saw there, ourselves excepted, was the Hofrath Heuschrecke, already known, by name and expectation, to the readers of these pages. To us, at that period, Herr Heuschrecke seemed one of those purse-mouthed, crane-necked, clean-brushed, pacific individuals, perhaps sufficiently distinguished in society by this fact, that, in dry weather or in wet, ' they never appear without their umbrella.' Had we not known with what ' little wisdom ' the world is governed; and how, in Germany as elsewhere, the ninety-and-nine Public Men can for most part be but mute train-bearers to the hundredth, perhaps but stalking-horses and willing or unwilling dupes,—it might have seemed wonderful how Herr Heuschrecke should be named a *Rath,* or Councillor, and Counsellor, even in Weissnichtwo. What counsel to any man, or to any woman, could this particular Hofrath give; in whose loose, zigzag figure; in whose thin visage, as it went jerking to and fro, in minute incessant fluctuation,—you traced rather confusion worse confounded; at most, Timidity and physical Cold? Some indeed said withal, he was ' the very Spirit of Love embodied ': blue earnest eyes, full of sadness and kindness; purse ever open, and so forth; the whole of which, we shall now hope, for many reasons, was not quite groundless. Nevertheless friend Teufelsdröckh's outline, who indeed handled the burin like few in these cases, was probably the best: *Er hat Gemüth und Geist, hat wenigstens gehabt, doch ohne Organ, ohne Schicksals-Gunst; ist gegenwärtig aber halb-zerrüttet, halb-erstarrt,* " He has heart and talent, at least has had such, yet without fit mode of utterance, or favour of Fortune; and so is now half-cracked, half-congealed."—What the Hofrath shall think of this when he sees it, readers may wonder : we, safe in the stronghold of Historical Fidelity, are careless.

The main point, doubtless, for us all, is his love of Teufelsdröckh, which indeed was also by far the most decisive feature of Heuschrecke himself. We are enabled to assert that he hung on the Professor with the fondness of a Boswell for his Johnson. And perhaps with the like return; for Teufelsdröckh treated his gaunt admirer with little outward regard, as some half-rational or altogether irrational friend, and at best loved him out of gratitude and by habit. On the other hand, it was

curious to observe with what reverent kindness, and a
sort of fatherly protection, our Hofrath, being the elder,
richer, and as he fondly imagined far more practically
influential of the two, looked and tended on his little
Sage, whom he seemed to consider as a living oracle.
Let but Teufelsdröckh open his mouth, Heuschrecke's
also unpuckered itself into a free doorway, besides his
being all eye and all ear, so that nothing might be lost:
and then, at every pause in the harangue, he gurgled-
out his pursy chuckle of a cough-laugh (for the machinery
of laughter took some time to get in motion, and seemed
crank and slack), or else his twanging nasal, *Bravo!
Das glaub' ich;* in either case, by way of heartiest approval. In short, if Teufelsdröckh was Dalai-Lama, of
which, except perhaps in his self-seclusion, and god-like
indifference, there was no symptom, then might Heuschrecke pass for his chief Talapoin, to whom no dough-
pill he could knead and publish was other than medicinal
and sacred.

In such environment, social, domestic, physical, did
Teufelsdröckh, at the time of our acquaintance, and
most likely does he still, live and meditate. Here,
perched-up in his high Wahngasse watch-tower, and
often, in solitude, outwatching the Bear, it was that the
indomitable Inquirer fought all his battles with Dulness
and Darkness; here, in all probability, that he wrote
this surprising Volume on *Clothes.* Additional particulars: of his age, which was of that standing middle
sort you could only guess at; of his wide surtout; the
colour of his trousers, fashion of his broad-brimmed
steeple-hat, and so forth, we might report, but do not.
The Wisest truly is, in these times, the Greatest; so
that an enlightened curiosity, leaving Kings and suchlike to rest very much on their own basis, turns more
and more to the Philosophic Class: nevertheless, what
reader expects that, with all our writing and reporting,
Teufelsdröckh could be brought home to him, till once
the Documents arrive? His Life, Fortunes, and Bodily
Presence, are as yet hidden from us, or matter only
of faint conjecture. But, on the other hand, does not
his Soul lie enclosed in this remarkable Volume, much
more truly than Pedro Garcia's did in the buried Bag

of Doubloons? To the soul of Diogenes Teufelsdröckh, to his opinions, namely, on the ' Origin and Influence of Clothes,' we for the present gladly return.

CHAPTER IV

CHARACTERISTICS

It were a piece of vain flattery to pretend that this Work on Clothes entirely contents us; that it is not, like all works of genius, like the very Sun, which, though the highest published creation, or work of genius, has nevertheless black spots and troubled nebulosities amid its effulgence,—a mixture of insight, inspiration, with dulness, double-vision, and even utter blindness.

Without committing ourselves to those enthusiastic praises and prophesyings of the *Weissnichtwo'sche Anzeiger*, we admitted that the Book had in a high degree excited us to self-activity, which is the best effect of any book; that it had even operated changes in our way of thought; nay, that it promised to prove, as it were, the opening of a new mine-shaft, wherein the whole world of Speculation might henceforth dig to unknown depths. More especially it may now be declared that Professor Teufelsdröckh's acquirements, patience of research, philosophic and even poetic vigour, are here made indisputably manifest; and unhappily no less his prolixity and tortuosity and manifold ineptitude; that, on the whole, as in opening new mine-shafts is not unreasonable, there is much rubbish in his Book, though likewise specimens of almost invaluable ore. A paramount popularity in England we cannot promise him. Apart from the choice of such a topic as Clothes, too often the manner of treating it betokens in the Author a rusticity and academic seclusion, unblamable, indeed inevitable in a German, but fatal to his success with our public.

Of good society Teufelsdröckh appears to have seen

little, or has mostly forgotten what he saw.   He speaks-
out with a strange plainness ; calls many things by their
mere dictionary names.   To him the Upholsterer is no
Pontiff, neither is any Drawing-room a Temple, were it
never so begilt and overhung : ' a whole immensity
of Brussels carpets, and pier-glasses, and or-molu,' as
he himself expresses it, ' cannot hide from me that such
Drawing-room is simply a section of Infinite Space,
where so many God-created Souls do for the time meet
together.'   To Teufelsdröckh the highest Duchess is
respectable, is venerable ; but nowise for her pearl brace-
lets and Malines laces : in his eyes, the star of a Lord
is little less and little more than the broad button of
Birmingham spelter in a Clown's smock ; ' each is an
implement,' he says, ' in its kind ; a tag for *hooking-
together ;* and, for the rest, was dug from the earth,
and hammered on a stithy before smith's fingers.'
Thus does the Professor look in men's faces with a
strange impartiality, a strange scientific freedom ; like
a man unversed in the higher circles, like a man dropped
thither from the Moon.   Rightly considered, it is in this
peculiarity, running through his whole system of
thought, that all these short-comings, over-shootings,
and multiform perversities, take rise : if indeed they
have not a second source, also natural enough, in his
Transcendental Philosophies, and humour of looking
at all Matter and Material things as Spirit ; whereby
truly his case were but the more hopeless, the more
lamentable.

To the Thinkers of this nation, however, of which
class it is firmly believed there are individuals yet
extant, we can safely recommend the Work : nay, who
knows but among the fashionable ranks too, if it be
true, as Teufelsdröckh maintains, that ' within the
most starched cravat there passes a windpipe and
weasand, and under the thickliest embroidered waistcoat beats a heart,'—the force of that rapt earnestness may be felt, and here and there an arrow of the
soul pierce through? In our wild Seer, shaggy, un-
kempt, like a Baptist living on locusts and wild honey,
there is an untutored energy, a silent, as it were unconscious, strength, which, except in the higher walks of

Literature, must be rare. Many a deep glance, and often with unspeakable precision, has he cast into mysterious Nature, and the still more mysterious Life of Man. Wonderful it is with what cutting words, now and then, he severs asunder the confusion; shears down, were it furlongs deep, into the true centre of the matter; and there not only hits the nail on the head, but with crushing force smites it home, and buries it.—On the other hand, let us be free to admit, he is the most unequal writer breathing. Often after some such feat, he will play truant for long pages, and go dawdling and dreaming, and mumbling and maundering the merest commonplaces, as if he were asleep with eyes open, which indeed he is.

Of his boundless Learning, and how all reading and literature in most known tongues, from *Sanchoniathon* to *Dr Lingard*, from your Oriental *Shasters*, and *Talmuds,* and *Korans,* with Cassini's *Siamese Tables,* and Laplace's *Mécanique Céleste,* down to *Robinson Crusoe* and the *Belfast Town and Country Almanack*, are familiar to him,—we shall say nothing: for unexampled as it is with us, to the Germans such universality of study passes without wonder, as a thing commendable, indeed, but natural, indispensable, and there of course. A man that devotes his life to learning, shall he not be learned?

In respect of style our Author manifests the same genial capability, marred too often by the same rudeness, inequality, and apparent want of intercourse with the higher classes. Occasionally, as above hinted, we find consummate vigour, a true inspiration; his burning thoughts step forth in fit burning words, like so many full-formed Minervas, issuing amid flame and splendour from Jove's head; a rich, idiomatic diction, picturesque allusions, fiery poetic emphasis, or quaint tricksy turns; all the graces and terrors of a wild Imagination, wedded to the clearest Intellect, alternate in beautiful vicissitude. Were it not that sheer sleeping and soporific passages; circumlocutions, repetitions, touches even of pure doting jargon, so often intervene ! On the whole, Professor Teufelsdröckh is not a cultivated writer. Of his sentences perhaps not more than

nine-tenths stand straight on their legs; the remainder
are in quite angular attitudes, buttressed-up by props
(of parentheses and dashes), and ever with this or the
other tagrag hanging from them; a few even sprawl-
out helplessly on all sides, quite broken-backed and
dismembered.   Nevertheless, in almost his very worst
moods, there lies in him a singular attraction.   A wild
tone pervades the whole utterance of the man, like its
keynote and regulator; now screwing itself aloft as
into the Song of Spirits, or else the shrill mockery of
Fiends; now sinking in cadences, not without melodious heartiness, though sometimes abrupt enough, into
the common pitch, when we hear it only as a monoton-
ous hum; of which hum the true character is extremely
difficult to fix.   Up to this hour we have never fully
satisfied ourselves whether it is a tone and hum of real
Humour, which we reckon among the very highest
qualities of genius, or some echo of mere Insanity and
Inanity, which doubtless ranks below the very lowest.

Under a like difficulty, in spite even of our personal
intercourse, do we still lie with regard to the Professor's
moral feeling.   Gleams of an ethereal Love burst forth
from him, soft wailings of infinite pity; he could clasp
the whole Universe into his bosom, and keep it warm;
it seems as if under that rude exterior there dwelt a
very seraph.   Then again he is so sly and still, so
imperturbably saturnine; shows such indifference,
malign coolness towards all that men strive after; and
ever with some half-visible wrinkle of a bitter sardonic
humour, if indeed it be not mere stolid callousness,—
that you look on him almost with a shudder, as on
some incarnate Mephistopheles, to whom this great
terrestrial and celestial Round, after all, were but some
huge foolish Whirligig, where kings and beggars, and
angels and demons, and stars and street-sweepings, were
chaotically whirled, in which only children could take
interest.   His look, as we mentioned, is probably the
gravest ever seen: yet it is not of that cast-iron gravity
frequent enough among our own Chancery suitors;
but rather the gravity as of some silent, high-encircled
mountain-pool, perhaps the crater of an extinct volcano; into whose black deeps you fear to gaze: those

eyes, those lights that sparkle in it, may indeed be reflexes of the heavenly Stars, but perhaps also glances from the region of Nether Fire!

Certainly a most involved, self-secluded, altogether enigmatic nature, this of Teufelsdröckh! Here, however, we gladly recall to mind that once we saw him *laugh;* once only, perhaps it was the first and last time in his life; but then such a peal of laughter, enough to have awakened the Seven Sleepers! It was of Jean Paul's doing: some single billow in that vast World-Mahlstrom of Humour, with its heaven-kissing coruscations, which is now, alas, all congealed in the frost of death! The large-bodied Poet and the small, both large enough in soul, sat talking miscellaneously together, the present Editor being privileged to listen; and now Paul, in his serious way, was giving one of those inimitable ' Extra-harangues '; and, as it chanced, On the Proposal for a *Cast-metal King:* gradually a light kindled in our Professor's eyes and face, a beaming, mantling, loveliest light; through those murky features, a radiant, ever-young Apollo looked; and he burst forth like the neighing of all Tattersall's,—tears streaming down his cheeks, pipe held aloft, foot clutched into the air,—loud, long-continuing, uncontrollable; a laugh not of the face and diaphragm only, but of the whole man from head to heel. The present Editor, who laughed indeed, yet with measure, began to fear all was not right: however, Teufelsdröckh composed himself, and sank into his old stillness; on his inscrutable countenance there was, if anything, a slight look of shame; and Richter himself could not rouse him again. Readers who have any tincture of Psychology know how much is to be inferred from this; and that no man who has once heartily and wholly laughed can be altogether irreclaimably bad. How much lies in Laughter: the cipher-key, wherewith we decipher the whole man! Some men wear an everlasting barren simper; in the smile of others lies a cold glitter as of ice: the fewest are able to laugh, what can be called laughing, but only sniff and titter and snigger from the throat outwards; or at best, produce some whiffling husky cachinnation, as if they were laughing through wool : of none such comes good. The man who cannot laugh is not only fit for treasons, stratagems, and spoils; but his whole life is already a treason and a stratagem.

Considered as an Author, Herr Teufelsdröckh has one scarcely pardonable fault, doubtless his worst : an almost total want of arrangement. In this remarkable Volume, it is true, his adherence to the mere course of Time produces, through the Narrative portions, a certain show of outward method; but of true logical method and sequence there is too little. Apart from its multifarious sections and subdivisions, the Work naturally falls into two Parts; a Historical-Descriptive, and a Philosophical-Speculative : but falls, unhappily, by no firm line of demarcation; in that labyrinthic combination, each Part overlaps, and indents, and indeed runs quite through the other. Many sections are of a debatable rubric, or even quite nondescript and unnameable; whereby the Book not only loses in accessibility, but too often distresses us like some mad banquet, wherein all courses had been confounded, and fish and flesh, soup and solid, oyster-sauce, lettuces, Rhine-wine and French mustard, were hurled into one huge tureen or trough, and the hungry Public invited to help itself. To bring what order we can out of this Chaos shall be part of our endeavour.

CHAPTER V

THE WORLD IN CLOTHES

' As Montesquieu wrote a *Spirit of Laws,*' observes our Professor, ' so could I write a *Spirit of Clothes;* thus, with an *Esprit des Lois,* properly an *Esprit de Coutumes,* we should have an *Esprit de Costumes.* For neither in tailoring nor in legislating does man proceed by mere Accident, but the hand is ever guided on by mysterious operations of the mind. In all his Modes, and habilatory endeavours, an Architectural

Idea will be found lurking; his Body and the Cloth are the site and materials whereon and whereby his beautified edifice, of a Person, is to be built. Whether he flow gracefully out in folded mantles, based on light sandals; tower-up in high headgear, from amid peaks, spangles and bell-girdles; swell-out in starched ruffs, buckram stuffings, and monstrous tuberosities; or girth himself into separate sections, and front the world an Agglomeration of four limbs,—will depend on the nature of such Architectural Idea: whether Grecian, Gothic, Later-Gothic, or altogether Modern, and Parisian or Anglo-Dandiacal. Again, what meaning lies in Colour! From the soberest drab to the high-flaming scarlet, spiritual idiosyncrasies unfold themselves in choice of Colour: if the Cut betoken Intellect and Talent, so does the Colour betoken Temper and Heart. In all which, among nations as among individuals, there is an incessant, indubitable, though infinitely complex working of Cause and Effect: every snip of the Scissors has been regulated and prescribed by ever-active Influences, which doubtless to Intelligences of a superior order are neither invisible nor illegible.

'For such superior Intelligences a Cause-and-Effect Philosophy of Clothes, as of Laws, were probably a comfortable winter-evening entertainment: nevertheless, for inferior Intelligences, like men, such Philosophies have always seemed to me uninstructive enough. Nay, what is your Montesquieu himself but a clever infant spelling Letters from a hieroglyphical prophetic Book, the lexicon of which lies in Eternity, in Heaven? —Let any Cause-and-Effect Philosopher explain, not why I wear such and such a Garment, obey such and such a Law; but even why *I* am *here,* to wear and obey anything!—Much, therefore, if not the whole, of that same *Spirit of Clothes* I shall suppress, as hypo-thetical, ineffectual, and even impertinent: naked Facts, and Deductions drawn therefrom in quite another than that omniscient style, are my humbler and proper province.'

Acting on which prudent restriction, Teufelsdröckh has nevertheless contrived to take-in a well-nigh *rhetor. trope*

boundless extent of field; at least, the boundaries too often lie quite beyond our horizon. Selection being indispensable, we shall here glance-over his First Part only in the most cursory manner. This First Part is, no doubt, distinguished by omnivorous learning, and utmost patience and fairness : at the same time, in its results and delineations, it is much more likely to interest the Compilers of some *Library* of General, Entertaining, Useful, or even Useless Knowledge than the miscellaneous readers of these pages. Was it this Part of the Book which Heuschrecke had in view, when he recommended us to that joint-stock vehicle of publication, 'at present the glory of British Literature'? If so, the Library Editors are welcome to dig in it for their own behoof.

To the First Chapter, which turns on Paradise and Fig-leaves, and leads us into interminable disquisitions of a mythological, metaphorical, cabalistico-sartorial and quite antediluvian cast, we shall content ourselves with giving an unconcerned approval. Still less have we to do with ' Lilis, Adam's first wife, whom, according to the Talmudists, he had before Eve, and who bore him, in that wedlock, the whole progeny of aerial, aquatic, and terrestrial Devils,'—very needlessly, we think. On this portion of the Work, with its profound glances into the *Adam-Kadmon,* or Primeval Element, here strangely brought into relation with the *Nifl* and *Muspel* (Darkness and Light) of the antique North, it may be enough to say, that its correctness of deduction, and depth of Talmudic and Rabbinical lore have filled perhaps not the worst Hebraist in Britain with something like astonishment.

But, quitting this twilight region, Teufelsdröckh hastens from the Tower of Babel, to follow the dispersion of Mankind over the whole habitable and habilable globe. Walking by the light of Oriental, Pelasgic, Scandinavian, Egyptian, Otaheitean, Ancient and Modern researches of every conceivable kind, he strives to give us in compressed shape (as the Nürnbergers give an *Orbis Pictus*) an *Orbis Vestitus;* or view of the costumes of all mankind, in all countries, in all times. It is here that to the Antiquarian, to the Historian, we

can triumphantly say: Fall to! Here is learning: an
irregular Treasury, if you will; but inexhaustible as
the Hoard of King Nibelung, which twelve wagons in
twelve days, at the rate of three journeys a day, could
not carry off. Sheepskin cloaks and wampum belts;
phylacteries, stoles, albs; chlamydes, togas, Chinese
silks, Afghaun shawls, trunk-hose, leather breeches,
Celtic philibegs (though breeches, as the name *Gallia
Braccata* indicates, are the more ancient), Hussar
cloaks, Vandyke tippets, ruffs, fardingales, are brought
vividly before us,—even the Kilmarnock nightcap is
not forgotten. For most part, too, we must admit
that the Learning, heterogeneous as it is, and tumbled-
down quite pell-mell, is true concentrated and purified
Learning, the drossy parts smelted out and thrown
aside.

Philosophical reflections intervene, and sometimes
touching pictures of human life. Of this sort the
following has surprised us. The first purpose of
Clothes, as our Professor imagines, was not warmth or
decency, but ornament. 'Miserable indeed,' says he,
'was the condition of the Aboriginal Savage, glaring
fiercely from under his fleece of hair, which with the
beard reached down to his loins, and hung round him
like a matted cloak; the rest of his body sheeted in
its thick natural fell. He loitered in the sunny glades
of the forest, living on wild-fruits; or, as the ancient
Caledonian, squatted himself in morasses, lurking for
his bestial or human prey; without implements, without arms, save the ball of heavy Flint, to which, that
his sole possession and defence might not be lost, he
had attached a long cord of plaited thongs; thereby
recovering as well as hurling it with deadly unerring
skill. Nevertheless, the pains of Hunger and Revenge
once satisfied, his next care was not Comfort but Decoration (*Putz*). Warmth he found in the toils of the
chase; or amid dried leaves, in his hollow tree, in his
bark shed, or natural grotto: but for Decoration he
must have Clothes. Nay, among wild people we find
tattooing and painting even prior to Clothes. The first
spiritual want of a barbarous man is Decoration, as

indeed we still see among the barbarous classes in civilised countries.

'Reader, the heaven-inspired melodious Singer; loftiest Serene Highness; nay thy own amber-locked, snow-and-rose-bloom Maiden, worthy to glide sylphlike almost on air, whom thou lovest, worshippest as a divine Presence, which, indeed, symbolically taken, she is,—has descended, like thyself, from that same hair-mantled, flint-hurling Aboriginal Anthropophagus! Out of the eater cometh forth meat; out of the strong cometh forth sweetness. What changes are wrought, not by time, yet in Time! For not Mankind only, but all that Mankind does or beholds, is in continual growth, regenesis and self-perfecting vitality. Cast forth thy Act, thy Word, into the ever-living, ever-working Universe: it is a seed-grain that cannot die; unnoticed to-day (says one), it will be found flourishing as a Banyan-grove (perhaps, alas, as a Hemlock-forest!) after a thousand years.

'He who first shortened the labour of Copyists by device of *Movable Types* was disbanding hired Armies, and cashiering most Kings and Senates, and creating a whole new Democratic world: he had invented the Art of Printing. The first ground handful of Nitre, Sulphur, and Charcoal drove Monk Schwartz's pestle through the ceiling: what will the last do? Achieve the final undisputed prostration of Force under Thought, of Animal courage under Spiritual. A simple invention it was in the old-world Grazier,—sick of lugging his slow Ox about the country till he got it bartered for corn or oil,—to take a piece of Leather, and thereon scratch or stamp the mere Figure of an Ox (or *Pecus*); put it in his pocket, and call it *Pecunia,* Money. Yet hereby did Barter grow Sale, the Leather Money is now Golden and Paper, and all miracles have been out-miracled: for there are Rothschilds and English National Debts; and whoso has sixpence is sovereign (to the length of sixpence) over all men; commands cooks to feed him, philosophers to teach him, kings to mount guard over him,—to the length of sixpence. —Clothes too, which began in foolishest love of Orna-

ment, what have they not become! Increased Security
and pleasurable Heat soon followed: but what of these?
Shame, divine Shame (*Schaam, Modesty*), as yet a
stranger to the Anthropophagous bosom, arose there
mysteriously under Clothes; a mystic grove-encircled
shrine for the Holy in man. Clothes gave us individuality, distinctions, social polity; Clothes have made
Men of us; they are threatening to make Clothes-
screens of us.

'But, on the whole,' continues our eloquent Professor, 'Man is a Tool-using Animal (*Handthierendes
Thier*). Weak in himself, and of small stature, he
stands on a basis, at most for the flattest-soled, of some
half-square foot, insecurely enough; has to straddle
out his legs, lest the very wind supplant him. Feeblest
of bipeds! Three quintals are a crushing load for him;
the steer of the meadow tosses him aloft, like a waste
rag. Nevertheless he can use Tools, can devise Tools:
with these the granite mountain melts into light dust
before him; he kneads glowing iron, as if it were soft
paste; seas are his smooth highway, winds and fire his
unwearying steeds. Nowhere do you find him without
Tools; without Tools he is nothing, with Tools he is all.'

Here may we not, for a moment, interrupt the stream
of Oratory with a remark, that this Definition of the
Tool-using Animal, appears to us, of all that Animal-
sort, considerably the precisest and best? Man is called
a Laughing Animal: but do not the apes also laugh, or
attempt to do it; and is the manliest man the greatest
and oftenest laugher? Teufelsdröckh himself, as we said,
laughed only once. Still less do we make of that other
French Definition of the Cooking Animal; which, indeed, for rigorous scientific purposes, is as good as useless. Can a Tartar be said to cook, when he only
readies his steak by riding on it? Again, what Cookery
does the Greenlander use, beyond stowing-up his
whale-blubber, as a marmot, in the like case, might do?
Or how would Monsieur Ude prosper among those
Orinocco Indians, who, according to Humboldt, lodge
in crow-nests, on the branches of trees; and, for half
the year, have no victuals but pipe-clay, the whole
country being under water? But, on the other hand,

show us the human being, of any period or climate, without his Tools : those very Caledonians, as we saw, had their Flint-ball, and Thong to it, such as no brute has or can have.

'Man is a Tool-using Animal,' concludes Teufelsdröckh in his abrupt way; 'of which truth Clothes are but one example : and surely if we consider the interval between the first wooden Dibble fashioned by man, and those Liverpool Steam-carriages, or the British House of Commons, we shall note what progress he has made. He digs up certain black stones from the bosom of the earth, and says to them, *Transport me and this luggage at the rate of five-and-thirty miles an hour;* and they do it : he collects, apparently by lot, six-hundred and fifty-eight miscellaneous individuals, and says to them, *Make this nation toil for us, bleed for us, hunger and sorrow and sin for us;* and they do it.'

CHAPTER VI

APRONS

ONE of the most unsatisfactory Sections in the whole Volume is that on *Aprons.* What though stout old Gao, the Persian Blacksmith, 'whose Apron, now indeed hidden under jewels, because raised in revolt which proved successful, is still the royal standard of that country'; what though John Knox's Daughter, 'who threatened Sovereign Majesty that she would catch her husband's head in her Apron, rather than he should lie and be a bishop '; what though the Landgravine Elizabeth, with many other Apron worthies,—figure here? An idle wire-drawing spirit, sometimes even a tone of levity, approaching to conventional satire, is too clearly discernible. What, for example, are we to make of such sentences as the following?

'Aprons are Defences; against injury to cleanliness, to safety, to modesty, sometimes to roguery. From the thin slip of notched silk (as it were, the Emblem and

beatified Ghost of an Apron), which some highest-bred
housewife, sitting at Nürnberg Workboxes and Toy-
boxes, has gracefully fastened on; to the thick-tanned
hide, girt round him with thongs, wherein the Builder
builds, and at evening sticks his trowel; or to those
jingling sheet-iron Aprons, wherein your otherwise
half-naked Vulcans hammer and smelt in their smelt-
furnace,—is there not range enough in the fashion and
uses of this Vestment? How much has been concealed,
how much has been defended in Aprons! Nay, rightly
considered, what is your whole Military and Police
Establishment, charged at uncalculated millions, but a
huge scarlet-coloured, iron-fastened Apron, wherein
Society works (uneasily enough); guarding itself from
some soil and stithy-sparks, in this Devil's-smithy
(*Teufelsschmiede*) of a world? But of all Aprons the
most puzzling to me hitherto has been the Episcopal or
Cassock. Wherein consists the usefulness of this
Apron? The Overseer (*Episcopus*) of Souls, I notice,
has tucked-in the corner of it, as if his day's work
were done: what does he shadow forth thereby?'
&c. &c.

Or again, has it often been the lot of our readers to
read such stuff as we shall now quote?

' I consider those printed Paper Aprons, worn by the
Parisian Cooks, as a new vent, though a slight one,
for Typography; therefore as an encouragement to
modern Literature, and deserving of approval: nor is
it without satisfaction that I hear of a celebrated London Firm having in view to introduce the same fashion,
with important extensions, in England.'—We who are
on the spot hear of no such thing; and indeed have
reason to be thankful that hitherto there are other vents
for our Literature, exuberant as it is.—Teufelsdröckh
continues : ' If such supply of printed Paper should
rise so far as to choke-up the highways and public
thoroughfares, new means must of necessity be had
recourse to. In a world existing by Industry, we
grudge to employ fire as a destroying element, and not
as a creating one. However, Heaven is omnipotent,
and will find us an outlet. In the mean while, is it not
beautiful to see five-million quintals of Rags picked

annually from the Laystall; and annually, after being
macerated, hot - pressed, printed - on, and sold,—returned thither; filling so many hungry mouths by the
way? Thus is the Laystall, especially with its Rags or
Clothes-rubbish, the grand Electric Battery, and Foun-
tain-of-motion, from which and to which the Social
Activities (like vitreous and resinous Electricities) circulate, in larger or smaller circles, through the mighty,
billowy, storm-tost Chaos of Life, which they keep
alive !'—Such passages fill us, who love the man, and
partly esteem him, with a very mixed feeling.

Farther down we meet with this : ' The Journalists
are now the true Kings and Clergy : henceforth Historians, unless they are fools, must write not of Bourbon Dynasties, and Tudors and Hapsburgs; but of
Stamped Broad-sheet Dynasties, and quite new successive Names, according as this or the other Able Editor,
or Combination of Able Editors, gains the world's ear.
Of the British Newspaper Press, perhaps the most
important of all, and wonderful enough in its secret
constitution and procedure, a valuable descriptive History already exists, in that language, under the title of
Satan's Invisible World Displayed; which, however,
by search in all the Weissnichtwo Libraries, I have not
yet succeeded in procuring (*vermöchte nicht aufzu-
treiben*).'

Thus does the good Homer not only nod, but snore.
Thus does Teufelsdröckh, wandering in regions where
he had little business, confound the old authentic
Presbyterian Witchfinder with a new, spurious, imagin-
ary Historian of the *Brittische Journalistik;* and so
stumble on perhaps the most egregious blunder in
Modern Literature !

CHAPTER VII

MISCELLANEOUS-HISTORICAL

HAPPIER is our Professor, and more purely scientific
and historic, when he reaches the Middle Ages in
Europe, and down to the end of the Seventeenth Century; the true era of extravagance in Costume. It is
here that the Antiquary and Student of Modes comes
upon his richest harvest. Fantastic garbs, beggaring
all fancy of a Teniers or a Callot, succeed each other,
like monster devouring monster in a Dream. The
whole too in brief authentic strokes, and touched not
seldom with that breath of genius which makes even
old raiment live. Indeed, so learned, precise, graphical,
and everyway interesting have we found these Chapters,
that it may be thrown-out as a pertinent question for
parties concerned, Whether or not a good English
Translation thereof might henceforth be profitably incorporated with Mr. Merrick's valuable Work *On
Ancient Armour?* Take, by way of example, the
following sketch; as authority for which Paulinus's
Zeitkürzende Lust (ii. 678) is, with seeming confidence,
referred to:

' Did we behold the German fashionable dress of the
Fifteenth Century, we might smile; as perhaps those
bygone Germans, were they to rise again, and see our
haberdashery, would cross themselves, and invoke the
Virgin. But happily no bygone German, or man, rises
again; thus the Present is not needlessly trammelled
with the Past; and only grows out of it, like a Tree,
whose roots are not intertangled with its branches, but
lie peaceably underground. Nay it is very mournful,
yet not useless, to see and know, how the Greatest and
Dearest, in a short while, would find his place quite
filled-up here, and no room for him; the very Napoleon,
the very Byron, in some seven years, has become obsolete, and were now a foreigner to his Europe. Thus
is the Law of Progress secured; and in Clothes, as in
all other external things whatsoever, no fashion will
continue.

'Of the military classes in those old times, whose
buff-belts, complicated chains and gorgets, huge churn-
boots, and other riding and fighting gear have been
bepainted in modern Romance, till the whole has
acquired somewhat of a sign-post character,—I shall
here say nothing : the civil and pacific classes, less
touched upon, are wonderful enough for us.

'Rich men, I find, have *Teusinke*' (a perhaps un-
translateable article); 'also a silver girdle, whereat
hang little bells; so that when a man walks, it is with
continual jingling. Some few, of musical turn, have a
whole chime of bells (*Glockenspiel*) fastened there;
which, especially in sudden whirls, and the other accidents of walking, has a grateful effect. Observe too
how fond they are of peaks, and Gothic-arch intersec-
tions. The male world wears peaked caps, an ell long,
which hang bobbing over the side (*schief*) : their shoes
are peaked in front, also to the length of an ell, and
laced on the side with tags; even the wooden shoes
have their ell-long noses : some also clap bells on the
peak. Further, according to my authority, the men
have breeches without seat (*ohne Gesäss*) : these they
fasten peakwise to their shirts; and the long round
doublet must overlap them.

'Rich maidens, again, flit abroad in gowns scolloped
out behind and before, so that back and breast are
almost bare. Wives of quality, on the other hand, have
train-gowns four or five ells in length; which trains
there are boys to carry. Brave Cleopatras, sailing in
their silk-cloth Galley, with a Cupid for steersman !
Consider their welts, a handbreadth thick, which waver
round them by way of hem; the long flood of silver
buttons, or rather silver shells, from throat to shoe,
wherewith these same welt-gowns are buttoned. The
maidens have bound silver snoods about their hair, with
gold spangles, and pendent flames (*Flammen*), that is,
sparkling hair-drops : but of their mother's headgear
who shall speak? Neither in love of grace is comfort
forgotten. In winter weather you behold the whole fair
creation (that can afford it) in long mantles, with skirts
wide below, and, for hem, not one but two sufficient
hand-broad welts; all ending atop in a thick well-

starched Ruff, some twenty inches broad : these are
their Ruff-mantles (*Kragenmäntel*).

' As yet among the womankind hoop-petticoats are
not ; but the men have doublets of fustian, under which
lie multiple ruffs of cloth, pasted together with batter
(*mit Teig zusammengekleistert*), which create protuber-
ance enough. Thus do the two sexes vie with each
other in the art of Decoration ; and as usual the stronger
carries it.'

Our Professor, whether he hath humour himself or
not, manifests a certain feeling of the Ludicrous, a sly
observance of it, which, could emotion of any kind be
confidently predicated of so still a man, we might call
a real love. None of those bell-girdles, bushel-breeches,
cornuted shoes, or other the like phenomena, of which
the History of Dress offers so many, escape him : more
especially the mischances, or striking adventures, incident to the wearers of such, are noticed with due
fidelity. Sir Walter Raleigh's fine mantle, which he
spread in the mud under Queen Elizabeth's feet, appears to provoke little enthusiasm in him ; he merely
asks, Whether at that period the Maiden Queen ' was
red-painted on the nose, and white-painted on the
cheeks, as her tire-women, when from spleen and
wrinkles she would no longer look in any glass, were
wont to serve her?' We can answer that Sir Walter
knew well what he was doing, and had the Maiden
Queen been stuffed parchment dyed in verdigris, would
have done the same.

Thus too, treating of those enormous habiliments,
that were not only slashed and galooned, but artificially swollen-out on the broader parts of the body, by
introduction of Bran,—our Professor fails not to comment on that luckless Courtier, who having seated himself on a chair with some projecting nail on it, and
therefrom rising, to pay his *devoir* on the entrance of
Majesty, instantaneously emitted several pecks of dry
wheat-dust : and stood there diminished to a spindle,
his galoons and slashes dangling sorrowful and flabby
round him. Whereupon the Professor publishes this
reflection :

' By what strange chances do we live in History?

Erostratus by a torch; Milo by a bullock; Henry Darnley, an unfledged booby and bustard, by his limbs; most Kings and Queens by being born under such and such a bed-tester; Boileau Despréaux (according to Helvetius) by the peck of a turkey; and this ill-starred individual by a rent in his breeches,—for no Memoirist of Kaiser Otto's Court omits him. Vain was the prayer of Themistocles for a talent of Forgetting : my Friends, yield cheerfully to Destiny, and read since it is written.'
—Has Teufelsdröckh to be put in mind that, nearly related to the impossible talent of Forgetting, stands that talent of Silence, which even travelling Englishmen manifest?

'The simplest costume,' observes our Professor, 'which I anywhere find alluded to in History, is that used as regimental, by Bolivar's Cavalry, in the late Columbian wars. A square Blanket, twelve feet in diagonal, is provided (some were wont to cut-off the corners, and make it circular): in the centre a slit is effected eighteen inches long; through this the mother-naked Trooper introduces his head and neck : and so rides shielded from all weather, and in battle from many strokes (for he rolls it about his left arm); and not only dressed, but harnessed and draperied.'

With which picture of a State of Nature, affecting by its singularity, and Old-Roman contempt of the superfluous, we shall quit this part of our subject.

CHAPTER VIII

THE WORLD OUT OF CLOTHES

IF in the Descriptive-Historical portion of this Volume, Teufelsdröckh, discussing merely the *Werden* (Origin and successive Improvement) of Clothes, has astonished many a reader, much more will he in the Speculative-Philosophical portion, which treats of their *Wirken*, or Influences. It is here that the present Editor first feels the pressure of his task; for here properly the higher and new Philosophy of Clothes commences : an untried, almost inconceivable region, or chaos; in venturing upon which, how difficult, yet how unspeakably important is it to know what course, of survey and conquest, is the true one; where the footing is firm substance and will bear us, where it is hollow, or mere cloud, and may engulf us ! Teufelsdröckh undertakes no less than to expound the moral, political, even religious Influences of Clothes; he undertakes to make manifest, in its thousandfold bearings, this grand Proposition, that Man's earthly interests 'are all hooked and buttoned together, and held up, by Clothes.' He says in so many words, ' Society is founded upon Cloth '; and again, ' Society sails through the Infinitude on Cloth, as on a Faust's Mantle, or rather like the Sheet of clean and unclean beasts in the Apostle's Dream; and without such Sheet or Mantle, would sink to endless depths, or mount to inane limboes, and in either case be no more.'

By what chains, or indeed infinitely complected tissues, of Meditation this grand Theorem is here unfolded, and innumerable practical Corollaries are drawn therefrom, it were perhaps a mad ambition to attempt exhibiting. Our Professor's method is not, in any case, that of common school Logic, where the truths all stand in a row, each holding by the skirts of the other; but at best that of practical Reason, proceeding by large Intuition over whole systematic groups and kingdoms; whereby, we might say, a noble complexity, almost like that of Nature, reigns in his Philosophy, or spiritual Picture of Nature : a mighty maze, yet, as faith whispers, not without a plan. Nay we complained above, that a certain ignoble complexity, what we must call mere confusion, was also discernible. Often, also, we have to exclaim : Would to Heaven those same Biographical Documents were come ! For it seems as if the demonstration lay much in the Author's individuality; as if it were not Argument that had taught him, but Experience. At present it is only in local glimpses, and by significant fragments, picked often at wide-enough intervals from the original Volume, and carefully collated, that we can hope to impart some outline or foreshadow of this Doctrine. Readers of any intelligence are once more invited to favour us with their most concentrated attention : let these, after intense consideration, and not till then, pronounce, Whether on the utmost verge of our actual horizon there is not a looming as of Land; a promise of new Fortunate Islands, perhaps whole undiscovered Americas, for such as have canvas to sail thither?—As exordium to the whole, stand here the following long citation :

‘With men of a speculative turn,’ writes Teufelsdröckh, ‘there come seasons, meditative, sweet, yet awful hours, when in wonder and fear you ask yourself that unanswerable question : Who am *I; the thing that can say " I " (das Wesen das sich* ICH *nennt*)? The world, with its loud trafficking, retires into the distance; and, through the paper-hangings, and stone-walls, and thick-plied tissues of Commerce and Polity, and all the living and lifeless integuments (of Society and a Body), wherewith your Existence sits surrounded,—the sight reaches forth into the void Deep, and you are alone with the Universe, and silently commune with it, as one mysterious Presence with another.

‘Who am I; what is this ME? A Voice, a Motion, an Appearance;—some embodied, visualised Idea in the Eternal Mind? *Cogito, ergo sum.* Alas, poor Cogitator, this takes us but a little way. Sure enough, I am; and lately was not : but Whence? How? Whereto? The answer lies around, written in all colours and motions, uttered in all tones of jubilee and wail, in thousand-figured, thousand-voiced, harmonious Nature : but where is the cunning eye and ear to whom that God-written Apocalypse will yield articulate meaning? We sit as in a boundless Phantasmagoria and Dreamgrotto; boundless, for the faintest star, the remotest century, lies not even nearer the verge thereof : sounds and many-coloured visions flit round our sense; but Him, the Unslumbering, whose work both Dream and Dreamer are, we see not; except in rare half-waking moments, suspect not. Creation, says one, lies before us, like a glorious Rainbow; but the Sun that made it lies behind us, hidden from us. Then, in that strange Dream, how we clutch at shadows as if they were substances; and sleep deepest while fancying ourselves most awake! Which of your Philosophical Systems is other than a dream-theorem; a net quotient, confidently given out, where divisor and dividend are both unknown? What are all your national Wars, with their Moscow Retreats, and sanguinary hate-filled Revolutions, but the Somnambulism of uneasy Sleepers? This Dreaming, this Somnambulism is what we on Earth call Life; wherein the most indeed undoubtingly wander, as if they knew right hand from left; yet they only are wise who know that they know nothing.

'Pity that all Metaphysics had hitherto proved so inexpressibly unproductive! The secret of Man's Being is still like the Sphinx's secret: a riddle that he cannot rede; and for ignorance of which he suffers death, the worst death, a spiritual. What are your Axioms, and Categories, and Systems, and Aphorisms? Words, words. High Air-castles are cunningly built of Words, the Words well bedded also in good Logic-mortar, wherein, however, no Knowledge will come to lodge. *The whole is greater than the part:* how exceedingly true! *Nature abhors a vacuum:* how exceedingly false and calumnious! Again, *Nothing can act but where it is:* with all my heart; only, WHERE is it? Be not the slave of Words: is not the Distant, the Dead, while I love it, and long for it, and mourn for it, Here, in the genuine sense, as truly as the floor I stand on? But that same WHERE, with its brother WHEN, are from the first the master-colours of our Dream-grotto; say rather, the Canvas (the warp and woof thereof) whereon all our Dreams and Life-visions are painted. Nevertheless, has not a deeper meditation taught certain of every climate and age, that the WHERE and WHEN, so mysteriously inseparable from all our thoughts, are but superficial terrestrial adhesions to thought; that the Seer may discern them where they mount up out of the celestial EVERYWHERE and FOREVER: have not all nations conceived their God as Omnipresent and Eternal; as existing in a universal HERE, an everlasting Now? Think well, thou too wilt find that Space is but a mode of our human Sense, so likewise Time; there *is* no Space and no Time: WE are—we know not what;—light-sparkles floating in the æther of Deity !

' So that this so solid-seeming World, after all, were but an air-image, our ME the only reality : and Nature, with its thousandfold production and destruction, but the reflex of our own inward Force, the " phantasy of our Dream " ; or what the Earth-Spirit in *Faust* names it, *the living visible Garment of God :*

> " In Being's floods, in Action's storm,
> I walk and work, above, beneath,
> Work and weave in endless motion !
>> Birth and Death,
>> An infinite ocean ;
>> A seizing and giving
>> The fire of Living :
> 'Tis thus at the roaring Loom of Time I ply,
> And weave for God the Garment thou seest Him by.'

Of twenty millions that have read and spouted this thunder-speech of the *Erdgeist,* are there yet twenty units of us that have learned the meaning thereof?

' It was in some such mood, when wearied and for-done with these high speculations, that I first came upon the question of Clothes. Strange enough, it strikes me, is this same fact of there being Tailors and Tailored. The Horse I ride has his own whole fell : strip him of the girths and flaps and extraneous tags I have fastened round him, and the noble creature is his own sempster and weaver and spinner ; nay his own bootmaker, jeweller, and man-milliner ; he bounds free through the valleys, with a perennial rain-proof court-suit on his body ; wherein warmth and easiness of fit have reached perfection ; nay, the graces also have been considered, and frills and fringes, with gay variety of colour, featly appended, and ever in the right place, are not wanting. While I—good Heaven !—have thatched myself over with the dead fleeces of sheep, the bark of vegetables, the entrails of worms, the hides of oxen or seals, the felt of furred beasts ; and walk abroad a moving Rag-screen, overheaped with shreds and tatters raked from the Charnel-house of Nature, where they would have rotted, to rot on me more slowly ! Day after day, I must thatch myself anew ; day after day,

this despicable thatch must lose some film of its thick-
ness; some film of it, frayed away by tear and wear,
must be brushed-off into the Ashpit, into the Laystall;
till by degrees the whole has been brushed thither, and
I, the dust-making, patent Rag-grinder, get new
material to grind down. O subter-brutish! vile! most
vile! For have not I too a compact all-enclosing Skin,
whiter or dingier? Am I a botched mass of tailors'
and cobblers' shreds, then; or a tightly-articulated,
homogeneous little Figure, automatic, nay alive?

  'Strange enough how creatures of the human-kind
shut their eyes to plainest facts; and by the mere inertia
of Oblivion and Stupidity, live at ease in the midst of
Wonders and Terrors. But indeed man is, and was
always, a blockhead and dullard; much readier to feel
and digest, than to think and consider. Prejudice,
which he pretends to hate, is his absolute lawgiver;
mere use-and-wont everywhere leads him by the nose;
thus let but a Rising of the Sun, let but a Creation of
the World happen *twice*, and it ceases to be marvellous,
to be noteworthy, or noticeable. Perhaps not once in
a lifetime does it occur to your ordinary biped, of any
country or generation, be he gold-mantled Prince or
russet-jerkined Peasant, that his Vestments and his
Self are not one and indivisible; that *he* is naked, without vestments, till he buy or steal such, and by forethought sew and button them.

  'For my own part, these considerations, of our
Clothes-thatch, and how, reaching inwards even to our
heart of hearts, it tailorises and demoralises us, fill me
with a certain horror at myself and mankind; almost
as one feels at those Dutch Cows, which, during the
wet season, you see grazing deliberately with jackets
and petticoats (of striped sacking), in the meadows of
Gouda. Nevertheless there is something great in the
moment when a man first strips himself of adventitious
wrappages; and sees indeed that he is naked, and, as
Swift has it, "a forked straddling animal with bandy
legs"; yet also a Spirit, and unutterable Mystery of
Mysteries.'

CHAPTER IX

ADAMITISM

LET no courteous reader take offence at the opinions
broached in the conclusion of the last Chapter. The
Editor himself, on first glancing over that singular
passage, was inclined to exclaim : What, have we got
not only a Sansculottist, but an enemy to Clothes in
the abstract? A new Adamite, in this century, which
flatters itself that it is the Nineteenth, and destructive
both to Superstition and Enthusiasm?

Consider, thou foolish Teufelsdröckh, what benefits
unspeakable all ages and sexes derive from Clothes.
For example, when thou thyself, a watery, pulpy, slob-
bery freshman and new-comer in this Planet, sattest
muling and puking in thy nurse's arms; sucking thy
coral, and looking forth into the world in the blankest
manner, what hadst thou been without thy blankets,
and bibs, and other nameless hulls? A terror to thyself
and mankind ! Or hast thou forgotten the day when
thou first receivedst breeches, and thy long clothes became short? The village where thou livedst was all
apprised of the fact; and neighbour after neighbour
kissed thy pudding-cheek, and gave thee, as handsel,
silver or copper coins, on that the first gala-day of thy
existence. Again, wert not thou, at one period of life,
a Buck, or Blood, or Macaroni, or Incroyable, or Dandy,
or by whatever name, according to year and place,
such phenomenon is distinguished? In that one word
lie included mysterious volumes. Nay, now when the
reign of folly is over, or altered, and thy clothes are
not for triumph but for defence, hast thou always worn
them perforce, and as a consequence of Man's Fall;
never rejoiced in them as in a warm movable House, a
Body round thy Body, wherein that strange THEE of
thine sat snug, defying all variations of Climate? Girt
with thick double-milled kerseys; half-buried under
shawls and broad-brims, and overalls and mud-boots,
thy very fingers cased in doeskin and mittens, thou hast
bestrode that ' Horse I ride '; and, though it were in

wild winter, dashed through the world, glorying in it as if thou wert its lord. In vain did the sleet beat round thy temples; it lighted only on thy impenetrable, felted or woven, case of wool. In vain did the winds howl,—forests sounding and creaking, deep calling unto deep,—and the storms heap themselves together into one huge Arctic whirlpool: thou flewest through the middle thereof, striking fire from the highway; wild music hummed in thy ears, thou too wert as a ' sailor of the air '; the wreck of matter and the crash of worlds was thy element and propitiously wafting tide. Without Clothes, without bit or saddle, what hadst thou been; what had thy fleet quadruped been?— Nature is good, but she is not the best: here truly was the victory of Art over Nature. A thunderbolt indeed might have pierced thee; all short of this thou couldst defy.

Or, cries the courteous reader, has your Teufels-dröckh forgotten what he said lately about ' Aboriginal Savages,' and their ' condition miserable indeed '? Would he have all this unsaid; and us betake ourselves again to the ' matted cloak,' and go sheeted in a ' thick natural fell '?

Nowise, courteous reader! The Professor knows full well what he is saying; and both thou and we, in our haste, do him wrong. If Clothes, in these times, ' so tailorise and demoralise us,' have they no re-deeming value; can they not be altered to serve better; must they of necessity be thrown to the dogs? The truth is, Teufelsdröckh, though a Sansculottist, is no Adamite; and much perhaps as he might wish to go forth before this degenerate age ' as a Sign,' would nowise wish to do it, as those old Adamites did, in a state of Nakedness. The utility of Clothes is alto-gether apparent to him: nay perhaps he has an insight into their more recondite, and almost mystic qualities, what we might call the omnipotent virtue of Clothes, such as was never before vouchsafed to any man. For example:

' You see two individuals,' he writes, ' one dressed in fine Red, the other in coarse threadbare Blue: Red says to Blue, " Be hanged and anatomised "; Blue hears

with a shudder, and (O wonder of wonders!) marches
sorrowfully to the gallows; is there noosed-up, vibrates
his hour, and the surgeons dissect him, and fit his bones
into a skeleton for medical purposes. How is this; or
what make ye of your *Nothing can act but where it is?*
Red has no physical hold of Blue, no *clutch* of him, is
nowise in *contact* with him : neither are those ministering Sheriffs and Lord-Lieutenants and Hangmen and
Tipstaves so related to commanding Red, that he can
tug them hither and thither; but each stands distinct
within his own skin. Nevertheless, as it is spoken, so
is it done : the articulated Word sets all hands in
Action; and Rope and Improved-drop perform their
work.

' Thinking reader, the reason seems to me twofold :
First, that *Man is a Spirit,* and bound by invisible bonds
to *All Men;* secondly, that *he wears Clothes,* which are
the visible emblems of that fact. Has not your Red
hanging-individual a horsehair wig, squirrel-skins, and
a plush-gown; whereby all mortals know that he is a
Judge?—Society, which the more I think of it astonishes
me the more, is founded upon Cloth.

' Often in my atrabiliar-moods, when I read of pomp-
ous ceremonials, Frankfort Coronations, Royal Draw-
ing-rooms, Levees, Couchees; and how the ushers and
macers and pursuivants are all in waiting; how Duke
this is presented by Archduke that, and Colonel A by
General B, and innumerable Bishops, Admirals, and
miscellaneous Functionaries, are advancing gallantly
to the Anointed Presence; and I strive, in my remote
privacy, to form a clear picture of that solemnity,—on
a sudden, as by some enchanter's wand, the—shall I
speak it?—the Clothes fly-off the whole dramatic corps;
and Dukes, Grandees, Bishops, Generals, Anointed
Presence itself, every mother's son of them, stand
straddling there, not a shirt on them; and I know not
whether to laugh or weep. This physical or psychical
infirmity, in which perhaps I am not singular, I have,
after hesitation, thought right to publish, for the solace
of those afflicted with the like.'

Would to Heaven, say we, thou hadst thought right
to keep it secret! Who is there now that can read the

five columns of Presentations in his Morning Newspaper
without a shudder? Hypochondriac men, and all men
are to a certain extent hypochondriac, should be more
gently treated. With what readiness our fancy, in this
shattered state of the nerves, follows out the consequences which Teufelsdröckh, with a devilish coolness,
goes on to draw:

'What would Majesty do, could such an accident
befall in reality; should the buttons all simultaneously
start, and the solid wool evaporate, in very Deed, as
here in Dream? *Ach Gott!* How each skulks into the
nearest hiding-place; their high State Tragedy (*Haupt-
und Staats-Action*) becomes a Pickleherring-Farce to
weep at, which is the worst kind of Farce; *the tables*
(according to Horace), and with them, the whole fabric
of Government, Legislation, Property, Police, and
Civilised Society, *are dissolved*, in wails and howls.'

Lives the man that can figure a naked Duke of
Windlestraw addressing a naked House of Lords?
Imagination, choked as in mephitic air, recoils on itself,
and will not forward with the picture. The Woolsack,
the Ministerial, the Opposition Benches—*infandum!
infandum!* And yet why is the thing impossible?
Was not every soul, or rather every body, of these
Guardians of our Liberties, naked, or nearly so, last
night; 'a forked Radish with a head fantastically
carved'? And why might he not, did our stern fate
so order it, walk out to St Stephen's, as well as into
bed, in that no-fashion; and there, with other similar
Radishes, hold a Bed of Justice? 'Solace of those
afflicted with the like!' Unhappy Teufelsdröckh, had
man ever such a 'physical or psychical infirmity'
before? And now how many, perhaps, may thy unparalleled confession (which we, even to the sounder
British world, and goaded-on by Critical and Biographical duty, grudge to re-impart) incurably infect
therewith! Art thou the malignest of Sansculottists,
or only the maddest?

'It will remain to be examined,' adds the inexorable
Teufelsdröckh, 'in how far the SCARECROW, as a
Clothed Person, is not also entitled to benefit of clergy,
and English trial by jury: nay perhaps, considering his

high function (for is not he too a Defender of Property, and Sovereign armed with the *terrors* of the Law?), to a certain royal Immunity and Inviolability; which, however, misers and the meaner class of persons are not always voluntarily disposed to grant him.' * * *
* * * ' O my Friends, we are (in Yorick Sterne's words) but as '' turkeys driven with a stick and red clout, to the market '': or if some drivers, as they do in Norfolk, take a dried bladder and put peas in it, the rattle thereof terrifies the boldest!'

CHAPTER X

PURE REASON

It must now be apparent enough that our Professor, as above hinted, is a speculative Radical, and of the very darkest tinge; acknowledging, for most part, in the solemnities and paraphernalia of civilised Life, which we make so much of, nothing but so many Cloth-rags, turkey-poles, and 'bladders with dried peas.' To linger among such speculations, longer than mere Science requires, a discerning public can have no wish. For our purposes the simple fact that such a *Naked World* is possible, nay actually exists (under the Clothed one), will be sufficient. Much, therefore, we omit about 'Kings wrestling naked on the green with Carmen,' and the Kings being thrown: 'dissect them with scalpels,' says Teufelsdröckh; 'the same viscera, tissues, livers, lights, and other life-tackle are there: examine their spiritual mechanism; the same great Need, great Greed, and little Faculty; nay ten to one but the Carman, who understands draught-cattle, the rimming of wheels, something of the laws of unstable and stable equilibrium, with other branches of wagon-science, and has actually put forth his hand and operated on Nature, is the more cunningly gifted of the two. Whence, then, their so unspeakable difference? From Clothes.' Much also we shall omit about confusion of

Ranks, and Joan and My Lady, and how it would be everywhere ' Hail fellow well met,' and Chaos were come again : all which to any one that has once fairly pictured-out the grand mother-idea, *Society in a state of nakedness,* will spontaneously suggest itself. Should some sceptical individual still entertain doubts whether in a world without Clothes, the smallest Politeness, Polity, or even Police, could exist, let him turn to the original Volume, and view there the boundless Serbonian Bog of Sansculottism, stretching sour and pestilential : over which we have lightly flown ; where not only whole armies but whole nations might sink ! If indeed the following argument, in its brief riveting emphasis, be not of itself incontrovertible and final :

' Are we Opossums ; have we natural Pouches, like the Kangaroo ? Or how, without Clothes, could we possess the master-organ, soul's seat, and true pineal gland of the Body Social : I mean, a Purse ?'

Nevertheless, it is impossible to hate Professor Teufelsdröckh ; at worst, one knows not whether to hate or to love him. For though, in looking at the fair tapestry of human Life, with its royal and even sacred figures, he dwells not on the obverse alone, but here chiefly on the reverse ; and indeed turns out the rough seams, tatters, and manifold thrums of that unsightly wrong-side, with an almost diabolic patience and indifference, which must have sunk him in the estimation of most readers,—there is that within which unspeakably distinguishes him from all other past and present Sansculottists. The grand unparalleled peculiarity of Teufelsdröckh is, that with all this Descendentalism, he combines a Transcendentalism, no less superlative ; whereby if on the one hand he degrade man below most animals, except those jacketed Gouda Cows, he, on the other, exalts him beyond the visible Heavens, almost to an equality with the Gods.

' To the eye of vulgar Logic,' says he, ' what is man ? An omnivorous Biped that wears Breeches. To the eye of Pure Reason what is he ? A Soul, a Spirit, and divine Apparition. Round his mysterious Me, there lies, under all those wool-rags, a Garment of Flesh (or of Senses), contextured in the Loom of

Heaven; whereby he is revealed to his like, and dwells
with them in UNION and DIVISION; and sees and fashions
for himself a Universe, with azure Starry Spaces, and
long Thousands of Years. Deep-hidden is he under
that strange Garment; amid Sounds and Colours and
Forms, as it were, swathed-in, and inextricably over-
shrouded: yet it is sky-woven, and worthy of a God.
Stands he not thereby in the centre of Immensities, in
the conflux of Eternities? He feels; power has been
given him to know, to believe; nay does not the spirit
of Love, free in its celestial primeval brightness, even
here, though but for moments, look through? Well
said Saint Chrysostom, with his lips of gold, " the true
SHEKINAH is Man ": where else is the GOD'S-PRESENCE
manifested not to our eyes only, but to our hearts, as
in our fellow-man?'

In such passages, unhappily too rare, the high
Platonic Mysticism of our Author, which is perhaps
the fundamental element of his nature, bursts forth, as
it were, in full flood: and, through all the vapour and
tarnish of what is often so perverse, so mean in his
exterior and environment, we seem to look into a whole
inward Sea of Light and Love;—though, alas, the grim
coppery clouds soon roll together again, and hide it from
view.

Such tendency to Mysticism is everywhere traceable
in this man; and indeed, to attentive readers, must
have been long ago apparent. Nothing that he sees
but has more than a common meaning, but has two
meanings: thus, if in the highest Imperial Sceptre and
Charlemagne-Mantle, as well as in the poorest Ox-goad
and Gipsy-Blanket, he finds Prose, Decay, Contempt-
ibility; there is in each sort Poetry also, and a reverend
Worth. For Matter, were it never so despicable, is
Spirit, the manifestation of Spirit: were it never so
honourable, can it be more? The thing Visible, nay
the thing Imagined, the thing in any way conceived as
Visible, what is it but a Garment, a Clothing of the
higher, celestial Invisible, ' unimaginable, formless,
dark with excess of bright '? Under which point of
view the following passage, so strange in purport, so
strange in phrase, seems characteristic enough:

'The beginning of all Wisdom is to look fixedly on Clothes, or even with armed eyesight, till they become *transparent*. "The Philosopher," says the wisest of this age, "must station himself in the middle": how true! The Philosopher is he to whom the Highest has descended, and the Lowest has mounted up; who is the equal and kindly brother of all.

'Shall we tremble before clothwebs and cobwebs, whether woven in Arkwright looms, or by the silent Arachnes that weave unrestingly in our imagination? Or, on the other hand, what is there that we cannot love; since all was created by God?

'Happy he who can look through the Clothes of a Man (the woollen, and fleshly, and official Bank-paper and State-paper Clothes) into the Man himself; and discern, it may be, in this or the other Dread Potentate, a more or less incompetent Digestive-apparatus; yet also an inscrutable venerable Mystery, in the meanest Tinker that sees with eyes!'

For the rest, as is natural to a man of this kind, he deals much in the feeling of Wonder; insists on the necessity and high worth of universal Wonder; which he holds to be the only reasonable temper for the denizen of so singular a Planet as ours. 'Wonder,' says he, 'is the basis of Worship: the reign of wonder is perennial, indestructible in Man; only at certain stages (as the present), it is, for some short season, a reign *in partibus infidelium*.' That progress of Science, which is to destroy Wonder, and in its stead substitute Mensuration and Numeration, finds small favour with Teufelsdröckh, much as he otherwise venerates these two latter processes.

'Shall your Science,' exclaims he, 'proceed in the small chink-lighted, or even oil-lighted, underground workshop of Logic alone; and man's mind become an Arithmetical Mill, whereof Memory is the Hopper, and mere Tables of Sines and Tangents, Codification, and Treatises of what you call Political Economy, are the Meal? And what is that Science, which the scientific head alone, were it screwed off, and (like the Doctor's in the Arabian Tale) set in a basin to keep it alive, could prosecute without shadow of a heart,—but one other of the mechanical and menial handicrafts, for which the Scientific Head (having a Soul in it) is too noble an organ? I mean that Thought without Reverence is barren, perhaps poisonous; at best, dies like cookery with the day that called it forth; does not live, like sowing, in successive tilths and wider-spreading harvests, bringing food and plenteous increase to all Time.'

In such wise does Teufelsdröckh deal hits, harder or softer, according to ability; yet ever, as we would fain persuade ourselves, with charitable intent. Above all, that class of ' Logic-choppers, and treble-pipe Scoffers, and professed Enemies to Wonder; who, in these days, so numerously patrol as night-constables about the Mechanics' Institute of Science, and cackle, like true Old-Roman geese and goslings round their Capitol, on any alarm, or on none; nay who often, as illuminated Sceptics, walk abroad into peaceable society, in full day-light, with rattle and lantern, and insist on guiding you and guarding you therewith, though the Sun is shining, and the street populous with mere justice-loving men ': that whole class is inexpressibly wearisome to him. Hear with what uncommon animation he perorates :

' The man who cannot wonder, who does not habitually wonder (and worship) were he President of innumerable Royal Societies, and carried the whole *Mécanique Céleste* and *Hegel's Philosophy*, and the epitome of all Laboratories and Observatories with their results, in his single head,—is but a Pair of Spectacles behind which there is no Eye. Let those who have Eyes look through him, then he may be useful.

' Thou wilt have no Mystery and Mysticism; wilt walk through thy world by the sunshine of what thou callest Truth, or even by the hand-lamp of what I call Attorney-Logic; and " explain " all, " account " for all, or believe nothing of it? Nay, thou wilt attempt laughter; whoso recognises the unfathomable, all-pervading domain of Mystery, which is everywhere under our feet and among our hands; to whom the Universe is an Oracle and Temple, as well as a Kitchen and Cattlestall,—he shall be a delirious Mystic; to him thou, with sniffing charity, wilt protrusively proffer thy hand-lamp, and shriek, as one injured, when he kicks his foot through it?—*Armer Teufel!* Doth not thy cow calve, doth not thy bull gender? Thou thyself, wert thou not born, wilt thou not die? " Explain " me all this, or do one of two things : Retire into private places with thy foolish cackle; or, what were better, give it up, and weep, not that the reign of wonder is done, and God's world all disembellished and prosaic, but that thou hitherto art a Dilettante and sandblind Pedant.'

CHAPTER XI

PROSPECTIVE

THE Philosophy of Clothes is now to all readers, as we predicted it would do, unfolding itself into new boundless expansions, of a cloudclapt, almost chimerical aspect, yet not without azure loomings in the far distance, and streaks as of an Elysian brightness; the highly questionable purport and promise of which it is becoming more and more important for us to ascertain. Is that a real Elysian brightness, cries many a timid wayfarer, or the reflex of Pandemonian lava? Is it of a truth leading us into beatific Asphodel meadows, or the yellow-burning marl of a Hell-on-Earth?

Our Professor, like other Mystics, whether delirious or inspired, gives an Editor enough to do. Ever higher and dizzier are the heights he leads us to; more piercing, all-comprehending, all-confounding are his views and glances. For example, this of Nature being not an Aggregate but a Whole :

' Well sang the Hebrew Psalmist: " If I take the wings of the morning and dwell in the uttermost parts of the universe, God is there." Thou thyself, O cultivated reader, who too probably art no Psalmist, but a Prosaist, knowing GOD only by tradition, knowest thou any corner of the world where at least FORCE is not? The drop which thou shakest from thy wet hand, rests not where it falls, but to-morrow thou findest it swept away; already on the wings of the Northwind, it is nearing the Tropic of Cancer. How came it to evaporate, and not lie motionless? Thinkest thou there is aught motionless; without Force, and utterly dead?

'As I rode through the Schwarzwald, I said to myself: That little fire which grows star-like across the dark-growing (*nachtende*) moor, where the sooty smith bends over his anvil, and thou hopest to replace thy lost horse-shoe,—is it a detached, separated speck, cut-off from the whole Universe; or indissolubly joined to the whole? Thou fool, that smithy-fire was (primarily) kindled at the Sun; is fed by air that circulates from before Noah's Deluge, from beyond the Dogstar; therein, with Iron Force, and Coal Force, and the far stranger Force of Man, are cunning affinities and battles and victories of Force brought about; it is a little ganglion, or nervous centre, in the great vital system of Immensity. Call it, if thou wilt, an unconscious Altar, kindled on the bosom of the All; whose iron sacrifice, whose iron smoke and influence reach quite through the All; whose dingy Priest, not by word, yet by brain and sinew, preaches forth the mystery of Force; nay preaches forth (exoterically enough) one little textlet from the Gospel of Freedom, the Gospel of Man's Force, commanding, and one day to be all-commanding.

'Detached, separated! I say there is no such separation: nothing hitherto was ever stranded, cast aside; but all, were it only a withered leaf, works together with all; is borne forward on the bottomless, shoreless flood of Action, and lives through perpetual metamorphoses. The withered leaf is not dead and lost, there are Forces in it and around it, though working in inverse order; else how could it *rot*? Despise not the rag from which man makes Paper, or the litter from which the earth makes Corn. Rightly viewed no meanest object is insignificant; all objects are as windows, through which the philosophic eye looks into Infinitude itself.'

Again, leaving that wondrous Schwarzwald Smithy-Altar, what vacant, high-sailing air-ships are these, and whither will they sail with us?

' All visible things are emblems; what thou seest is not there on its own account; strictly taken, is not there at all: Matter exists only spiritually, and to represent some Idea, and *body* it forth. Hence Clothes, as despicable as we think them, are so unspeakably significant. Clothes, from the King's mantle downwards, are emblematic, not of want only, but of a manifold cunning Victory over Want. On the other hand, all Emblematic things are properly Clothes, thought-woven or hand-woven: must not the Imagination weave Garments, visible Bodies, wherein the else invisible creations and inspirations of our Reason are, like Spirits, revealed, and first become all-powerful;—the rather if, as we often see, the Hand too aid her, and (by wool Clothes or otherwise) reveal such even to the outward eye?

' Men are properly said to be clothed with Authority, clothed with Beauty, with Curses, and the like. Nay, if you consider it, what is Man himself, and his whole terrestrial Life, but an Emblem; a Clothing or visible Garment for that divine ME of his, cast hither, like a light-particle, down from Heaven? Thus is he said also to be clothed with a Body.

' Language is called the Garment of Thought: however, it should rather be, Language is the Flesh-Garment, the Body, of thought. I said that Imagination wove this Flesh-Garment; and does not she? Metaphors are her stuff: examine Language; what, if you except some few primitive elements (of natural sound), what is it all but Metaphors, recognised as such, or no longer recognised; still fluid and florid, or now solid-grown and colourless? If those same primitive elements are the osseous fixtures in the Flesh-Garment, Language,—then are Metaphors its muscles and tissues and living integuments. An unmetaphorical style you shall in vain seek for: is not your very *Attention* a *Stretching-to?* The difference lies here: some styles are lean, adust, wiry, the muscle itself seems osseous; some are even quite pallid, hunger-bitten and dead-looking; while others again glow in the flush of health and vigorous self-growth, sometimes (as in my own case) not without an apoplectic tendency. Moreover, there are sham Metaphors, which overhanging that same Thought's-Body (best naked), and deceptively bedizening, or bolstering it out, may be called its false stuffings, superfluous show-cloaks (*Putz-Mäntel*), and tawdry woollen rags : whereof he that runs and reads may gather whole hampers,—and burn them.'

Than which paragraph on Metaphors did the reader ever chance to see a more surprisingly metaphorical? However, that is not our chief grievance; the Professor continues :

' Why multiply instances? It is written, the Heavens and the Earth shall fade away like a Vesture; which indeed they are : the Time-vesture of the Eternal. Whatsoever sensibly exists, whatsoever represents Spirit to Spirit, is properly a Clothing, a suit of Raiment, put on for a season, and to be laid off. Thus in this one pregnant subject of CLOTHES, rightly understood, is included all that men have thought, dreamed, done, and been : the whole External Universe and what it holds is but Clothing; and the essence of all Science lies in the PHILOSOPHY OF CLOTHES.'

Towards these dim infinitely-expanded regions, close-bordering on the impalpable Inane, it is not without apprehension, and perpetual difficulties, that the Editor sees himself journeying and struggling. Till lately a cheerful daystar of hope hung before him, in the expected Aid of Hofrath Heuschrecke; which daystar, however, melts now, not into the red of morning, but into a vague, gray half-light, uncertain whether dawn of day or dusk of utter darkness. For the last week, these so-called Biographical Documents are in his hand. By the kindness of a Scottish Hamburg Merchant, whose name, known to the whole mercantile world, he must not mention; but whose honourable courtesy, now and often before spontaneously manifested to him, a mere literary stranger, he cannot soon forget,—the bulky Weissnichtwo Packet, with all its Custom-house seals, foreign hieroglyphs, and miscellaneous tokens of Travel, arrived here in perfect safety, and free of cost. The reader shall now fancy with what hot haste it was broken up, with what breathless expectation glanced over; and, alas, with what unquiet disappointment it has, since then, been often thrown down, and again taken up.

Hofrath Heuschrecke, in a too long-winded Letter, full of compliments, Weissnichtwo politics, dinners, dining repartees, and other ephemeral trivialities, proceeds to remind us of what we know well already : that however it may be with Metaphysics, and other abstract Science originating in the Head (*Verstand*) alone, no Life-Philosophy (*Lebensphilosophie*), such as this of Clothes pretends to be, which originates equally in the Character (*Gemüth*), and equally speaks thereto, can attain its significance till the Character itself is known and seen; 'till the Author's View of the World (*Weltansicht*), and how he actively and passively came by such view, are clear : in short till a Biography of him has been philosophico-poetically written, and philosophico-poetically read.' 'Nay,' adds he, 'were the speculative scientific Truth even known, you still, in this inquiring age, ask yourself, Whence came it, and Why, and How?—and rest not, till, if no better may be, Fancy have shaped-out an answer; and either in the authentic lineaments of Fact, or the forged ones of Fiction, a complete picture and Genetical History of the Man and his spiritual Endeavour lies before you. But why,' says the Hofrath, and indeed say we, 'do I dilate on the uses of our Teufelsdröckh's Biography? The great Herr Minister von Goethe has penetratingly remarked that "Man is properly the *only* object that interests man" : thus I too have noted, that in Weissnichtwo our whole conversation is little or nothing else but Biography or Auto-Biography; ever humanoanecdotical (*menschlich-anekdotisch*). Biography is by nature the most universally profitable, universally pleasant of all things : especially Biography of distinguished individuals.

'By this time, *mein Verehrtester* (my Most Esteemed),' continues he, with an eloquence which, unless the words be purloined from Teufelsdröckh, or some trick of his, as we suspect, is well-nigh unaccountable, 'by this time you are fairly plunged (*vertieft*) in that mighty forest of Clothes-Philosophy; and looking

round, as all readers do, with astonishment enough.
Such portions and passages as you have already
mastered, and brought to paper, could not but awaken
a strange curiosity touching the mind they issued from;
the perhaps unparalleled psychical mechanism, which
manufactured such matter, and emitted it to the light
of day. Had Teufelsdröckh also a father and mother;
did he, at one time, wear drivel-bibs, and live on spoon-
meat? Did he ever, in rapture and tears, clasp a friend's
bosom to his; looks he also wistfully into the long
burial-aisle of the Past, where only winds, and their
low harsh moan, give inarticulate answer? Has he
fought duels;—good Heaven! how did he comport himself when in Love? By what singular stair-steps, in
short, and subterranean passages, and sloughs of Despair, and steep Pisgah hills, has he reached this wonderful prophetic Hebron (a true Old-Clothes Jewry) where
he now dwells?

'To all these natural questions the voice of public
History is as yet silent. Certain only that he has been,
and is, a Pilgrim, and Traveller from a far Country;
more or less footsore and travel-soiled; has parted with
road-companions; fallen among thieves, been poisoned
by bad cookery, blistered with bug-bites; nevertheless,
at every stage (for they have let him pass), has had the
Bill to discharge. But the whole particulars of his
Route, his Weather-observations, the picturesque
Sketches he took, though all regularly jotted down (in
indelible sympathetic-ink by an invisible interior Penman), are these nowhere forthcoming? Perhaps quite
lost: one other leaf of that mighty Volume (of human
Memory) left to fly abroad, unprinted, unpublished,
unbound up, as waste paper; and to rot, the sport of
rainy winds?

'No, *verehrtester Herr Herausgeber*, in no wise! I
here, by the unexampled favour you stand in with our
Sage, send not a Biography only, but an Autobiography:
at least the materials for such; wherefrom, if I mis-
reckon not, your perspicacity will draw fullest insight:
and so the whole Philosophy and Philosopher of Clothes
will stand clear to the wondering eyes of England, nay

thence, through America, through Hindostan, and the antipodal New Holland, finally conquer (*einnehmen*) great part of this terrestrial Planet!'

And now let the sympathising reader judge of our feeling when, in place of this same Autobiography with 'fullest insight,' we find—Six considerable PAPER-BAGS, carefully sealed, and marked successively, in gilt China-ink, with the symbols of the Six southern Zodiacal Signs, beginning at Libra; in the inside of which sealed Bags lie miscellaneous masses of Sheets, and oftener Shreds and Snips, written in Professor Teufelsdröckh's scarce legible *cursiv-schrift;* and treating of all imaginable things under the Zodiac and above it, but of his own personal history only at rare intervals, and then in the most enigmatic manner.

Whole fascicles there are, wherein the Professor, or, as he here, speaking in the third person, calls himself, 'the Wanderer,' is not once named. Then again, amidst what seems to be a Metaphysico-theological Disquisition, 'Detached Thoughts on the Steam-engine,' or, 'The continued Possibility of Prophecy,' we shall meet with some quite private, not unimportant Biographical fact. On certain sheets stand Dreams, authentic or not, while the circumjacent waking Actions are omitted. Anecdotes, oftenest without date of place or time, fly loosely on separate slips, like Sibylline leaves. Interspersed also are long purely Autobiographical delineations; yet without connexion, without recognisable coherence; so unimportant, so superfluously minute, they almost remind us of 'P.P. Clerk of this Parish.' Thus does famine of intelligence alternate with waste. Selection, order, appears to be unknown to the Professor. In all Bags the same imbroglio; only perhaps in the Bag *Capricorn,* and those near it, the confusion a little worse confounded. Close by a rather eloquent Oration, 'On receiving the Doctor's-Hat,' lie washbills, marked *bezahlt* (settled). His Travels are indicated by the Street-Advertisements of the various cities he has visited; of which Street-Advertisements, in most living tongues, here is perhaps the completest collection extant.

So that if the Clothes-Volume itself was too like a

Chaos, we have now instead of the solar Luminary that should still it, the airy Limbo which by intermixture will farther volatilise and discompose it! As we shall perhaps see it our duty ultimately to deposit these Six Paper-Bags in the British Museum, farther description, and all vituperation of them, may be spared. Biography or Autobiography of Teufelsdröckh there is, clearly enough, none to be gleaned here : at most some sketchy, shadowy fugitive likeness of him may, by unheard-of efforts, partly of intellect, partly of imagination, on the side of Editor and of Reader, rise up between them. Only as a gaseous-chaotic Appendix to that aqueous-chaotic Volume can the contents of the Six Bags hover round us, and portions thereof be incorporated with our delineation of it.

Daily and nightly does the Editor sit (with green spectacles) deciphering these unimaginable Documents from their perplexed *cursiv-schrift;* collating them with the almost equally unimaginable Volume, which stands in legible print. Over such a universal medley of high and low, of hot, cold, moist and dry, is he here struggling (by union of like with like, which is Method) to build a firm Bridge for British travellers. Never perhaps since our first Bridge-builders, Sin and Death, built that stupendous Arch from Hell-gate to the Earth, did any Pontifex, or Pontiff, undertake such a task as the present Editor. For in this Arch too, leading, as we humbly presume, far otherwards than that grand primeval one, the materials are to be fished-up from the weltering deep, and down from the simmering air, here one mass, there another, and cunningly cemented, while the elements boil beneath : nor is there any supernatural force to do it with; but simply the Diligence and feeble thinking Faculty of an English Editor, endeavouring to evolve printed Creation out of a German printed and written Chaos, wherein, as he shoots to and fro in it, gathering, clutching, piercing the Why to the far-distant Wherefore, his whole Faculty and Self are like to be swallowed up.

Patiently, under these incessant toils and agitations, does the Editor, dismissing all anger, see his otherwise robust health declining; some fraction of his allotted

natural sleep nightly leaving him, and little but an
inflamed nervous-system to be looked for.   What is the
use of health, or of life, if not to do some work therewith? And what work nobler than transplanting foreign
Thought into the barren domestic soil; except indeed
planting Thought of your own, which the fewest are
privileged to do?   Wild as it looks, this Philosophy of
Clothes, can we ever reach its real meaning, promises
to reveal new-coming Eras, the first dim rudiments and
already-budding germs of a nobler Era, in Universal
History.   Is not such a prize worth some striving?
Forward with us, courageous reader; be it towards
failure, or towards success! The latter thou sharest
with us; the former also is not all our own.

BOOK SECOND

CHAPTER I

GENESIS

In a psychological point of view, it is perhaps questionable whether from birth and genealogy, how closely scrutinised soever, much insight is to be gained. Nevertheless, as in every phenomenon the Beginning remains always the most notable moment; so, with regard to any great man, we rest not till, for our scientific profit or not, the whole circumstances of his first appearance in this Planet, and what manner of Public Entry he made, are with utmost completeness rendered manifest. To the Genesis of our Clothes-Philosopher, then, be this First Chapter consecrated. Unhappily, indeed, he seems to be of quite obscure extraction; uncertain, we might almost say, whether of any: so that this Genesis of his can properly be nothing but an Exodus (or transit out of Invisibility into Visibility); whereof the preliminary portion is nowhere forthcoming.

'In the village of Entepfuhl,' thus writes he, in the Bag *Libra,* on various Papers, which we arrange with difficulty, ' dwelt Andreas Futteral and his wife; childless, in still seclusion, and cheerful though now verging towards old age. Andreas had been grenadier Sergeant, and even regimental Schoolmaster under Frederick the Great; but now, quitting the halbert and ferule for the spade and pruning-hook, cultivated a little Orchard, on the produce of which he, Cincinnatus-like, lived not without dignity. Fruits, the peach, the apple, the grape, with other varieties came in their season; all which Andreas knew how to sell: on evenings he smoked largely, or read (as beseemed a regimental Schoolmaster), and talked to neighbours that would listen about the Victory of Rossbach; and how Fritz the Only (*der Einzige*) had once with his own royal lips spoken to him, had been pleased to say, when Andreas as camp-sentinel demanded the pass-word, " *Schweig Hund* (Peace, hound)!" before any of his staff-adjutants could answer. " *Das nenn' ich mir einen König*, There is what I call a King," would Andreas exclaim : " but the smoke of Kunersdorf was still smarting his eyes."

' Gretchen, the housewife, won like Desdemona by the deeds rather than the looks of her now veteran Othello, lived not in altogether military subordination ; for, as Andreas said, " the womankind will not drill (*wer kann die Weiberchen dressiren*)" : nevertheless she at heart loved him both for valour and wisdom ; to her a Prussian grenadier Sergeant and Regiment's Schoolmaster was little other than a Cicero and Cid : what you see, yet cannot see over, is as good as infinite. Nay, was not Andreas in very deed a man of order, courage, downrightness (*Geradheit*) ; that understood Büsching's *Geography,* had been in the victory of Rossbach, and left for dead in the camisade of Hochkirch ? The good Gretchen, for all her fretting, watched over him and hovered round him as only a true housemother can : assiduously she cooked and sewed and scoured for him ; so that not only his old regimental sword and grenadier-cap, but the whole habitation and environment, where on pegs of honour they hung, looked ever trim and gay : a roomy painted Cottage, embowered in fruit-trees and forest-trees, evergreens and honeysuckles ; rising many-coloured from amid shaven grassplots, flowers struggling-in through the very windows ; under its long projecting eaves nothing but gardentools in methodic piles (to screen them from rain), and seats where, especially on summer nights, a King might have wished to sit and smoke, and call it his. Such a *Bauergut* (Copyhold) had Gretchen given her veteran ; whose sinewy arms, and long-disused gardening talent, had made it what you saw.

' Into this umbrageous Man's-nest, one meek yellow evening or dusk, when the Sun, hidden indeed from terrestrial Entepfuhl, did nevertheless journey visible and radiant along the celestial Balance (*Libra*), it was that a Stranger of reverend aspect entered ; and, with grave salutation, stood before the two rather astonished housemates. He was close-muffled in a wide mantle ;

which without further parley unfolding, he deposited
therefrom what seemed some Basket, overhung with
green Persian silk; saying only : *Ihr lieben Leute, hier
bringe ein unschätzbares Verleihen; nehmt es in aller
Acht, sorgfältigst benützt es : mit hohem Lohn, oder
wohl mit schweren Zinsen, wird's einst zurückgefordert.*
" Good Christian people, here lies for you an invaluable
Loan ; take all heed thereof, in all carefulness employ
it : with high recompense, or else with heavy penalty,
will it one day be required back." Uttering which
singular words, in a clear, bell-like, forever memorable
tone, the Stranger gracefully withdrew ; and before
Andreas or his wife, gazing in expectant wonder, had
time to fashion either question or answer, was clean
gone. Neither out of doors could aught of him be seen
or heard ; he had vanished in the thickets, in the dusk ;
the Orchard-gate stood quietly closed : the Stranger
was gone once and always. So sudden had the whole
transaction been, in the autumn stillness and twilight,
so gentle, noiseless, that the Futterals could have
fancied it all a trick of Imagination, or some visit from
an authentic Spirit. Only that the green-silk Basket,
such as neither Imagination nor authentic Spirits are
wont to carry, still stood visible and tangible on their
little parlour-table. Towards this the astonished couple,
now with lit candle, hastily turned their attention. Lifting the green veil, to see what invaluable it hid, they
descried there, amid down and rich white wrappages,
no Pitt Diamond or Hapsburg Regalia, but, in the
softest sleep, a little red-coloured Infant ! Beside it,
lay a roll of gold Friedrichs, the exact amount of which
was never publicly known ; also a *Taufschein* (baptismal
certificate), wherein unfortunately nothing but the Name
was decipherable ; other document or indication none
whatever.

 ' To wonder and conjecture was unavailing, then and
always thenceforth. Nowhere in Entepfuhl, on the
morrow or next day, did tidings transpire of any such
figure as the Stranger ; nor could the Traveller, who had
passed through the neighbouring Town in coach-and-
four, be connected with this Apparition, except in the
way of gratuitous surmise. Meanwhile, for Andreas and

D 278

his wife, the grand practical problem was : What to do with this little sleeping red-coloured Infant? Amid amazements and curiosities, which had to die away without external satisfying, they resolved, as in such circumstances charitable prudent people needs must, on nursing it, though with spoon-meat, into whiteness, and if possible into manhood. The Heavens smiled on their endeavour : thus has that same mysterious Individual ever since had a status for himself in this visible Universe, some modicum of victual and lodging and parade-ground; and now expanded in bulk, faculty and knowledge of good and evil, he, as HERR DIOGENES TEUFELSDRÖCKH, professes or is ready to profess, perhaps not altogether without effect, in the new University of Weissnichtwo, the new Science of Things in General.'

Our Philosopher declares here, as indeed we should think he well might, that these facts, first communicated, by the good Gretchen Futteral, in his twelfth year, 'produced on the boyish heart and fancy a quite indelible impression. Who this Reverend Personage,' he says, 'that glided into the Orchard Cottage when the Sun was in Libra, and then, as on spirit's wings, glided out again, might be? An inexpressible desire, full of love and of sadness, has often since struggled within me to shape an answer. Ever, in my distresses and my loneliness, has Fantasy turned, full of longing (*sehnsuchtsvoll*), to that unknown Father, who perhaps far from me, perhaps near, either way invisible, might have taken me to his paternal bosom, there to lie screened from many a woe. Thou beloved Father, dost thou still, shut out from me only by thin penetrable curtains of earthly Space, wend to and fro among the crowd of the living? Or art thou hidden by those far thicker curtains of the Everlasting Night, or rather of the Everlasting Day, through which my mortal eye and outstretched arms need not strive to reach? Alas, I know not, and in vain vex myself to know. More than once, heart-deluded, have I taken for thee this and the other noble-looking Stranger; and approached him wistfully, with infinite regard; but he too had to repel me; he too was not thou.

'And yet, O Man born of Woman,' cries the Autobiographer, with one of his sudden whirls, 'wherein is my case peculiar? Hadst thou, any more than I, a Father whom thou knowest? The Andreas and Gretchen, or the Adam and Eve, who led thee into Life, and for a time suckled and pap-fed thee there, whom thou namest Father and Mother; these were, like mine, but thy nursing-father and nursing-mother: thy true Beginning and Father is in Heaven, whom with the bodily eye thou shalt never behold, but only with the spiritual.'

'The little green veil,' adds he, among much similar moralising, and embroiled discoursing, 'I yet keep; still more inseparably the Name, Diogenes Teufelsdröckh. From the veil can nothing be inferred: a piece of now quite faded Persian silk, like thousands of others. On the Name I have many times meditated and conjectured; but neither in this lay there any clue. That it was my unknown Father's name I must hesitate to believe. To no purpose have I searched through all the Herald's Books, in and without the German Empire, and through all manner of Subscriber-Lists (*Pränumeranten*), Militia-Rolls, and other Name-catalogues; extraordinary names as we have in Germany, the name Teufelsdröckh, except as appended to my own person, nowhere occurs. Again, what may the unchristian rather than Christian "Diogenes" mean? Did that reverend Basket-bearer intend, by such designation, to shadow-forth my future destiny, or his own present malign humour? Perhaps the latter, perhaps both. Thou ill-starred Parent, who like an Ostrich hadst to leave thy ill-starred offspring to be hatched into self-support by the mere sky-influences of Chance, can thy pilgrimage have been a smooth one? Beset by Misfortune thou doubtless hast been; or indeed by the worst figure of Misfortune, by Misconduct. Often have I fancied how, in thy hard life-battle, thou wert shot at, and slung at, wounded, hand-fettered, hamstrung, browbeaten and bedevilled by the Time-Spirit (*Zeitgeist*) in thyself and others, till the good soul first given thee was seared into grim rage; and thou hadst nothing for it but to leave in me an indignant appeal to the Future, and living speaking Protest against the Devil, as that same Spirit not of the Time only, but of Time itself, is well named! Which Appeal and Protest, may I now modestly add, was not perhaps quite lost in air.

'For indeed, as Walter Shandy often insisted, there is much, nay almost all, in Names. The Name is the earliest Garment you wrap round the earth-visiting ME; to which it thenceforth cleaves, more tenaciously (for there are Names that have lasted nigh thirty centuries) than the very skin. And now from without, what mystic influences does it not send inwards, even to the centre; especially in those plastic first-times, when the whole soul is yet infantine, soft, and the invisible seedgrain will grow to be an all overshadowing tree! Names? Could I unfold the influence of Names, which are the most important of all Clothings, I were a second greater Trismegistus. Not only all common Speech, but Science, Poetry itself is no other, if thou consider it, than a right *Naming*. Adam's first task was giving names to natural Appearances: what is ours still but a continuation of the same; be the Appearances exotic-vegetable, organic, mechanic, stars or starry movements (as in Science); or (as in Poetry) passions, virtues, calamities, God-attributes, Gods?—In a very plain sense the Proverb says, *Call one a thief, and he will steal;* in an almost similar sense may we not perhaps say, *Call one Diogenes Teufelsdröckh, and he will open the Philosophy of Clothes?*'

'Meanwhile the incipient Diogenes, like others, all ignorant of his Why, his How or Whereabout, was opening his eyes to the kind Light; sprawling-out his ten fingers and toes; listening, tasting, feeling; in a word, by all his Five Senses, still more by his Sixth Sense of Hunger, and a whole infinitude of inward, spiritual, half-awakened Senses, endeavouring daily to acquire for himself some knowledge of this strange Universe where he had arrived, be his task therein what it might. Infinite was his progress; thus in some fifteen months, he could perform the miracle of—Speech! To breed a fresh Soul, is it not like brooding a fresh (celestial) Egg; wherein as yet all is formless, power-less; yet by degrees organic elements and fibres shoot through the watery albumen; and out of vague Sensation grows Thought, grows Fantasy and Force, and we have Philosophies, Dynasties, nay Poetries and Religions!

'Young Diogenes, or rather young Gneschen, for by such diminutive had they in their fondness named him, travelled forward to those high consummations, by quick yet easy stages. The Futterals, to avoid vain talk, and moreover keep the roll of gold Friedrichs safe, gave-out that he was a grand-nephew; the orphan of some sister's daughter, suddenly deceased, in Andreas's distant Prussian birthland; of whom, as of her indigent sorrowing widower, little enough was known at Entepfuhl. Heedless of all which, the Nurseling took to his spoon-meat, and throve. I have heard him noted as a still infant, that kept his mind much to himself; above all, that seldom or never cried. He already felt that time was precious; that he had other work cut-out for him than whimpering.'

Such, after utmost painful search and collation among these miscellaneous Paper-masses, is all the notice we can gather of Herr Teufelsdröckh's genealogy. More imperfect, more enigmatic it can seem to few readers than to us. The Professor, in whom truly we more and more discern a certain satirical turn, and deep undercurrents of roguish whim, for the present stands pledged in honour, so we will not doubt him: but seems it not conceivable that, by the ' good Gretchen Futteral,' or some other perhaps interested party, he has himself been deceived? Should these sheets, translated or not, ever reach the Entepfuhl Circulating Library, some cultivated native of that district might feel called to afford explanation. Nay, since Books, like invisible scouts, permeate the whole habitable globe, and Timbuctoo itself is not safe from British Literature, may not some Copy find out even the mysterious basket-bearing Stranger, who in a state of extreme senility perhaps still exists; and gently force even him to disclose himself; to claim openly a son, in whom any father may feel pride?

CHAPTER II

IDYLLIC

'HAPPY season of Childhood!' exclaims Teufelsdröckh: 'Kind Nature, that art to all a bountiful
mother; that visitest the poor man's hut with auroral
radiance; and for thy Nurseling hast provided a soft
swathing of Love and infinite Hope, wherein he waxes
and slumbers, danced-round (*umgaukelt*) by sweetest
Dreams! If the paternal Cottage still shuts us in, its
roof still screens us; with a Father we have as yet a
prophet, priest and king, and an Obedience that makes
us free. The young spirit has awakened out of Eternity,
and knows not what we mean by Time; as yet Time
is no fast-hurrying stream, but a sportful sunlit ocean;
years to the child are as ages: ah! the secret of Vicissitude, of that slower or quicker decay and ceaseless down-
rushing of the universal World-fabric, from the granite
mountain to the man or day-moth, is yet unknown; and
in a motionless Universe, we taste, what afterwards in
this quick-whirling Universe is forever denied us, the
balm of Rest. Sleep on, thou fair Child, for thy long
rough journey is at hand! A little while, and thou too
shalt sleep no more, but thy very dreams shall be mimic
battles; thou too, with old Arnauld, wilt have to say in
stern patience: "Rest? Rest? Shall I not have all
Eternity to rest in?" Celestial Nepenthe! though a
Pyrrhus conquer empires, and an Alexander sack the
world, he finds thee not; and thou hast once fallen
gently, of thy own accord, on the eyelids, on the heart
of every mother's child. For as yet, sleep and waking
are one: the fair Life-garden rustles infinite around, and
everywhere is dewy fragrance, and the budding of Hope;
which budding, if in youth, too frostnipt, it grow to
flowers, will in manhood yield no fruit, but a prickly,
bitter-rinded stone-fruit, of which the fewest can find
the kernel.'

In such rose-coloured light does our Professor, as
Poets are wont, look back on his childhood; the historical details of which (to say nothing of much other

vague oratorical matter) he accordingly dwells on with
an almost wearisome minuteness. We hear of Entepfuhl standing 'in trustful derangement' among the
woody slopes; the paternal Orchard flanking it as
extreme out-post from below; the little Kuhbach gushing kindly by, among beech-rows, through river after
river, into the Donau, into the Black Sea, into the Atmosphere and Universe; and how 'the brave old Linden,'
stretching like a parasol of twenty ells in radius, over-
topping all other rows and clumps, towered-up from the
central *Agora* and *Campus Martius* of the Village, like
its Sacred Tree; and how the old men sat talking under
its shadow (Gneschen often greedily listening), and the
wearied labourers reclined, and the unwearied children
sported, and the young men and maidens often danced
to flute-music. 'Glorious summer twilights,' cries
Teufelsdröckh, 'when the Sun, like a proud Conqueror
and Imperial Taskmaster, turned his back, with his
gold-purple emblazonry, and all his fireclad body-guard
(of Prismatic Colours); and the tired brickmakers of
this clay Earth might steal a little frolic, and those few
meek Stars would not tell of them!'

Then we have long details of the *Weinlesen* (Vintage),
the Harvest-Home, Christmas, and so forth; with a
whole cycle of the Entepfuhl Children's-games, differing apparently by mere superficial shades from those
of other countries. Concerning all which, we shall here,
for obvious reasons, say nothing. What cares the world
for our as yet miniature Philosopher's achievements
under that 'brave old Linden'? Or even where is the
use of such practical reflections as the following? 'In
all the sports of Children, were it only in their wanton
breakages and defacements, you shall discern a creative
instinct (*schaffenden Trieb*): the Mankin feels that he
is a born Man, that his vocation is to work. The
choicest present you can make him is a Tool; be it
knife or pen-gun, for construction or for destruction;
either way it is for Work, for Change. In gregarious
sports of skill or strength, the Boy trains himself to Co-
operation, for war or peace, as governor or governed:
the little Maid again, provident of her domestic destiny,
takes with preference to Dolls.'

Perhaps, however, we may give this anecdote, considering who it is that relates it : ' My first short-clothes were of yellow serge; or rather, I should say, my first short-cloth, for the vesture was one and indivisible, reaching from neck to ankle, a mere body with four limbs : of which fashion how little could I then divine the architectural, how much less the moral significance !'

More graceful is the following little picture : ' On fine evenings I was wont to carry-forth my supper (bread-crumb boiled in milk), and eat it out-of-doors. On the coping of the Orchard-wall, which I could reach by climbing, or still more easily if Father Andreas would set-up the pruning-ladder, my porringer was placed : there, many a sunset, have I, looking at the distant western Mountains, consumed, not without relish, my evening meal. Those hues of gold and azure, that hush of World's expectation as Day died, were still a Hebrew Speech for me; nevertheless I was looking at the fair illuminated Letters, and had an eye for their gilding.'

With ' the little one's friendship for cattle and poultry ' we shall not much intermeddle. It may be that hereby he acquired a ' certain deeper sympathy with animated Nature ' : but when, we would ask, saw any man, in a collection of Biographical Documents, such a piece as this : ' Impressive enough (*bedeutungs-voll*) was it to hear, in early morning, the Swineherd's horn; and know that so many hungry happy quadrupeds were, on all sides, starting in hot haste to join him, for breakfast on the Heath. Or to see them at eventide, all marching-in again, with short squeak, almost in military order; and each, topographically correct, trotting-off in succession to the right or left, through its own lane, to its own dwelling; till old Kunz, at the Village-head, now left alone, blew his last blast, and retired for the night. We are wont to love the Hog chiefly in the form of Ham; yet did not these bristly thick-skinned beings here manifest intelligence, perhaps humour of character; at any rate, a touching, trustful submissiveness to Man,—who, were he but a Swineherd, in darned gabardine, and leather breeches more resembling slate or discoloured-tin breeches, is still the Hierarch of this lower world?'

It is maintained, by Helvetius and his set, that an infant of genius is quite the same as any other infant, only that certain surprisingly favourable influences accompany him through life, especially through childhood, and expand him, while others lie closefolded and continue dunces. Herein, say they, consists the whole difference between an inspired Prophet and a double-barrelled Game-preserver : the inner man of the one has been fostered into generous development; that of the other, crushed-down perhaps by vigour of animal digestion, and the like, has exuded and evaporated, or at best sleeps now irresuscitably stagnant at the bottom of his stomach. ' With which opinion,' cries Teufelsdröckh, ' I should as soon agree as with this other, that an acorn might, by favourable or unfavourable influences of soil and climate, be nursed into a cabbage, or the cabbage-seed into an oak.

' Nevertheless,' continues he, ' I too acknowledge the all-but omnipotence of early culture and nurture : hereby we have either a doddered dwarf bush, or a high-towering, wide-shadowing tree; either a sick yellow cabbage, or an edible luxuriant green one. Of a truth, it is the duty of all men, especially of all philosophers, to note-down with accuracy the characteristic circumstances of their Education, what furthered, what hindered, what in any way modified it : to which duty, nowadays so pressing for many a German Autobiographer, I also zealously address myself.'—Thou rogue! Is it by short-clothes of yellow serge, and swineherd horns, that an infant of genius is educated? And yet, as usual, it ever remains doubtful whether he is laughing in his sleeve at these Autobiographical times of ours, or writing from the abundance of his own fond ineptitude. For he continues : ' If among the ever-streaming currents of Sights, Hearings, Feelings for Pain or Pleasure, whereby, as in a Magic Hall, young Gneschen went about environed, I might venture to select and specify, perhaps these following were also of the number :

' Doubtless, as childish sports call forth Intellect,

Activity, so the young creature's Imagination was stirred up, and a Historical tendency given him by the narrative habits of Father Andreas; who, with his battle-reminiscences, and gay austere yet hearty patriarchal aspect, could not but appear another Ulysses and "much-enduring Man." Eagerly I hung upon his tales, when listening neighbours enlivened the hearth; from these perils and these travels, wild and far almost as Hades itself, a dim world of Adventure expanded itself within me. Incalculable also was the knowledge I acquired in standing by the Old Men under the Linden-tree: the whole of Immensity was yet new to me; and had not these reverend seniors, talkative enough, been employed in partial surveys thereof for nigh fourscore years? With amazement I began to discover that Entepfuhl stood in the middle of a Country, of a World; that there was such a thing as History, as Biography; to which I also, one day, by hand and tongue, might contribute.

'In a like sense worked the *Postwagen* (Stage-coach), which, slow-rolling under its mountains of men and luggage, wended through our Village: northwards, truly, in the dead of night; yet southwards visibly at eventide. Not till my eighth year did I reflect that this Postwagen could be other than some terrestrial Moon, rising and setting by mere Law of Nature, like the heavenly one; that it came on made highways, from far cities towards far cities; weaving them like a monstrous shuttle into closer and closer union. It was then that, independently of Schiller's *Wilhelm Tell,* I made this not quite insignificant reflection (so true also in spiritual things): *Any road, this simple Entepfuhl road, will lead you to the end of the world!*

'Why mention our Swallows, which, out of far Africa, as I learned, threading their way over seas and mountains, corporate cities and belligerent nations, yearly found themselves, with the month of May, snug-lodged in our Cottage Lobby? The hospitable Father (for cleanliness' sake) had fixed a little bracket plumb under their nest: there they built, and caught flies, and twittered, and bred; and all, I chiefly, from the heart loved them. Bright, nimble creatures, who taught *you* the mason-craft; nay, stranger still, gave you a masonic

incorporation, almost social police? For if, by ill
chance, and when time pressed, your House fell, have I
not seen five neighbourly Helpers appear next day; and
swashing to and fro, with animated, loud, long-drawn
chirpings, and activity almost super-hirundine, complete
it again before nightfall?

'But undoubtedly the grand summary of Entepfuhl
child's-culture, where as in a funnel its manifold influences were concentrated and simultaneously poured-
down on us, was the annual Cattle-fair. Here, assem-
bling from all the four winds, came the elements of an
unspeakable hurly-burly. Nutbrown maids and nutbrown men, all clear-washed, loud-laughing, bedizened
and beribanded; who came for dancing, for treating,
and if possible, for happiness. Topbooted Graziers
from the North; Swiss Brokers, Italian Drovers, also
topbooted, from the South; these with their subalterns
in leather jerkins, leather skull-caps, and long oxgoads;
shouting in half-articulate speech, amid the inarticulate
barking and bellowing. Apart stood Potters from far
Saxony, with their crockery in fair rows; Nürnberg
Pedlars, in booths that to me seemed richer than Ormuz
bazaars; Showmen from the Lago Maggiore; detach-
ments of the *Wiener Schub* (Offscourings of Vienna)
vociferously superintending games of chance. Ballad-
singers brayed, Auctioneers grew hoarse; cheap New
Wine (*heuriger*) flowed like water, still worse confound-
ing the confusion; and high over all, vaulted, in ground-
and-lofty tumbling, a particoloured Merry-Andrew, like
the genius of the place and of Life itself.

'Thus encircled by the mystery of Existence; under
the deep heavenly Firmament; waited-on by the four
golden Seasons, with their vicissitudes of contribution,
for even grim Winter brought its skating-matches and
shooting-matches, its snow-storms and Christmas-
carols,—did the Child sit and learn. These things were
the Alphabet, whereby in aftertime he was to syllable
and partly read the grand Volume of the World; what
matters it whether such Alphabet be in large gilt letters
or in small ungilt ones, so you have an eye to read it?
For Gneschen, eager to learn, the very act of looking
thereon was a blessedness that gilded all: his existence
was a bright, soft element of Joy; out of which, as in

Prospero's Island, wonder after wonder bodied itself forth, to teach by charming.

'Nevertheless, I were but a vain dreamer to say, that even then my felicity was perfect. I had, once for all, come down from Heaven into the Earth. Among the rainbow colours that glowed on my horizon, lay even in childhood a dark ring of Care, as yet no thicker than a thread, and often quite overshone; yet always it reappeared, nay ever waxing broader and broader; till in after-years it almost over-shadowed my whole canopy, and threatened to engulf me in final night. It was the ring of Necessity whereby we are all begirt; happy he for whom a kind heavenly Sun brightens it into a ring of Duty, and plays round it with beautiful prismatic diffractions; yet ever, as basis and as bourne for our whole being, it is there.

'For the first few years of our terrestrial Apprenticeship, we have not much work to do; but, boarded and lodged gratis, are set down mostly to look about us over the workshop, and see others work, till we have understood the tools a little, and can handle this and that. If good Passivity alone, and not good Passivity and good Activity together, were the thing wanted, then was my early position favourable beyond the most. In all that respects openness of Sense, affectionate Temper, ingenuous Curiosity, and the fostering of these, what more could I have wished? On the other side, however, things went not so well. My Active Power (*Thatkraft*) was unfavourably hemmed-in; of which misfortune how many traces yet abide with me! In an orderly house, where the litter of children's sports is hateful enough, your training is too stoical; rather to bear and forbear than to make and do. I was forbid much: wishes in any measure bold I had to renounce; everywhere a strait bond of Obedience inflexibly held me down. Thus already Freewill often came in painful collision with Necessity; so that my tears flowed, and at seasons the Child itself might taste that root of bitterness, wherewith the whole fruitage of our life is mingled and tempered.

'In which habituation to Obedience, truly, it was

beyond measure safer to err by excess than by defect. Obedience is our universal duty and destiny; wherein whoso will not bend must break: too early and too thoroughly we cannot be trained to know that Would, in this world of ours, is as mere zero to Should, and for most part as the smallest of fractions even to Shall. Hereby was laid for me the basis of worldly Discretion, nay, of Morality itself. Let me not quarrel with my upbringing! It was rigorous, too frugal, compressively secluded, everyway unscientific: yet in that very strictness and domestic solitude might there not lie the root of deeper earnestness, of the stem from which all noble fruit must grow? Above all, how unskilful soever, it was loving, it was well-meant, honest; whereby every deficiency was helped. My kind Mother, for as such I must ever love the good Gretchen, did me one altogether invaluable service: she taught me, less indeed by word than by act and daily reverent look and habitude, her own simple version of the Christian Faith. Andreas too attended Church; yet more like a parade-duty, for which he in the other world expected pay with arrears, —as, I trust, he has received; but my Mother, with a true woman's heart, and fine though uncultivated sense, was in the strictest acceptation Religious. How indestructibly the Good grows, and propagates itself, even among the weedy entanglements of Evil! The highest whom I knew on Earth I here saw bowed down, with awe unspeakable, before a Higher in Heaven: such things, especially in infancy, reach inwards to the very core of your being; mysteriously does a Holy of Holies build itself into visibility in the mysterious deeps; and Reverence, the divinest in man, springs forth undying from its mean envelopment of Fear. Wouldst thou rather be a peasant's son that knew, were it never so rudely, there was a God in Heaven and in Man; or a duke's son that only knew there were two-and-thirty quarters on the family-coach?'

To which last question we must answer: Beware, O Teufelsdröckh, of spiritual pride!

CHAPTER III

PEDAGOGY

HITHERTO we see young Gneschen, in his indivisible
case of yellow serge, borne forward mostly on the arms
of kind Nature alone; seated, indeed, and much to his
mind, in the terrestrial workshop; but (except his soft
hazel eyes, which we doubt not already gleamed with a
still intelligence) called upon for little voluntary movement there. Hitherto, accordingly, his aspect is rather
generic, that of an incipient Philosopher and Poet in
the abstract; perhaps it would trouble Herr Heuschrecke
himself to say wherein the special Doctrine of Clothes
is as yet foreshadowed or betokened. For with Gneschen, as with others, the Man may indeed stand pictured
in the Boy (at least all the pigments are there); yet only
some half of the Man stands in the Child, or young
Boy, namely, his Passive endowment, not his Active.
The more impatient are we to discover what figure he
cuts in this latter capacity; how when, to use his own
words, ' he understands the tools a little, and can
handle this or that,' he will proceed to handle it.

Here, however, may be the place to state that, in
much of our Philosopher's history, there is something
of an almost Hindoo character: nay perhaps in that
so well-fostered and everyway excellent ' Passivity '
of his, which, with no free development of the antagon-
ist Activity, distinguished his childhood, we may detect
the rudiments of much that, in after days, and still in
these present days, astonishes the world. For the
shallow-sighted, Teufelsdröckh is oftenest a man without Activity of any kind, a No-man; for the deep-
sighted, again, a man with Activity almost superabund-
ant, yet so spiritual, close-hidden, enigmatic, that no
mortal can foresee its explosions, or even when it has
exploded, so much as ascertain its significance. A
dangerous, difficult temper for the modern European;
above all, disadvantageous in the hero of a Biography!
Now as heretofore it will behove the Editor of these
pages, were it never so unsuccessfully, to do his
endeavour.

Among the earliest tools of any complicacy which a man, especially a man of letters, gets to handle, are his Class-books. On this portion of his History, Teufelsdröckh looks down professedly as indifferent. Reading he ' cannot remember ever to have learned '; so perhaps had it by nature. He says generally : ' Of the insignificant portion of my Education, which depended on Schools, there need almost no notice be taken. I learned what others learn; and kept it stored-by in a corner of my head, seeing as yet no manner of use in it. My Schoolmaster, a downbent, brokenhearted, underfoot martyr, as others of that guild are, did little for me, except discover that he could do little : he, good soul, pronounced me a genius, fit for the learned professions; and that I must be sent to the Gymnasium, and one day to the University. Meanwhile, what printed thing soever I could meet with I read. My very copper pocket-money I laid-out on stall-literature; which, as it accumulated, I with my own hands sewed into volumes. By this means was the young head furnished with a considerable miscellany of things and shadows of things : History in authentic fragments lay mingled with Fabulous chimeras, wherein also was reality; and the whole not as dead stuff, but as living pabulum, tolerably nutritive for a mind as yet so peptic.'

That the Entepfuhl Schoolmaster judged well, we now know. Indeed, already in the youthful Gneschen, with all his outward stillness, there may have been manifest an inward vivacity that promised much; symptoms of a spirit singularly open, thoughtful, almost poetical. Thus, to say nothing of his Suppers on the Orchard-wall, and other phenomena of that earlier period, have many readers of these pages stumbled, in their twelfth year, on such reflections as the following? ' It struck me much, as I sat by the Kuhbach, one silent noontide, and watched it flowing, gurgling, to think how this same streamlet had flowed and gurgled, through all changes of weather and of fortune, from beyond the earliest date of History. Yes, probably on the morning when Joshua forded Jordan; even as at the midday when Cæsar, doubtless with difficulty, swam the Nile, yet kept his *Commentaries* dry,—this little

Kuhbach, assiduous as Tiber, Eurotas or Siloa, was
murmuring on across the wilderness, as yet unnamed,
unseen : here, too, as in the Euphrates and the Ganges,
is a vein or veinlet of the grand World-circulation of
Waters, which, with its atmospheric arteries, has lasted
and lasts simply with the World. Thou fool! Nature
alone is antique, and the oldest art a mushroom; that
idle crag thou sittest on is six-thousand years of age.'
In which little thought, as in a little fountain, may
there not lie the beginning of those well-nigh unutterable
meditations on the grandeur and mystery of TIME, and
its relation to ETERNITY, which play such a part in this
Philosophy of Clothes?

Over his Gymnasic and Academic years the Professor
by no means lingers so lyrical and joyful as over his
childhood. Green sunny tracts there are still; but intersected by bitter rivulets of tears, here and there stagnat-
ing into sour marshes of discontent. 'With my first
view of the Hinterschlag Gymnasium,' writes he, ' my
evil days began. Well do I still remember the red
sunny Whitsuntide morning, when, trotting full of hope
by the side of Father Andreas, I entered the main street
of the place, and saw its steeple-clock (then striking
Eight) and *Schuldthurm* (Jail), and the aproned or dis-
aproned Burghers moving-in to breakfast : a little dog,
in mad terror, was rushing past; for some human imps
had tied a tin-kettle to its tail; thus did the agonised
creature, loud-jingling, career through the whole length
of the Borough, and become notable enough. Fit emblem of many a Conquering Hero, to whom Fate
(wedding Fantasy to Sense, as it often elsewhere does)
has malignantly appended a tin-kettle of Ambition, to
chase him on; which the faster he runs, urges him the
faster, the more loudly and more foolishly! Fit emblem
also of much that awaited myself, in that mischievous
Den; as in the World, whereof it was a portion and
epitome !

' Alas, the kind beech-rows of Entepfuhl were hidden
in the distance : I was among strangers, harshly, at
best indifferently, disposed towards me; the young heart
felt, for the first time, quite orphaned and alone.' His
schoolfellows, as is usual, persecuted him : ' They were

Boys,' he says, ' mostly rude Boys, and obeyed the
impulse of rude Nature, which bids the deerherd fall
upon any stricken hart, the duck-flock put to death any
broken-winged brother or sister, and on all hands the
strong tyrannise over the weak.' He admits, that
though ' perhaps in an unusual degree morally courageous,' he succeeded ill in battle, and would fain have
avoided it; a result, as would appear, owing less to
his small personal stature (for in passionate seasons he
was ' incredibly nimble '), than to his ' virtuous principles ' : ' if it was disgraceful to be beaten,' says
he, ' it was only a shade less disgraceful to have so
much as fought; thus was I drawn two ways at once,
and in this important element of school-history, the war-
element, had little but sorrow.' On the whole, that
same excellent ' Passivity,' so notable in Teufelsdröckh's childhood, is here visibly enough again getting
nourishment. ' He wept often; indeed to such a degree
that he was nicknamed *Der Weinende* (the Tearful),
which epithet, till towards his thirteenth year, was
indeed not quite unmerited. Only at rare intervals did
the young soul burst-forth into fire-eyed rage, and, with
a stormfulness (*Ungestüm*) under which the boldest
quailed, assert that he too had Rights of Man, or at
least of Mankin.' In all which, who does not discern
a fine flower-tree and cinnamon-tree (of genius) nigh
choked among pumpkins, reed-grass and ignoble shrubs;
and forced if it would live, to struggle upwards only,
and not outwards; into a *height* quite sickly, and dis-
proportioned to its *breadth?*

We find, moreover, that his Greek and Latin were
' mechanically ' taught; Hebrew scarce even mechanically; much else which they called History, Cosmo-
graphy, Philosophy, and so forth, no better than not at
all. So that, except inasmuch as Nature was still busy;
and he himself ' went about, as was of old his wont,
among the Craftsmen's workshops, there learning many
things '; and farther lighted on some small store of
curious reading, in Hans Wachtel the Cooper's house,
where he lodged,—his time, it would appear, was utterly
wasted. Which facts the Professor has not yet learned
to look upon with any contentment. Indeed, through-

out the whole of this Bag *Scorpio,* where we now are, and often in the following Bag, he shows himself unusually animated on the matter of Education, and not without some touch of what we might presume to be anger.

' My Teachers,' says he, ' were hide-bound Pedants, without knowledge of man's nature, or of boy's; or of aught save their lexicons and quarterly account-books. Innumerable dead Vocables (no dead Language, for they themselves knew no Language) they crammed into us, and called it fostering the growth of mind. How can an inanimate, mechanical Gerund-grinder, the like of whom will, in a subsequent century, be manufactured at Nürnberg out of wood and leather, foster the growth of anything; much more of Mind, which grows, not like a vegetable (by having its roots littered with etymological compost), but like a spirit, by mysterious contact of Spirit; Thought kindling itself at the fire of living Thought? How shall *he* give kindling, in whose own inward man there is no live coal, but all is burnt-out to a dead grammatical cinder? The Hinterschlag Professors knew syntax enough; and of the human soul thus much: that it had a faculty called Memory, and could be acted-on through the muscular integument by appliance of birch-rods.

' Alas, so is it everywhere, so will it ever be; till the Hodman is discharged, or reduced to hodbearing, and an Architect is hired, and on all hands fitly encouraged: till communities and individuals discover, not without surprise, that fashioning the souls of a generation by Knowledge can rank on a level with blowing their bodies to pieces by Gunpowder; that with Generals and Fieldmarshals for killing, there should be world-honoured Dignitaries, and were it possible, true God-ordained Priests, for teaching. But as yet, though the Soldier wears openly, and even parades, his butchering-tool, nowhere, far as I have travelled, did the Schoolmaster make show of his instructing-tool: nay, were he to walk abroad with birch girt on thigh, as if he therefrom expected honour, would there not, among the idler class, perhaps a certain levity be excited?'

In the third year of this Gymnasic period, Father

Andreas seems to have died : the young Scholar, otherwise so maltreated, saw himself for the first time clad
outwardly in sables, and inwardly in quite inexpressible
melancholy. ' The dark bottomless Abyss, that lies under
our feet, had yawned open ; the pale kingdoms of Death,
with all their innumerable silent nations and generations, stood before him ; the inexorable word, NEVER !
now first showed its meaning. My Mother wept, and
her sorrow got vent ; but in my heart there lay a whole
lake of tears, pent-up in silent desolation. Nevertheless the unworn Spirit is strong ; Life is so healthful
that it even finds nourishment in Death : these stern
experiences, planted down by Memory in my Imagination, rose there to a whole cypress-forest, sad but
beautiful ; waving, with not unmelodious sighs, in dark
luxuriance, in the hottest sunshine, through long years
of youth :—as in manhood also it does, and will do ; for
I have now pitched my tent under a Cypress-tree ; the
Tomb is now my inexpugnable Fortress, ever close by
the gate of which I look upon the hostile armaments,
and pains and penalties of tyrannous Life placidly
enough, and listen to its loudest threatenings with a
still smile. O ye loved ones, that already sleep in the
noiseless Bed of Rest, whom in life I could only weep
for and never help ; and ye, who wide-scattered still
toil lonely in the monster-bearing Desert, dyeing the
flinty ground with your blood,—yet a little while, and
we shall all meet THERE, and our Mother's bosom will
screen us all ; and Oppression's harness, and Sorrow's
fire-whip, and all the Gehenna Bailiffs that patrol and
inhabit ever-vexed Time, cannot thenceforth harm us
any more !'

Close by which rather beautiful apostrophe, lies a
laboured Character of the deceased Andreas Futteral ;
of his natural ability, his deserts in life (as Prussian
Sergeant) ; with long historical inquiries into the genealogy of the Futteral Family, here traced back as far
as Henry the Fowler : the whole of which we pass
over, not without astonishment. It only concerns us
to add, that now was the time when Mother Gretchen
revealed to her foster-son that he was not at all of this
kindred, or indeed of any kindred, having come into

historical existence in the way already known to us.
'Thus was I doubly orphaned,' says he; 'bereft not
only of Possession, but even of Remembrance. Sorrow
and Wonder, here suddenly united, could not but produce abundant fruit. Such a disclosure, in such a
season, struck its roots through my whole nature : ever
till the years of mature manhood, it mingled with my
whole thoughts, was as the stem whereon all my day-
dreams and night-dreams grew. A certain poetic elevation, yet also a corresponding civic depression, it
naturally imparted : *I was like no other ;* in which fixed-
idea, leading sometimes to highest, and oftener to
frightfullest results, may there not lie the first spring
of Tendencies, which in my Life have become remarkable enough? As in birth, so in action, speculation,
and social position, my fellows are perhaps not numerous.'

In the Bag *Sagittarius,* as we at length discover,
Teufelsdröckh has become a University man; though,
how, when, or of what quality, will nowhere disclose
itself with the smallest certainty. Few things, in the
way of confusion and capricious indistinctness, can now
surprise our readers ; not even the total want of dates,
almost without parallel in a Biographical work. So
enigmatic, so chaotic we have always found, and must
always look to find, these scattered Leaves. In *Sagittarius,* however, Teufelsdröckh begins to show himself
even more than usually Sibylline : fragments of all
sorts ; scraps of regular Memoir, College-Exercises,
Programs, Professional Testimoniums, Milkscores, torn
Billets, sometimes to appearance of an amatory cast ;
all blown together as if by merest chance, henceforth
bewilder the sane Historian. To combine any picture
of these University, and the subsequent, years ; much
more, to decipher therein any illustrative primordial
elements of the Clothes-Philosophy, becomes such a
problem as the reader may imagine.

So much we can see ; darkly, as through the foliage
of some wavering thicket : a youth of no common
endowment, who has passed happily through Childhood,
less happily yet still vigorously through Boyhood, now

at length perfect in ' dead vocables,' and set down, as he hopes, by the living Fountain, there to superadd Ideas and Capabilities. From such Fountain he draws, diligently, thirstily, yet never or seldom with his whole heart, for the water nowise suits his palate; discouragements, entanglements, aberrations are discoverable or supposable. Nor perhaps are even pecuniary distresses wanting; for ' the good Gretchen, who in spite of advices from not disinterested relatives has sent him hither, must after a time withdraw her willing but too feeble hand.' Nevertheless in an atmosphere of Poverty and manifold Chagrin, the Humour of that young Soul, what character is in him, first decisively reveals itself; and, like strong sunshine in weeping skies, gives out variety of colours, some of which are prismatic. Thus, with the aid of Time and of what Time brings, has the stripling Diogenes Teufelsdröckh waxed into manly stature; and into so questionable an aspect, that we ask with new eagerness, How he specially came by it, and regret anew that there is no more explicit answer. Certain of the intelligible and partially significant fragments, which are few in number, shall be extracted from that Limbo of a Paper-bag, and presented with the usual preparation.

As if, in the Bag *Scorpio,* Teufelsdröckh had not already expectorated his antipedagogic spleen; as if, from the name *Sagittarius,* he had thought himself called upon to shoot arrows, we here again fall-in with such matter as this : ' The University where I was educated still stands vivid enough in my remembrance, and I know its name well; which name, however, I, from tenderness to existing interests and persons, shall in nowise divulge. It is my painful duty to say that, out of England and Spain, ours was the worst of all hitherto discovered Universities. This is indeed a time when right Education is, as nearly as may be, impossible : however, in degrees of wrongness there is no limit : nay, I can conceive a worse system than that of the Nameless itself; as poisoned victual may be worse than absolute hunger.

' It is written, When the blind lead the blind, both shall fall into the ditch : wherefore, in such circum-

stances, may it not sometimes be safer, if both leader
and led simply—sit still? Had you, anywhere in Crim
Tartary; walled-in a square enclosure; furnished it
with a small, ill-chosen Library; and then turned loose
into it eleven-hundred Christian striplings, to tumble
about as they listed, from three to seven years : certain
persons, under the title of Professors, being stationed
at the gates, to declare aloud that it was a University,
and exact considerable admission-fees,—you had, not
indeed in mechanical structure, yet in spirit and result,
some imperfect resemblance of our High Seminary. I
say, imperfect; for if our mechanical structure was
quite other, so neither was our result altogether the
same : unhappily, we were not in Crim Tartary, but in
a corrupt European city, full of smoke and sin; moreover, in the middle of a Public, which, without far
costlier apparatus than that of the Square Enclosure,
and Declaration aloud, you could not be sure of gulling.

  ' Gullible, however, by fit apparatus, all Publics are;
and gulled, with the most surprising profit. Towards
anything like a *Statistics of Imposture,* indeed, little as
yet has been done : with a strange indifference, our
Economists, nigh buried under Tables for minor
Branches of Industry, have altogether overlooked the
grand all-overtopping Hypocrisy Branch; as if our
whole arts of Puffery, of Quackery, Priestcraft, King-
craft, and the innumerable other crafts and mysteries
of that genus, had not ranked in Productive Industry
at all! Can any one, for example, so much as say,
What moneys, in Literature and Shoeblacking, are
realised by actual Instruction and actual jet Polish;
what by fictitious-persuasive Proclamation of such;
specifying, in distinct items, the distributions, circula-
tions, disbursements, incomings of said moneys, with
the smallest approach to accuracy? But to ask, How
far, in all the several infinitely-complected departments
of social business, in government, education, in manual,
commercial, intellectual fabrication of every sort, man's
Want is supplied by true Ware; how far by the mere
Appearance of true Ware :—in other words, To what
extent, by what methods, with what effects, in various
times and countries, Deception takes the place of wages

of Performance : here truly is an Inquiry big with
results for the future time, but to which hitherto only
the vaguest answer can be given. If for the present,
in our Europe, we estimate the ratio of Ware to Appearance of Ware so high even as at One to a Hundred
(which, considering the Wages of a Pope, Russian
Autocrat, or English Game-Preserver, is probably not
far from the mark),—what almost prodigious saving
may there not be anticipated, as the *Statistics of Imposture* advances, and so the manufacturing of Shams (that
of Realities rising into clearer and clearer distinction
therefrom) gradually declines, and at length becomes
all but wholly unnecessary !

'This for the coming golden ages. What I had to
remark, for the present brazen one, is, that in several
provinces, as in Education, Polity, Religion, where so
much is wanted and indispensable, and so little can as
yet be furnished, probably Imposture is of sanative,
anodyne nature, and man's Gullibility not his worst
blessing. Suppose your sinews of war quite broken ; I
mean your military chest insolvent, forage all but exhausted ; and that the whole army is about to mutiny,
disband, and cut your and each other's throat,—then
were it not well could you, as if by miracle, pay them
in any sort of fairy-money, feed them on coagulated
water, or mere imagination of meat; whereby, till the
real supply came up, they might be kept together and
quiet? Such perhaps was the aim of Nature, who does
nothing without aim, in furnishing her favourite, Man,
with this his so omnipotent or rather omnipatient Talent
of being Gulled.

'How beautifully it works, with a little mechanism ;
nay, almost makes mechanism for itself ! These Professors in the Nameless lived with ease, with safety,
by a mere Reputation, constructed in past times, and
then too with no great effort, by quite another class of
persons. Which Reputation, like a strong, brisk-going
undershot wheel, sunk into the general current, bade
fair, with only a little annual repainting on their part,
to hold long together, and of its own accord assiduously
grind for them. Happy that it was so, for the Millers !
They themselves needed not to work ; their attempts

at working, at what they called Educating, now when I look back on it, filled me with a certain mute admiration.

'Besides all this, we boasted ourselves a Rational University; in the highest degree hostile to Mysticism; thus was the young vacant mind furnished with much talk about Progress of the Species, Dark Ages, Prejudice, and the like; so that all were quickly enough blown out into a state of windy argumentativeness; whereby the better sort had soon to end in sick, impotent Scepticism; the worser sort explode (*crepiren*) in finished Self-conceit, and to all spiritual intents become dead.—But this too is portion of mankind's lot. If our era is the Era of Unbelief, why murmur under it; is there not a better coming, nay come? As in long-drawn Systole and long-drawn Diastole, must the period of Faith alternate with the period of Denial; must the vernal growth, the summer luxuriance of all Opinions, Spiritual Representations and Creations, be followed by, and again follow, the autumnal decay, the winter dissolution. For man lives in Time, has his whole earthly being, endeavour and destiny shaped for him by Time: only in the transitory Time-Symbol is the ever-motionless Eternity we stand on made manifest. And yet, in such winter-seasons of Denial, it is for the nobler-minded perhaps a comparative misery to have been born, and to be awake and work; and for the duller a felicity, if, like hibernating animals, safe-lodged in some Salamanca University, or Sybaris City, or other superstitious or voluptuous Castle of Indolence, they can slumber-through, in stupid dreams, and only awaken when the loud-roaring hailstorms have all done their work, and to our prayers and martyrdoms the new Spring has been vouchsafed.'

That in the environment, here mysteriously enough shadowed forth, Teufelsdröckh must have felt ill at ease, cannot be doubtful. 'The hungry young,' he says, 'looked up to their spiritual Nurses; and, for food, were bidden eat the east-wind. What vain jargon of controversial Metaphysic, Etymology, and mechanical Manipulation falsely named Science, was current there, I indeed learned, better perhaps than the most. Among

eleven-hundred Christian youths, there will not be
wanting some eleven eager to learn. By collision with
such, a certain warmth, a certain polish was communicated; by instinct and happy accident, I took less to
rioting (*renommiren*), than to thinking and reading,
which latter also I was free to do. Nay from the chaos
of that Library, I succeeded in fishing-up more books
perhaps than had been known to the very keepers thereof. The foundation of a Literary Life was hereby laid:
I learned, on my own strength, to read fluently in almost
all cultivated languages, on almost all subjects and
sciences; farther, as man is ever the prime object to
man, already it was my favourite employment to read
character in speculation, and from the Writing to construe the Writer. A certain groundplan of Human
Nature and Life began to fashion itself in me; wondrous
enough, now when I look back on it; for my whole
Universe, physical and spiritual, was as yet a Machine!
However, such a conscious, recognised groundplan, the
truest I had, *was* beginning to be there, and by additional experiments might be corrected and indefinitely
extended.'

Thus from poverty does the strong educe nobler
wealth; thus in the destitution of the wild desert does
our young Ishmael acquire for himself the highest of all
possessions, that of Self-help. Nevertheless a desert
this was, waste, and howling with savage monsters.
Teufelsdröckh gives us long details of his 'fever-
paroxysms of Doubt'; his Inquiries concerning
Miracles, and the Evidences of religious Faith; and
how 'in the silent night-watches, still darker in his
heart than over sky and earth, he has cast himself before
the All-seeing, and with audible prayers cried vehemently
for Light, for deliverance from Death and the Grave.
Not till after long years, and unspeakable agonies, did
the believing heart surrender; sink into spell-bound
sleep, under the night-mare, Unbelief; and, in this hag-
ridden dream, mistake God's fair living world for a
pallid, vacant Hades and extinct Pandemonium. But
through such Purgatory pain,' continues he, 'it is
appointed us to pass; first must the dead Letter of
Religion own itself dead, and drop piecemeal into dust,

if the living Spirit of Religion, freed from this its charnel-house, is to arise on us, newborn of Heaven, and with new healing under its wings.'

To which Purgatory pains, seemingly severe enough, if we add a liberal measure of Earthly distresses, want of practical guidance, want of sympathy, want of money, want of hope; and all this in the fervid season of youth, so exaggerated in imagining, so boundless in desires, yet here so poor in means,—do we not see a strong incipient spirit oppressed and overloaded from without and from within; the fire of genius struggling-up among fuel-wood of the greenest, and as yet with more of bitter vapour than of clear flame?

From various fragments of Letters and other documentary scraps, it is to be inferred that Teufelsdröckh, isolated, shy, retiring as he was, had not altogether escaped notice: certain established men are aware of his existence; and, if stretching-out no helpful hand, have at least their eyes on him. He appears, though in dreary enough humour, to be addressing himself to the Profession of Law;—whereof, indeed, the world has since seen him a public graduate. But omitting these broken, unsatisfactory thrums of Economical relation, let us present rather the following small thread of Moral relation; and therewith, the reader for himself weaving it in at the right place, conclude our dim arras-picture of these University years.

' Here also it was that I formed acquaintance with Herr Towgood, or, as it is perhaps better written, Herr Toughgut; a young person of quality (*von Adel*), from the interior parts of England. He stood connected, by blood and hospitality, with the Counts von Zähdarm, in this quarter of Germany; to which noble Family I likewise was, by his means, with all friendliness, brought near. Towgood had a fair talent, unspeakably ill-cultivated; with considerable humour of character: and, bating his total ignorance, for he knew nothing except Boxing and a little Grammar, showed less of that aristocratic impassivity, and silent fury, than for most part belongs to Travellers of his nation. To him I owe my first practical knowledge of the English and their ways; perhaps also something of the partiality with which I

have ever since regarded that singular people. Towgood was not without an eye, could he have come at
any light. Invited doubtless by the presence of the
Zähdarm Family, he had travelled hither, in the almost
frantic hope of perfecting his studies; he, whose studies
had as yet been those of infancy, hither to a University
where so much as the notion of perfection, not to say
the effort after it, no longer existed! Often we would
condole over the hard destiny of the Young in this era :
how, after all our toil, we were to be turned-out into the
world, with beards on our chins indeed, but with few
other attributes of manhood; no existing thing that we
were trained to Act on, nothing that we could so much
as Believe. "How has our head on the outside a
polished Hat," would Towgood exclaim, "and in the
inside Vacancy, or a froth of Vocables and Attorney-
Logic! At a small cost men are educated to make
leather into shoes; but at a great cost, what am I
educated to make? By Heaven, Brother! what I have
already eaten and worn, as I came thus far, would
endow a considerable Hospital of Incurables."—"Man,
indeed," I would answer, "has a Digestive Faculty,
which must be kept working, were it even partly by
stealth. But as for our Mis-education, make not bad
worse; waste not the time yet ours, in trampling on
thistles because they have yielded us no figs. *Frisch zu,
Bruder!* Here are Books, and we have brains to read
them; here is a whole Earth and a whole Heaven, and
we have eyes to look on them : *Frisch zu!*"

' Often also our talk was gay; not without brilliancy,
and even fire. We looked-out on Life, with its strange
scaffolding, where all at once harlequins dance, and
men are beheaded and quartered : motley, not unterrific
was the aspect; but we looked on it like brave youths.
For myself, these were perhaps my most genial hours.
Towards this young warmhearted, strongheaded and
wrongheaded Herr Towgood I was even near experienc-
ing the now obsolete sentiment of Friendship. Yes,
foolish Heathen that I was, I felt that, under certain
conditions, I could have loved this man, and taken him
to my bosom, and been his brother once and always.
By degrees, however, I understood the new time, and

its wants. If man's *Soul* is indeed, as in the Finnish Language, and Utilitarian Philosophy, a kind of *Stomach,* what else is the true meaning of Spiritual Union but an Eating together? Thus we, instead of Friends, are Dinner-guests; and here as elsewhere have cast away chimeras.'

So ends, abruptly as is usual, and enigmatically, this little incipient romance. What henceforth becomes of the brave Herr Towgood, or Toughgut? He has dived-under, in the Autobiographical Chaos, and swims we see not where. Does any reader ' in the interior parts of England ' know of such a man?

CHAPTER IV

GETTING UNDER WAY

' THUS, nevertheless,' writes our autobiographer, apparently as quitting College, ' was there realised Somewhat; namely, I, Diogenes Teufelsdröckh : a visible Temporary Figure (*Zeitbild*), occupying some cubic feet of Space, and containing within it Forces both physical and spiritual; hopes, passions, thoughts; the whole wondrous furniture, in more or less perfection, belonging to that mystery, a Man. Capabilities there were in me to give battle, in some small degree, against the great Empire of Darkness : does not the very Ditcher and Delver, with his spade, extinguish many a thistle and puddle; and so leave a little Order, where he found the opposite? Nay your very Daymoth has capabilities in this kind; and ever organises something (into its own Body, if no otherwise), which was before Inorganic; and of mute dead air makes living music, though only of the faintest, by humming.

' How much more, one whose capabilities are spiritual; who has learned, or begun learning, the grand thaumaturgic art of Thought ! Thaumaturgic I name it; for hitherto all Miracles have been wrought thereby, and henceforth innumerable will be wrought; whereof we, even in these days, witness some. Of the Poet's and Prophet's inspired Message, and how it makes and unmakes whole worlds, I shall forbear mention : but cannot the dullest hear Steam-engines clanking around him? Has he not seen the Scottish Brassmith's IDEA (and this but a mechanical one) travelling on fire-wings round the Cape, and across two Oceans; and stronger than any other Enchanter's Familiar, on all hands unweariedly fetching and carrying : at home, not only weaving Cloth, but rapidly enough overturning the whole old system of Society; and, for Feudalism and Preservation of the Game, preparing us, by indirect but sure methods, Industrialism and the Government of the Wisest? Truly a Thinking Man is the worst enemy the Prince of Darkness can have; every time such a one announces himself, I doubt not, there runs a shudder through the Nether Empire; and new Emissaries are trained, with new tactics, to, if possible, entrap him, and hoodwink and handcuff him.

' With such high vocation had I too, as denizen of the Universe, been called. Unhappy it is, however, that though born to the amplest Sovereignty, in this way, with no less than sovereign right of Peace and War against the Time-Prince (*Zeitfürst*), or Devil, and all his Dominions, your coronation-ceremony costs such trouble, your sceptre is so difficult to get at, or even to get eye on !'

By which last wiredrawn similitude does Teufelsdröckh mean no more than that young men find obstacles in what we call 'getting under way'? ' Not what I Have,' continues he, ' but what I Do is my Kingdom. To each is given a certain inward Talent, a certain outward Environment of Fortune; to each, by wisest combination of these two, a certain maximum of Capability. But the hardest problem were ever this first : To find by study of yourself, and of the ground you stand on, what your combined inward and outward Capability specially is. For, alas, our young soul is all budding with Capabilities, and we see not yet which is the main and true one. Always too the new man is in a new time, under new conditions; his course can be the *fac-simile* of no prior one, but is by its nature original. And then how seldom will the outward Capability fit the inward : though talented wonderfully enough, we are poor, unfriended, dyspeptical, bashful; nay what is worse than all, we are foolish. Thus, in a whole imbroglio of Capabilities, we go stupidly groping about, to grope which is ours, and often clutch the wrong one : in this mad work must several years of our small term be spent, till the purblind Youth, by practice, acquire notions of distance, and become a seeing Man. Nay, many so spend their whole term, and in ever-new expectation, ever-new disappointment, shift from enterprise to enterprise, and from side to side : till at length, as exasperated striplings of threescore-and-ten, they shift into their last enterprise, that of getting buried.

'Such, since the most of us are too ophthalmic, would be the general fate; were it not that one thing saves us : our Hunger. For on this ground, as the prompt nature of Hunger is well known, must a prompt choice be made : hence have we, with wise foresight, Indentures and Apprenticeships for our irrational young; whereby, in due season, the vague universality of a Man shall find himself ready-moulded into a specific Craftsman; and so thenceforth work, with much or with little waste of Capability as it may be; yet not with the worst waste, that of time. Nay even in matters spiritual, since the spiritual artist too is born blind, and does not, like certain other creatures, receive sight in nine days, but far later, sometimes never,—is it not well that there should be what we call Professions, or Bread-studies (*Brodzwecke*), pre-appointed us? Here, circling like the gin-horse, for whom partial or total blindness is no evil, the Bread-artist can travel contentedly round and round, still fancying that it is forward and forward; and realise much : for himself victual; for the world an additional horse's power in the grand corn-mill or hemp-mill of Economic Society. For me too had such a leading-string been provided; only that it proved a neck-halter, and had nigh throttled me, till I broke it off. Then, in the words of Ancient Pistol, did the world generally become mine oyster, which I, by strength or cunning, was to open, as I would and could. Almost had I deceased (*fast wär ich umgekommen*), so obstinately did it continue shut.'

We see here, significantly foreshadowed, the spirit
of much that was to befall our Autobiographer; the
historical embodiment of which, as it painfully takes
shape in his Life, lies scattered, in dim disastrous
details, through this Bag *Pisces*, and those that follow.
A young man of high talent, and high though still
temper, like a young mettled colt, ' breaks-off his neck-
halter,' and bounds forth, from his peculiar manger,
into the wide world; which, alas, he finds all rigorously
fenced-in. Richest clover-fields tempt his eye; but to
him they are forbidden pasture: either pining in progressive starvation, he must stand; or, in mad exasperation, must rush to and fro, leaping against sheer stone-
walls, which he cannot leap over, which only lacerate
and lame him; till at last, after thousand attempts and
endurances, he, as if by miracle, clears his way; not
indeed into luxuriant and luxurious clover, yet into a
certain bosky wilderness where existence is still possible, and Freedom, though waited on by Scarcity, is
not without sweetness. In a word, Teufelsdröckh
having thrown-up his legal Profession, finds himself
without landmark of outward guidance; whereby his
previous want of decided Belief, or inward guidance, is
frightfully aggravated. Necessity urges him on; Time
will not stop, neither can he, a Son of Time; wild
passions without solacement, wild faculties without
employment, ever vex and agitate him. He too must
enact that stern Monodrama, *No Object and no Rest;*
must front its successive destinies, work through to its
catastrophe, and deduce therefrom what moral he can.

Yet let us be just to him, let us admit that his ' neck-
halter ' sat nowise easy on him; that he was in some
degree forced to break it off. If we look at the young
man's civic position, in this Nameless capital, as he
emerges from its Nameless University, we can discern
well that it was far from enviable. His first Law-
Examination he has come through triumphantly; and
can even boast that the *Examen Rigorosum* need not
have frightened him: but though he is hereby ' an
Auscultator of respectability,' what avails it? There
is next to no employment to be had. Neither, for a
youth without connexions, is the process of Expecta-

tion very hopeful in itself; nor for one of his disposition
much cheered from without. 'My fellow Auscultators,' he says, 'were Auscultators: they dressed,
and digested, and talked articulate words; other vitality
showed they almost none. Small speculation in those
eyes, that they did glare withal! Sense neither for the
high nor for the deep, nor for aught human or divine,
save only for the faintest scent of coming Preferment.'
In which words, indicating a total estrangement on the
part of Teufelsdröckh, may there not also lurk traces
of a bitterness as from wounded vanity? Doubtless
these prosaic Auscultators may have sniffed at him,
with his strange ways; and tried to hate, and what was
much more impossible, to despise him. Friendly communion, in any case, there could not be: already has
the young Teufelsdröckh left the other young geese;
and swims apart, though as yet uncertain whether he
himself is cygnet or gosling.

Perhaps, too, what little employment he had was
performed ill, at best unpleasantly. 'Great practical
method and expertness' he may brag of; but is there
not also great practical pride, though deep-hidden, only
the deeper-seated? So shy a man can never have been
popular. We figure to ourselves, how in those days he
may have played strange freaks with his independence,
and so forth: do not his own words betoken as much?
'Like a very young person, I imagined it was with
Work alone, and not also with Folly and Sin, in myself
and others, that I had been appointed to struggle.' Be
this as it may, his progress from the passive Auscultatorship, towards any active Assessorship, is evidently
of the slowest. By degrees, those same established
men, once partially inclined to patronise him, seem to
withdraw their countenance, and give him up as 'a
man of genius': against which procedure he, in these
Papers, loudly protests. 'As if,' says he, 'the
higher did not presuppose the lower; as if he who can
fly into heaven, could not also walk post if he resolved
on it! But the world is an old woman, and mistakes
any gilt farthing for a gold coin; whereby being often
cheated, she will thenceforth trust nothing but the
common copper.'

How our winged sky-messenger, unaccepted as a terrestrial runner, contrived, in the mean while, to keep himself from flying skyward without return, is not too clear from these Documents. Good old Gretchen seems to have vanished from the scene, perhaps from the Earth; other Horn of Plenty, or even of Parsimony, nowhere flows for him; so that 'the prompt nature of Hunger being well known,' we are not without our anxiety. From private Tuition, in never so many languages and sciences, the aid derivable is small; neither, to use his own words, 'does the young Adventurer hitherto suspect in himself any literary gift; but at best earns bread-and-water wages, by his wide faculty of Translation. Nevertheless,' continues he, 'that I subsisted is clear, for you find me even now alive.' Which fact, however, except upon the principle of our true-hearted, kind old Proverb, that 'there is always life for a living one,' we must profess ourselves unable to explain.

Certain Landlords' Bills, and other economic Documents, bearing the mark of Settlement, indicate that he was not without money; but, like an independent Hearth-holder, if not House-holder, paid his way. Here also occur, among many others, two little mutilated Notes, which perhaps throw light on his condition. The first has now no date, or writer's name, but a huge Blot; and runs to this effect: 'The (*Inkblot*), tied-down by previous promise, cannot, except by best wishes, forward the Herr Teufelsdröckh's views on the Assessorship in question; and sees himself under the cruel necessity of forbearing, for the present, what were otherwise his duty and joy, to assist in opening the career for a man of genius, on whom far higher triumphs are yet waiting.' The other is on gilt paper; and interests us like a sort of epistolary mummy now dead, yet which once lived and beneficently worked. We give it in the original: '*Herr Teufelsdröckh wird von der Frau Gräfinn, auf Donnerstag, zum* ÆSTHETISCHEN THEE *schönstens eingeladen.*'

Thus, in answer to a cry for solid pudding, whereof there is the most urgent need, comes, epigrammatically enough, the invitation to a wash of quite fluid

Æsthetic Tea! How Teufelsdröckh, now at actual handgrips with Destiny herself, may have comported himself among these Musical and Literary Dilettanti of both sexes, like a hungry lion invited to a feast of chickenweed, we can only conjecture. Perhaps in expressive silence, and abstinence : otherwise if the lion, in such case, is to feast at all, it cannot be on the chickenweed, but only on the chickens. For the rest, as this Frau Gräfinn dates from the *Zähdarm House*, she can be no other than the Countess and mistress of the same; whose intellectual tendencies, and good-will to Teufelsdröckh, whether on the footing of Herr Towgood, or on his own footing, are hereby manifest. That some sort of relation, indeed, continued, for a time, to connect our Autobiographer, though perhaps feebly enough, with this noble House, we have elsewhere express evidence. Doubtless, if he expected patronage, it was in vain ; enough for him if he here obtained occasional glimpses of the great world, from which we at one time fancied him to have been always excluded. ' The Zähdarms,' says he, ' lived in the soft, sumptuous garniture of Aristocracy ; whereto Literature and Art, attracted and attached from without, were to serve as the handsomest fringing. It was to the *Gnädigen Frau* (her Ladyship) that this latter improvement was due : assiduously she gathered, dextrously she fitted-on, what fringing was to be had ; lace or cobweb, as the place yielded.' Was Teufelsdröckh also a fringe, of lace or cobweb ; or promising to be such ? ' With his *Excellenz* (the Count),' continues he, ' I have more than once had the honour to converse ; chiefly on general affairs, and the aspect of the world, which he, though now past middle life, viewed in no unfavourable light ; finding indeed, except the Outrooting of Journalism (*die auszurottende Journalistik*), little to desiderate therein. On some points, as his *Excellenz* was not uncholeric, I found it more pleasant to keep silence. Besides, his occupation being that of Owning Land, there might be faculties enough, which, as superfluous for such use, were little developed in him.'

That to Teufelsdröckh the aspect of the world was nowise so faultless, and many things besides ' the Outrooting of Journalism ' might have seemed improve-

ments, we can readily conjecture. With nothing but
a barren Auscultatorship from without, and so many
mutinous thoughts and wishes from within, his position
was no easy one. 'The Universe,' he says, 'was as
a mighty Sphinx-riddle, which I knew so little of, yet
must rede, or be devoured. In red streaks of unspeakable grandeur, yet also in the blackness of darkness,
was Life, to my too-unfurnished Thought, unfolding
itself. A strange contradiction lay in me; and I as yet
knew not the solution of it; knew not that spiritual
music can spring only from discords set in harmony;
that but for Evil there were no Good, as victory is only
possible by battle.'

'I have heard affirmed (surely in jest),' observes he
elsewhere, 'by not unphilanthropic persons, that it
were a real increase of human happiness, could all
young men from the age of nineteen be covered under
barrels, or rendered otherwise invisible; and there left
to follow their lawful studies and callings, till they
emerged, sadder and wiser, at the age of twenty-five.
With which suggestion, at least as considered in the
light of a practical scheme, I need scarcely say that I
nowise coincide. Nevertheless it is plausibly urged
that, as young ladies (*Mädchen*) are, to mankind, precisely the most delightful in those years; so young
gentlemen (*Bübchen*) do then attain their maximum of
detestability. Such gawks (*Gecken*) are they; and
foolish peacocks, and yet with such a vulturous hunger
for self-indulgence; so obstinate, obstreperous, vain-
glorious; in all senses, so froward and so forward. No
mortal's endeavour or attainment will, in the smallest,
content the as yet unendeavouring, unattaining young
gentleman; but he could make it all infinitely better,
were it worthy of him. Life everywhere is the most
manageable matter, simple as a question in the Rule-
of-Three : multiply your second and third term together,
divide the product by the first, and your quotient will
be the answer,—which you are but an ass if you cannot
come at. The booby has not yet found-out, by any
trial, that, do what one will, there is ever a cursed
fraction, oftenest a decimal repeater, and no net integer
quotient so much as to be thought of.'

In which passage does not there lie an implied confession that Teufelsdröckh himself, besides his outward obstructions, had an inward, still greater, to contend with; namely, a certain temporary, youthful, yet still afflictive derangement of head? Alas, on the former side alone, his case was hard enough. ' It continues ever true,' says he, ' that Saturn, or Chronos, or what we call TIME, devours all his Children: only by incessant Running, by incessant Working, may you (for some threescore-and-ten years) escape him; and you too he devours at last. Can any Sovereign, or Holy Alliance of Sovereigns, bid Time stand still; even in thought, shake themselves free of Time? Our whole terrestrial being is based on Time, and built of Time; it is wholly a Movement, a Time-impulse; Time is the author of it, the material of it. Hence also our Whole Duty, which is to move, to work,—in the right direction. Are not our Bodies and our Souls in continual movement, whether we will or not; in a continual Waste, requiring a continual Repair? Utmost satisfaction of our whole outward and inward Wants were but satisfaction for a space of Time; thus, whatso we have done, is done, and for us annihilated, and ever must we go and do anew. O Time-Spirit, how hast thou environed and imprisoned us, and sunk us so deep in thy troublous dim Time-Element, that only in lucid moments can so much as glimpses of our upper Azure Home be revealed to us ! Me, however, as a Son of Time, unhappier than some others, was Time threatening to eat quite prematurely; for, strive as I might, there was no good Running, so obstructed was the path, so gyved were the feet.' That is to say, we presume, speaking in the dialect of this lower world, that Teufelsdröckh's whole duty and necessity was, like other men's, ' to work,—in the right direction,' and that no work was to be had; whereby he became wretched enough. As was natural : with haggard Scarcity threatening him in the distance; and so vehement a soul languishing in restless inaction, and forced thereby, like Sir Hudibras's sword by rust,

> To eat into itself for lack
> Of something else to hew and hack !

But on the whole, that same ' excellent Passivity,'

as it has all along done, is here again vigorously
flourishing; in which circumstance may we not trace
the beginnings of much that now characterises our Professor; and perhaps, in faint rudiments, the origin of
the Clothes-Philosophy itself? Already the attitude he
has assumed towards the World is too defensive; not,
as would have been desirable, a bold attitude of attack.
'So far hitherto,' he says, 'as I had mingled with
mankind, I was notable, if for anything, for a certain
stillness of manner, which, as my friends often rebuk-
ingly declared, did but ill express the keen ardour of
my feelings. I, in truth, regarded men with an excess
both of love and of fear. The mystery of a Person,
indeed, is ever divine to him that has a sense for the
God-like. Often, notwithstanding, was I blamed, and
by half-strangers hated, for my so-called Hardness
(*Härte*), my Indifferentism towards men; and the
seemingly ironic tone I had adopted, as my favourite
dialect in conversation. Alas, the panoply of Sarcasm
was but as a buckram case, wherein I had striven to
envelop myself; that so my own poor Person might live
safe there, and in all friendliness, being no longer exasperated by wounds. Sarcasm I now see to be, in
general, the language of the Devil; for which reason I
have long since as good as renounced it. But how
many individuals did I, in those days, provoke into
some degree of hostility thereby! An ironic man, with
his sly stillness, and ambuscading ways, more especially
an ironic young man, from whom it is least expected,
may be viewed as a pest to society. Have we not seen
persons of weight and name coming forward, with
gentlest indifference, to tread such a one out of sight,
as an insignificancy and worm, start ceiling-high (*bal-
kenhoch*), and thence fall shattered and supine, to be
borne home on shutters, not without indignation, when
he proved electric and a torpedo!'

Alas, how can a man with this devilishness of temper
make way for himself in Life; where the first problem,
as Teufelsdröckh too admits, is 'to unite yourself with
some one and with somewhat (*sich anzuschliessen*)'?
Division, not union, is written on most part of his
procedure. Let us add too that, in no great length of

time, the only important connexion he had ever succeeded in forming, his connexion with the Zähdarm
Family, seems to have been paralysed, for all practical
uses, by the death of the ' not uncholeric ' old Count.
This fact stands recorded, quite incidentally, in a certain *Discourse on Epitaphs*, huddled into the present
Bag, among so much else; of which Essay the learning and curious penetration are more to be approved
of than the spirit. His grand principle is, that lapidary
inscriptions, of what sort soever, should be Historical
rather than Lyrical. ' By request of that worthy
Nobleman's survivors,' says he, ' I undertook to compose his Epitaph; and not unmindful of my own rules,
produced the following; which however, for an alleged
defect of Latinity, a defect never yet fully visible to myself, still remains unengraven ';—wherein, we may
predict, there is more than the Latinity that will surprise an English reader :

HIC JACET

PHILIPPUS ZAEHDARM, COGNOMINE MAGNUS,

ZAEHDARMI COMES,
EX IMPERII CONCILIO,
VELLERIS AUREI, PERISCELIDIS, NECNON VULTURIS NIGRI
EQUES.

QUI DUM SUB LUNA AGEBAT,

QUINQUIES MILLE PERDICES

PLUMBO CONFECIT :

VARII CIBI

CENTUMPONDIA MILLIES CENTENA MILLIA,
PER SE, PERQUE SERVOS QUADRUPEDES BIPEDESVE,
HAUD SINE TUMULTU DEVOLVENS,

IN STERCUS

PALAM CONVERTIT.

NUNC A LABORE REQUIESCENTEM
OPERA SEQUUNTUR.

SI MONUMENTUM QUÆRIS,
FIMETUM ADSPICE.

PRIMUM IN ORBE DEJECIT [*sub dato*]; POSTREMUM [*sub dato*].

CHAPTER V

ROMANCE

'For long years,' writes Teufelsdröckh, 'had the poor Hebrew, in this Egypt of an Auscultatorship, painfully toiled, baking bricks without stubble, before ever the question once struck him with entire force: For what?—*Beym Himmel!* For Food and Warmth! And are Food and Warmth nowhere else, in the whole wide Universe, discoverable?—Come of it what might, I resolved to try.'

Thus then are we to see him in a new independent capacity, though perhaps far from an improved one. Teufelsdröckh is now a man without Profession. Quitting the common Fleet of herring-busses and whalers, where indeed his leeward, laggard condition was painful enough, he desperately steers-off, on a course of his own, by sextant and compass of his own. Unhappy Teufelsdröckh! Though neither Fleet, nor Traffic, nor Commodores pleased thee, still was it not *a Fleet*, sailing in prescribed track, for fixed objects; above all, in combination, wherein, by mutual guidance, by all manner of loans and borrowings, each could manifoldly aid the other? How wilt thou sail in unknown seas; and for thyself find that shorter North-west Passage to thy fair Spice-country of a Nowhere?—A solitary rover, on such a voyage, with such nautical tactics, will meet with adventures. Nay, as we forthwith discover, a certain Calypso-Island detains him at the very outset; and as it were falsifies and oversets his whole reckoning.

'If in youth,' writes he once, 'the Universe is majestically unveiling, and everywhere Heaven revealing itself on Earth, nowhere to the Young Man does this Heaven on Earth so immediately reveal itself as in the Young Maiden. Strangely enough, in this strange life of ours, it has been so appointed. On the whole, as I have often said, a Person (*Persönlichkeit*) is ever holy to us: a certain orthodox Anthropomorphism connects my *Me* with all *Thees* in bonds of Love: but it is in this approximation of the Like and Unlike, that such heavenly attraction, as between Negative and Positive, first burns-out into a flame. Is the pitifullest mortal Person, think you, indifferent to us? Is it not rather our heartfelt wish to be made one with him; to unite him to us, by gratitude, by admiration, even by fear; or failing all these, unite ourselves to him? But how much more, in this case of the Like-Unlike! Here is conceded us the higher mystic possibility of such a union, the highest in our Earth; thus, in the conducting medium of Fantasy, flames-forth that *fire*-development of the universal Spiritual Electricity, which, as unfolded between man and woman, we first emphatically denominate LOVE.

' In every well-conditioned stripling, as I conjecture, there already blooms a certain prospective Paradise, cheered by some fairest Eve; nor, in the stately vistas, and flowerage and foliage of that Garden, is a Tree of Knowledge, beautiful and awful in the midst thereof, wanting. Perhaps too the whole is but the lovelier, if Cherubim and a Flaming Sword divide it from all footsteps of men; and grant him, the imaginative stripling, only the view, not the entrance. Happy season of virtuous youth, when shame is still an impassable celestial barrier; and the sacred air-cities of Hope have not shrunk into the mean clay-hamlets of Reality; and man, by his nature, is yet infinite and free!

' As for our young Forlorn,' continues Teufelsdröckh, evidently meaning himself, ' in his secluded way of life, and with his glowing Fantasy, the more fiery that it burnt under cover, as in a reverberating furnace, his feeling towards the Queens of this Earth was, and indeed is, altogether unspeakable. A visible Divinity dwelt in them; to our young Friend all women were holy, were heavenly. As yet he but saw them flitting past, in their many-coloured angel-plumage; or hovering mute and inaccessible on the outskirts of *Æsthetic Tea*: all of air they were, all Soul and Form; so lovely, like mysterious priestesses, in whose hand was the invisible Jacob's-ladder, whereby man might mount into very Heaven. That he, our poor Friend, should ever win for himself one of these Gracefuls (*Holden*)—*Ach Gott!* how could he hope it; should he

not have died under it? There was a certain delirious
vertigo in the thought.

' Thus was the young man, if all-sceptical of Demons
and Angels such as the vulgar had once believed in,
nevertheless not unvisited by hosts of true Sky-born,
who visibly and audibly hovered round him whereso he
went; and they had that religious worship in his
thought, though as yet it was by their mere earthly
and trivial name that he named them. But now, if on
a soul so circumstanced, some actual Air-maiden,
incorporated into tangibility and reality, should cast
any electric glance of kind eyes, saying thereby,
" Thou too mayest love and be loved "; and so kindle
him,—good Heaven, what a volcanic, earthquake-
bringing, all-consuming fire were probably kindled !'

Such a fire, it afterwards appears, did actually burst-
forth, with explosions more or less Vesuvian, in the
inner man of Herr Diogenes; as indeed how could it
fail? A nature, which, in his own figurative style, we
might say, had now not a little carbonised tinder, of
Irritability; with so much nitre of latent Passion, and
sulphurous Humour enough; the whole lying in such
hot neighbourhood, close by ' a reverberating furnace
of Fantasy ': have we not here the components of
driest Gunpowder, ready, on occasion of the smallest
spark, to blaze-up? Neither, in this our Life-element,
are sparks anywhere wanting. Without doubt, some
Angel, whereof so many hovered round, would one day,
leaving ' the outskirts of Æsthetic Tea,' flit nigher;
and, by electric Promethean glance, kindle no despicable firework. Happy, if it indeed proved a Firework,
and flamed-off rocketwise, in successive beautiful bursts
of splendour, each growing naturally from the other,
through the several stages of a happy Youthful Love;
till the whole were safely burnt-out; and the young
soul relieved with little damage ! Happy, if it did not
rather prove a Conflagration and mad Explosion; painfully lacerating the heart itself; nay perhaps bursting
the heart in pieces (which were Death); or at best,
bursting the thin walls of your ' reverberating furnace,'
so that it rage thenceforth all unchecked among the
contiguous combustibles (which were Madness): till

of the so fair and manifold internal world of our Diogenes, there remained Nothing, or only the 'crater of an extinct volcano!'

From multifarious Documents in this Bag *Capricornus*, and in the adjacent ones on both sides thereof, it becomes manifest that our philosopher, as stoical and cynical as he now looks, was heartily and even frantically in Love: here therefore may our old doubts whether his heart were of stone or of flesh give way. He loved once; not wisely but too well. And once only: for as your Congreve needs a new case or wrappage for every new rocket, so each human heart can properly exhibit but one Love, if even one; the 'First Love which is infinite' can be followed by no second like unto it. In more recent years, accordingly, the Editor of these Sheets was led to regard Teufelsdröckh as a man not only who would never wed, but who would never even flirt; whom the grand-climacteric itself, and *St. Martin's Summer* of incipient Dotage, would crown with no new myrtle-garland. To the Professor, women are henceforth Pieces of Art; of Celestial Art, indeed; which celestial pieces he glories to survey in galleries, but has lost thought of purchasing.

Psychological readers are not without curiosity to see how Teufelsdröckh, in this for him unexampled predicament, demeans himself; with what specialties of successive configuration, splendour and colour, his Firework blazes-off. Small, as usual, is the satisfaction that such can meet with here. From amid these confused masses of Eulogy and Elegy, with their mad Petrarchan and Werterean ware lying madly scattered among all sorts of quite extraneous matter, not so much as the fair one's name can be deciphered. For, without doubt, the title *Blumine*, whereby she is here designated, and which means simply Goddess of Flowers, must be fictitious. Was her real name Flora, then? But what was her surname, or had she none? Of what station in Life was she; of what parentage, fortune, aspect? Specially, by what Pre-established Harmony of occurrences did the Lover and the Loved meet one another in so wide a world; how did they behave in such meeting? To all which questions, not

unessential in a Biographic work, mere Conjecture must
for most part return answer. 'It was appointed,'
says our Philosopher, ' that the high celestial orbit of
Blumine should intersect the low sublunary one of our
Forlorn; that he, looking in her empyrean eyes, should
fancy the upper Sphere of Light was come down into
this nether sphere of Shadows; and finding himself
mistaken, make noise enough.'

We seem to gather that she was young, hazel-eyed,
beautiful, and some one's Cousin; highborn, and of
high spirit; but unhappily dependent and insolvent;
living, perhaps, on the not-too-gracious bounty of
monied relatives. But how came ' the Wanderer '
into her circle? Was it by the humid vehicle of
Æsthetic Tea, or by the arid one of mere Business?
Was it on the hand of Herr Towgood; or of the Gnädige
Frau, who, as ornamental Artist, might sometimes like
to promote flirtation, especially for young cynical
Nondescripts? To all appearance, it was chiefly by
Accident, and the grace of Nature.

' Thou fair Waldschloss,' writes our Autobiographer, ' what stranger ever saw thee, were it even
an absolved Auscultator, officially bearing in his pocket
the last *Relatio ex Actis* he would ever write, but must
have paused to wonder! Noble Mansion! There
stoodest thou, in deep Mountain Amphitheatre, on
umbrageous lawns, in thy serene solitude; stately,
massive, all of granite; glittering in the western sun-
beams, like a palace of El Dorado, overlaid with
precious metal. Beautiful rose up, in wavy curvature,
the slope of thy guardian Hills; of the greenest was
their sward, embossed with its dark-brown frets of crag,
or spotted by some spreading solitary Tree and its
shadow. To the unconscious Wayfarer thou wert also
as an Ammon's Temple, in the Libyan Waste; where,
for joy and woe, the tablet of his Destiny lay written.
Well might he pause and gaze; in that glance of his
were prophecy and nameless forebodings.'

But now let us conjecture that the so presentient
Auscultator has handed-in his *Relatio ex Actis;* been
invited to a glass of Rhine-wine; and so, instead of
returning dispirited and athirst to his dusty Town-home,

is ushered into the Gardenhouse, where sit the choicest party of dames and cavaliers : if not engaged in Æsthetic Tea, yet in trustful evening conversation, and perhaps Musical Coffee, for we hear of ' harps and pure voices making the stillness live.' Scarcely, it would seem, is the Gardenhouse inferior in respectability to the noble Mansion itself. ' Embowered amid rich foliage, rose-clusters, and the hues and odours of thousand flowers, here sat that brave company; in front, from the wide-opened doors, fair outlook over blossom and bush, over grove and velvet green, stretching, undulating onwards to the remote Mountain peaks : so bright, so mild, and everywhere the melody of birds and happy creatures : it was all as if man had stolen a shelter from the Sun in the bosom-vesture of Summer herself. How came it that the Wanderer advanced thither with such forecasting heart (*ahndungsvoll*), by the side of his gay host? Did he feel that to these soft influences his hard bosom ought to be shut; that here, once more, Fate had it in view to try him; to mock him, and see whether there were Humour in him?

' Next moment he finds himself presented to the party; and especially by name to—Blumine ! Peculiar among all dames and damosels glanced Blumine, there in her modesty, like a star among earthly lights. Noblest maiden ! whom he bent to, in body and in soul; yet scarcely dared look at, for the presence filled him with painful yet sweetest embarrassment.

' Blumine's was a name well known to him; far and wide was the fair one heard of, for her gifts, her graces, her caprices : from all which vague colourings of Rumour, from the censures no less than from the praises, had our friend painted for himself a certain imperious Queen of Hearts, and blooming warm Earth-angel, much more enchanting than your mere white Heaven-angels of women, in whose placid veins circulates too little naphtha-fire. Herself also he had seen in public places; that light yet so stately form; those dark tresses, shading a face where smiles and sunlight played over earnest deeps : but all this he had seen only as a magic vision, for him inaccessible, almost without reality. Her sphere was too far from his; how should

she ever think of him; O Heaven! how should they so
much as once meet together? And now that Rose-
goddess sits in the same circle with him; the light of
her eyes has smiled on him; if he speak, she will hear
it! Nay, who knows, since the heavenly Sun looks
into lowest valleys, but Blumine herself might have
aforetime noted the so unnotable; perhaps, from his
very gainsayers, as he had from hers, gathered wonder,
gathered favour for him? Was the attraction, the
agitation mutual, then; pole and pole trembling towards
contact, when once brought into neighbourhood? Say
rather, heart swelling in presence of the Queen of
Hearts; like the Sea swelling when once near its Moon!
With the Wanderer it was even so : as in heavenward
gravitation, suddenly as at the touch of a Seraph's
wand, his whole soul is roused from its deepest recesses;
and all that was painful and that was blissful there,
dim images, vague feelings of a whole Past and a whole
Future, are heaving in unquiet eddies within him.

' Often, in far less agitating scenes, had our still
Friend shrunk forcibly together; and shrouded-up his
tremors and flutterings, of what sort soever, in a safe
cover of Silence, and perhaps of seeming Stolidity.
How was it, then, that here, when trembling to the
core of his heart, he did not sink into swoons, but rose
into strength, into fearlessness and clearness? It was
his guiding Genius (*Dämon*) that inspired him; he must
go forth and meet his Destiny. Show thyself now,
whispered it, or be forever hid. Thus sometimes it is
even when your anxiety becomes transcendental, that
the soul first feels herself able to transcend it; that she
rises above it, in fiery victory; and borne on new-
found wings of victory, moves so calmly, even because
so rapidly, so irresistibly. Always must the Wanderer
remember, with a certain satisfaction and surprise, how
in this case he sat not silent, but struck adroitly into
the stream of conversation; which thenceforth, to speak
with an apparent not a real vanity, he may say that he
continued to lead. Surely, in those hours, a certain
inspiration was imparted him, such inspiration as is
still possible in our late era. The self-secluded unfolds
himself in noble thoughts, in free, glowing words; his

soul is as one sea of light, the peculiar home of Truth and Intellect; wherein also Fantasy bodies-forth form after form, radiant with all prismatic hues.'

It appears, in this otherwise so happy meeting, there talked one ' Philistine '; who even now, to the general weariness, was dominantly pouring-forth Philistinism (*Philistriositäten*); little witting what hero was here entering to demolish him! We omit the series of Socratic, or rather Diogenic utterances, not unhappy in their way, whereby the monster, ' persuaded into silence,' seems soon after to have withdrawn for the night. ' Of which dialectic marauder,' writes our hero, ' the discomfiture was visibly felt as a benefit by most: but what were all applauses to the glad smile, threatening every moment to become a laugh, where-with Blumine herself repaid the victor? He ventured to address her, she answered with attention: nay what if there were a slight tremor in that silver voice; what if the red glow of evening were hiding a transient blush!

' The conversation took a higher tone, one fine thought called forth another: it was one of those rare seasons, when the soul expands with full freedom, and man feels himself brought near to man. Gaily in light, graceful abandonment, the friendly talk played round that circle; for the burden was rolled from every heart; the barriers of Ceremony, which are indeed the laws of polite living, had melted as into vapour; and the poor claims of *Me* and *Thee,* no longer parted by rigid fences, now flowed softly into one another; and Life lay all harmonious, many-tinted, like some fair royal cham-paign, the sovereign and owner of which were Love only. Such music springs from kind hearts, in a kind environment of place and time. And yet as the light grew more aërial on the mountain-tops, and the shadows fell longer over the valley, some faint tone of sadness may have breathed through the heart; and, in whispers more or less audible, reminded every one that as this bright day was drawing towards its close, so likewise must the Day of Man's Existence decline into dust and darkness; and with all its sick toilings, and joyful and mournful noises sink in the still Eternity.

' To our Friend the hours seemed moments; holy

was he and happy : the words from those sweetest lips
came over him like dew on thirsty grass ; all better
feelings in his soul seemed to whisper : It is good for us
to be here. At parting, the Blumine's hand was in his :
in the balmy twilight, with the kind stars above them,
he spoke something of meeting again, which was not
contradicted ; he pressed gently those small soft fingers,
and it seemed as if they were not hastily, not angrily
withdrawn.'

Poor Teufelsdröckh ! it is clear to demonstration
thou art smit : the Queen of Hearts would see a ' man
of genius ' also sigh for her ; and there, by art-magic,
in that preternatural hour, has she bound and spell-
bound thee. ' Love is not altogether a Delirium,'
says he elsewhere ; ' yet has it many points in common
therewith. I call it rather a discerning of the Infinite
in the Finite, of the Idea made Real ; which discerning
again may be either true or false, either seraphic or
demoniac, Inspiration or Insanity. But in the former
case too, as in common Madness, it is Fantasy that
superadds itself to sight ; on the so petty domain of
the Actual plants its Archimedes-lever, whereby to move
at will the infinite Spiritual. Fantasy I might call the
true Heaven-gate and Hell-gate of man : his sensuous
life is but the small temporary stage (*Zeitbühne*), whereon thick-streaming influences from both these far yet
near regions meet visibly, and act tragedy and melo-
drama. Sense can support herself handsomely, in most
countries, for some eighteenpence a day ; but for
Fantasy planets and solar-systems will not suffice.
Witness your Pyrrhus conquering the world, yet drink-
ing no better red wine than he had before.' Alas !
witness also your Diogenes, flame-clad, scaling the
upper Heaven, and verging towards Insanity, for prize
of a ' high-souled Brunette,' as if the earth held but
one and not several of these !

He says that, in Town, they met again : ' day after
day, like his heart's sun, the blooming Blumine shone
on him. Ah ! a little while ago, and he was yet in all
darkness ; him what Graceful (*Holde*) would ever love?
Disbelieving all things, the poor youth had never learned
to believe in himself. Withdrawn, in proud timidity,

within his own fastnesses; solitary from men, yet baited by night-spectres enough, he saw himself, with a sad indignation, constrained to renounce the fairest hopes of existence. And now, O now! "She looks on thee," cried he: "she the fairest, noblest; do not her dark eyes tell thee, thou art not despised? The Heaven's-Messenger! All Heaven's blessings be hers!" Thus did soft melodies flow through his heart; tones of an infinite gratitude; sweetest intimations that he also was a man, that for him also unutterable joys had been provided.

'In free speech, earnest or gay, amid lambent glances, laughter, tears, and often with the inarticulate mystic speech of Music: such was the element they now lived in; in such a many-tinted, radiant Aurora, and by this fairest of Orient Light-bringers must our Friend be blandished, and the new Apocalypse of Nature unrolled to him. Fairest Blumine! And, even as a Star, all Fire and humid Softness, a very Light-ray incarnate! Was there so much as a fault, a "caprice," he could have dispensed with? Was she not to him in very deed a Morning-Star; did not her presence bring with it airs from Heaven? As from Æolian Harps in the breath of dawn, as from the Memnon's Statue struck by the rosy finger of Aurora, unearthly music was around him, and lapped him into untried balmy Rest. Pale Doubt fled away to the distance; Life bloomed-up with happiness and hope. The past, then, was all a haggard dream; he had been in the Garden of Eden, then, and could not discern it! But lo now! the black walls of his prison melt away; the captive is alive, is free. If he loved his Disenchantress? *Ach Gott!* His whole heart and soul and life were hers, but never had he named it Love: existence was all a Feeling, not yet shaped into a Thought.'

Nevertheless, into a Thought, nay into an Action, it must be shaped; for neither Disenchanter nor Disenchantress, mere 'Children of Time,' can abide by Feeling alone. The Professor knows not, to this day, 'how in her soft, fervid bosom the Lovely found determination, even on hest of Necessity, to cut-asunder these so blissful bonds.' He even appears surprised at the

' Duenna Cousin,' whoever she may have been, ' in whose meagre, hunger-bitten philosophy, the religion of young hearts was, from the first, faintly approved of.' We, even at such distance, can explain it without necromancy. Let the Philosopher answer this one question : What figure, at that period, was a Mrs. Teufelsdröckh likely to make in polished society? Could she have driven so much as a brass-bound Gig, or even a simple iron-spring one? Thou foolish ' absolved Auscultator,' before whom lies no prospect of capital, will any yet known ' religion of young hearts ' keep the human kitchen warm? Pshaw ! thy divine Blumine when she ' resigned herself to wed some richer,' shows more philosophy, though but ' a woman of genius,' than thou, a pretended man.

Our readers have witnessed the origin of this Love-mania, and with what royal splendour it waxes, and rises. Let no one ask us to unfold the glories of its dominant state; much less the horrors of its almost instantaneous dissolution. How from such inorganic masses, henceforth madder than ever, as lie in these Bags, can even fragments of a living delineation be organised? Besides, of what profit were it? We view, with a lively pleasure, the gay silk Montgolfier start from the ground, and shoot upwards, cleaving the liquid deeps, till it dwindle to a luminous star : but what is there to look longer on, when once, by natural elasticity, or accident of fire, it has exploded? A hapless air-navigator, plunging amid torn parachutes, sand-bags, and confused wreck, fast enough into the jaws of the Devil ! Suffice it to know that Teufelsdröckh rose into the highest regions of the Empyrean, by a natural parabolic track, and returned thence in a quick perpendicular one. For the rest, let any feeling reader, who has been unhappy enough to do the like, paint it out for himself : considering only that if he, for his perhaps comparatively insignificant mistress, underwent such agonies and frenzies, what must Teufelsdröckh's have been, with a fire-heart, and for a nonpareil Blumine ! We glance merely at the final scene :

' One morning, he found his Morning - Star all dimmed and dusky-red; the fair creature was silent, absent, she seemed to have been weeping. Alas, no longer a Morning-star, but a troublous skyey Portent, announcing that the Doomsday had dawned! She said, in a tremulous voice, They were to meet no more.' The thunder-struck Air-sailor is not wanting to himself in this dread hour: but what avails it? We omit the passionate expostulations, entreaties, indignations, since all was vain, and not even an explanation was conceded him; and hasten to the catastrophe. '"Farewell, then, Madam!" said he, not without sternness, for his stung pride helped him. She put her hand in his, she looked in his face, tears started to her eyes: in wild audacity he clasped her to his bosom; their lips were joined, their two souls, like two dew-drops, rushed into one,—for the first time, and for the last!' Thus was Teufelsdröckh made immortal by a kiss. And then? Why, then—' thick curtains of Night rushed over his soul, as rose the immeasurable Crash of Doom; and through the ruins as of a shivered Universe was he falling, falling, towards the Abyss.'

CHAPTER VI

SORROWS OF TEUFELSDRÖCKH

WE have long felt that, with a man like our Professor, matters must often be expected to take a course of their own; that in so multiplex, intricate a nature, there might be channels, both for admitting and emitting, such as the Psychologist had seldom noted; in short, that on no grand occasion and convulsion, neither in the joy-storm nor in the woe-storm, could you predict his demeanour.

To our less philosophical readers, for example, it is now clear that the so passionate Teufelsdröckh, precipitated through ' a shivered Universe ' in this extraordinary way, has only one of three things which he can next do: Establish himself in Bedlam; begin writing Satanic Poetry; or blow-out his brains. In the progress towards any of which consummations, do not such readers anticipate extravagance enough; breast-beating, brow-beating (against walls), lion-bellowings of blasphemy and the like, stampings, smitings, breakages of furniture, if not arson itself?

Nowise so does Teufelsdröckh deport him. He quietly lifts his *Pilgerstab* (Pilgrim-staff), 'old business being soon wound-up'; and begins a perambulation and circumambulation of the terraqueous Globe! Curious it is, indeed, how with such vivacity of conception, such intensity of feeling, above all, with these unconscionable habits of Exaggeration in speech, he combines that wonderful stillness of his, that stoicism in external procedure. Thus, if his sudden bereavement, in this matter of the Flower-goddess, is talked of as a real Doomsday and Dissolution of Nature, in which light doubtless it partly appeared to himself, his own nature is nowise dissolved thereby; but rather is compressed closer. For once, as we might say, a Blumine by magic appliances has unlocked that shut heart of his, and its hidden things rush-out tumultuous, boundless, like genii enfranchised from their glass phial: but no sooner are your magic appliances withdrawn, than the strange casket of a heart springs-to again; and perhaps there is now no key extant that will open it; for a Teufelsdröckh, as we remarked, will not love a second time. Singular Diogenes! No sooner has that heart-rending occurrence fairly taken place, than he affects to regard it as a thing natural, of which there is nothing more to be said. 'One highest hope, seemingly legible in the eyes of an Angel, had recalled him as out of Death-shadows into celestial Life: but a gleam of Tophet passed-over the face of his Angel; he was rapt away in whirlwinds, and heard the laughter of Demons. It was a Calenture,' adds he, 'whereby the Youth saw green Paradise-groves in the waste Ocean-waters: a lying vision, yet not wholly a lie, for *he* saw it.' But what things soever passed in him, when he ceased to see it; what ragings and despairings soever Teufelsdröckh's soul was the scene of, he has the goodness to conceal under a quite opaque cover of Silence. We know it well; the first mad paroxysm past, our brave Gneschen collected his dismembered philosophies, and buttoned himself together; he was meek, silent, or spoke of the weather and the Journals: only by a transient knitting of those shaggy brows, by some deep flash of those eyes, glancing one knew not whether with tear-dew or with fierce fire,—might you have guessed what a Gehenna was within; that a whole Satanic School were spouting, though inaudibly, there. To consume your own choler, as some chimneys consume their own smoke; to keep a whole Satanic School spouting, if it must spout, inaudibly, is a negative yet no slight virtue, nor one of the commonest in these times.

Nevertheless, we will not take upon us to say, that in the strange measure he fell upon, there was not a touch of latent Insanity; whereof indeed the actual condition of these Documents in *Capricornus* and *Aquarius* is no bad emblem. His so unlimited Wanderings, toilsome enough, are without assigned or perhaps assignable aim; internal Unrest seems his sole guidance; he wanders, wanders, as if that curse of the Prophet had fallen on him, and he were 'made like unto a wheel.' Doubtless, too, the chaotic nature of these Paper-bags aggravates our obscurity. Quite without note of preparation, for example, we come upon the following slip: 'A peculiar feeling it is that will rise in the Traveller, when turning some hill-range in his desert road, he descries lying far below, embosomed among its groves and green natural bulwarks, and all diminished to a toybox, the fair Town, where so many souls, as it were seen and yet unseen, are driving their multifarious traffic. Its white steeple is then truly a starward-pointing finger; the canopy of blue smoke seems like a sort of Life-breath: for always, of its own unity, the soul gives unity to whatsoever it looks on with love; thus does the little Dwelling place of men, in itself a congeries of houses and huts, become for us an individual, almost a person. But what thousand other thoughts unite thereto, if the place has to ourselves been the arena of joyous or mournful experiences; if perhaps the cradle we were rocked in still stands there, if our Loving ones still dwell there, if our Buried ones there slumber!' Does Teufelsdröckh, as the wounded eagle is said to make for its own eyrie, and indeed military deserters, and all hunted outcast creatures, turn as if by instinct in the direction of their birthland,—fly first, in this extremity, towards his native Entepfuhl; but reflecting that there no help awaits him, take but one wistful look from the distance, and then wend elsewhither?

Little happier seems to be his next flight: into the wilds of Nature; as if in her mother-bosom he would seek healing. So at least we incline to interpret the following Notice, separated from the former by some considerable space, wherein, however, is nothing noteworthy:

'Mountains were not new to him; but rarely are Mountains seen in such combined majesty and grace as here. The rocks are of that sort called Primitive by the mineralogists, which always arrange themselves in masses of a rugged, gigantic character; which ruggedness, however, is here tempered by a singular airiness of form, and softness of environment: in a climate favourable to vegetation, the gray cliff, itself covered with lichens, shoots-up through a garment of foliage or verdure; and white, bright cottages, tree-shaded, cluster round the everlasting granite. In fine vicissitude, Beauty alternates with Grandeur: you ride through stony hollows, along straight passes, traversed by torrents, overhung by high walls of rock; now winding amid broken shaggy chasms, and huge fragments; now suddenly emerging into some emerald valley, where the streamlet collects itself into a Lake, and man has again found a fair dwelling, and it seems as if Peace had established herself in the bosom of Strength.

'To Peace, however, in this vortex of existence, can the Son of Time not pretend: still less if some Spectre haunt him from the Past; and the future is wholly a Stygian Darkness, spectre-bearing. Reasonably might the Wanderer exclaim to himself: Are not the gates of this world's happiness inexorably shut against thee; hast thou a hope that is not mad? Nevertheless, one may still murmur audibly, or in the original Greek if that suit better: " Whoso can look on Death will start at no shadows."

'From such meditations is the Wanderer's attention called outwards; for now the Valley closes-in abruptly, intersected by a huge mountain mass, the stony water-worn ascent of which is not to be accomplished on horse-back. Arrived aloft, he finds himself again lifted into the evening sunset light; and cannot but pause, and gaze round him, some moments there. An upland irregular expanse of wold, where valleys in complex branchings are suddenly or slowly arranging their descent towards every quarter of the sky. The moun-tain-ranges are beneath your feet, and folded together: only the loftier summits look down here and there as on a second plain; lakes also lie clear and earnest in their solitude. No trace of man now visible; unless indeed it were he who fashioned that little visible link of Highway, here, as would seem, scaling the inacces-sible, to unite Province with Province. But sunwards, lo you! how it towers sheer up, a world of Mountains, the diadem and centre of the mountain region! A hundred and a hundred savage peaks, in the last light of Day; all glowing, of gold and amethyst, like giant spirits of the wilderness; there in their silence, in their solitude, even as on the night when Noah's Deluge first dried! Beautiful, nay solemn, was the sudden aspect to our Wanderer. He gazed over those stupendous masses with wonder, almost with longing desire; never till this hour had he known Nature, that she was One, that she was his Mother, and divine. And as the ruddy glow was fading into clearness in the sky, and the Sun had now departed, a murmur of Eternity and Im-mensity, of Death and of Life, stole through his soul; and he felt as if Death and Life were one, as if the Earth were not dead, as if the Spirit of the Earth had its throne in that splendour, and his own spirit were therewith holding communion.

' The spell was broken by a sound of carriage-wheels. Emerging from the hidden Northward, to sink soon into the hidden Southward, came a gay Barouche-and-four: it was open; servants and postillions wore wedding-favours: that happy pair, then, had found each other, it was their marriage evening! Few moments brought them near: *Du Himmel!* It was Herr Towgood and —— Blumine! With slight unrecognising salutation they passed me; plunged down amid the neighbouring

thickets, onwards, to Heaven, and to England; and I,
in my friend Richter's words, *I remained alone, behind
them, with the Night.*'

Were it not cruel in these circumstances, here might
be the place to insert an observation, gleaned long ago
from the great *Clothes-Volume,* where it stands with
quite other intent : ' Some time before Small-pox was
extirpated,' says the Professor, ' there came a new
malady of the spiritual sort on Europe : I mean the
epidemic, now endemical, of View-hunting. Poets of
old date, being privileged with Senses, had also enjoyed
external Nature; but chiefly as we enjoy the crystal cup
which holds good or bad liquor for us; that is to say,
in silence, or with slight incidental commentary : never,
as I compute, till after the *Sorrows of Werter,* was
there man found who would say : Come let us make
a Description ! Having drunk the liquor, come let us
eat the glass ! Of which endemic the Jenner is unhappily still to seek.' Too true !

We reckon it more important to remark that the
Professor's Wanderings, so far as his stoical and cynical
envelopment admits us to clear insight, here first take
their permanent character, fatuous or not. That Basilisk-glance of the Barouche-and-four seems to have
withered-up what little remnant of a purpose may have
still lurked in him : Life has become wholly a dark
labyrinth; wherein, through long years, our Friend,
flying from spectres, has to stumble about at random,
and naturally with more haste than progress.

Foolish were it in us to attempt following him, even
from afar, in this extraordinary world-pilgrimage of
his; the simplest record of which, were clear record
possible, would fill volumes. Hopeless is the obscurity,
unspeakable the confusion. He glides from country to
country, from condition to condition; vanishing and re-
appearing, no man can calculate how or where.
Through all quarters of the world he wanders, and
apparently through all circles of society. If in any
scene, perhaps difficult to fix geographically, he settles
for a time, and forms connexions, be sure he will snap
them abruptly asunder. Let him sink out of sight as
Private Scholar (*Privatisirender*), living by the grace of

God in some European capital, you may next find him as Hadjee in the neighbourhood of Mecca. It is an inexplicable Phantasmagoria, capricious, quick-changing; as if our Traveller, instead of limbs and high-ways, had transported himself by some wishing-carpet, or Fortunatus' Hat. The whole, too, imparted emblematically, in dim multifarious tokens (as that collection of Street-Advertisements); with only some touch of direct historical notice sparingly interspersed: little light-islets in the world of haze! So that, from this point, the Professor is more of an enigma than ever. In figurative language, we might say he becomes, not indeed a spirit, yet spiritualised, vaporised Fact unparalleled in Biography: The river of his History, which we have traced from its tiniest fountains, and hoped to see flow onward, with increasing current, into the ocean, here dashes itself over that terrific Lover's Leap; and, as a mad-foaming cataract, flies wholly into tumultuous clouds of spray! Low down it indeed collects again into pools and plashes; yet only at a great distance, and with difficulty, if at all, into a general stream. To cast a glance into certain of those pools and plashes, and trace whither they run, must, for a chapter or two, form the limit of our endeavour.

For which end doubtless those direct historical Notices, where they can be met with, are the best. Nevertheless, of this sort too there occurs much, which, with our present light, it were questionable to emit. Teufelsdröckh, vibrating everywhere between the highest and the lowest levels, comes into contact with public History itself. For example, those conversations and relations with illustrious Persons, as Sultan Mahmoud, the Emperor Napoleon, and others, are they not as yet rather of a diplomatic character than of a biographic? The Editor, appreciating the sacredness of crowned heads, nay perhaps suspecting the possible trickeries of a Clothes-Philosopher, will eschew this province for the present; a new time may bring new insight and a different duty.

If we ask now, not indeed with what ulterior Purpose, for there was none, yet with what immediate outlooks: at all events, in what mood of mind, the Professor undertook and prosecuted this world-pilgrimage,—the answer is more distinct than favourable. 'A nameless Unrest,' says he, 'urged me forward; to which the outward motion was some momentary lying solace. Whither should I go? My Loadstars were blotted out, in that canopy of grim fire shone no star. Yet forward must I; the ground burnt under me; there was no rest for the sole of my foot. I was alone, alone! Ever too the strong inward longing shaped Fantasms for itself: towards these, one after the other, must I fruitlessly wander. A feeling I had, that for my fever-thirst there was and must be somewhere a healing Fountain. To many fondly imagined Fountains, the Saints' Wells of these days, did I pilgrim; to great Men, to great Cities, to great Events: but found there no healing. In strange countries, as in the well-known; in savage deserts, as in the press of corrupt civilisation, it was ever the same: how could your Wanderer escape from—*his own Shadow?* Nevertheless still Forward! I felt as if in great haste; to do I saw not what. From the depths of my own heart, it called to me, Forwards! The winds and the streams, and all Nature sounded to me, Forwards! *Ach Gott,* I was even, once for all, a Son of Time.'

From which is it not clear that the internal Satanic School was still active enough? He says elsewhere: 'The *Enchiridion of Epictetus* I had ever with me, often as my sole rational companion; and regret to mention that the nourishment it yielded was trifling.' Thou foolish Teufelsdröckh! How could it else? Hadst thou not Greek enough to understand thus much: *The end of Man is an Action, and not a Thought,* though it were the noblest?

'How I lived?' writes he once: 'Friend, hast thou considered the "rugged all-nourishing Earth," as Sophocles well names her; how she feeds the sparrow on the house-top, much more her darling, man? While thou stirrest and livest, thou hast a probability of victual. My breakfast of tea has been cooked by a Tartar woman, with water of the Amur, who wiped her earthen kettle with a horse-tail. I have roasted wild-eggs in the sand of Sahara; I have awakened in Paris *Estrapades* and

Vienna *Malzleins*, with no prospect of breakfast beyond elemental liquid. That I had my Living to seek saved me from Dying,—by suicide. In our busy Europe, is there not an everlasting demand for Intellect, in the chemical, mechanical, political, religious, educational, commercial departments? In Pagan countries, cannot one write Fetishes? Living! Little knowest thou what alchemy is in an inventive Soul; how, as with its little finger, it can create provision enough for the body (of a Philosopher); and then, as with both hands, create quite other than provision; namely, spectres to torment itself withal.'

Poor Teufelsdröckh! Flying with Hunger always parallel to him; and a whole Infernal Chase in his rear; so that the countenance of Hunger is comparatively a friend's! Thus must he, in the temper of ancient Cain, or of the modern Wandering Jew,—save only that he feels himself not guilty and but suffering the pains of guilt,—wend to and fro with aimless speed. Thus must he, over the whole surface of the Earth (by footprints), write his *Sorrows of Teufelsdröckh;* even as the great Goethe, in passionate words, had to write his *Sorrows of Werter,* before the spirit freed herself, and he could become a Man. Vain truly is the hope of your swiftest Runner to escape 'from his own Shadow'! Nevertheless, in these sick days, when the Born of Heaven first descries himself (about the age of twenty) in a world such as ours, richer than usual in two things, in Truths grown obsolete, and Trades grown obsolete,—what can the fool think but that it is all a Den of Lies, wherein whoso will not speak Lies and act Lies, must stand idle and despair? Whereby it happens that, for your nobler minds, the publishing of some such Work of Art, in one or the other dialect, becomes almost a necessity. For what is it properly but an Altercation with the Devil, before you begin honestly Fighting him? Your Byron publishes his *Sorrows of Lord George,* in verse and in prose, and copiously otherwise: your Bonaparte represents his *Sorrows of Napoleon* Opera, in an all-too stupendous style; with music of cannon-volleys, and murder-shrieks of a world; his stage-lights are the fires of Conflagration; his rhyme and recitative are the tramp of embattled Hosts and the sound of falling Cities.—Happier is he who, like our Clothes-Philosopher, can write such matter, since it must be written, on the insensible Earth, with his shoe-soles only; and also survive the writing thereof!

CHAPTER VII

THE EVERLASTING NO

UNDER the strange nebulous envelopment, wherein our Professor has now shrouded himself, no doubt but his spiritual nature is nevertheless progressive, and growing: for how can the 'Son of Time,' in any case, stand still? We behold him, through those dim years, in a state of crisis, of transition: his mad Pilgrimings, and general solution into aimless Discontinuity, what is all this but a mad Fermentation; wherefrom, the fiercer it is, the clearer product will one day evolve itself?

Such transitions are ever full of pain: thus the Eagle when he moults is sickly; and, to attain his new beak, must harshly dash-off the old one upon rocks. What Stoicism soever our Wanderer, in his individual acts and motions, may affect, it is clear that there is a hot fever of anarchy and misery raging within; coruscations of which flash out: as, indeed, how could there be other? Have we not seen him disappointed, bemocked of Destiny, through long years? All that the young heart might desire and pray for has been denied; nay, as in the last worst instance, offered and then snatched away. Ever an 'excellent Passivity'; but of useful, reasonable Activity, essential to the former as Food to Hunger, nothing granted: till at length, in this wild Pilgrimage, he must forcibly seize for himself an Activity, though useless, unreasonable. Alas, his cup of bitterness, which had been filling drop by drop, ever since that first 'ruddy morning' in the Hinterschlag Gymnasium, was at the very lip; and then with that poison-drop, of the Towgood-and-Blumine business, it runs over, and even hisses over in a deluge of foam.

He himself says once, with more justice than originality: 'Man is, properly speaking, based upon Hope, he has no other possession but Hope; this world of his is emphatically the Place of Hope.' What, then, was our Professor's possession? We see him, for the present, quite shut-out from Hope; looking not into the golden orient, but vaguely all round into a dim copper firmament, pregnant with earthquake and tornado.

Alas, shut-out from Hope, in a deeper sense than we yet dream of! For, as he wanders wearisomely through this world, he has now lost all tidings of another and higher. Full of religion, or at least of religiosity, as our Friend has since exhibited himself, he hides not that, in those days, he was wholly irreligious: 'Doubt had darkened into Unbelief,' says he; 'shade after shade goes grimly over your soul, till you have the fixed, starless, Tartarean black.' To such readers as have reflected, what can be called reflecting, on man's life, and happily discovered, in contradiction to much Profit-and-loss Philosophy, speculative and practical, that Soul is *not* synonymous with Stomach; who understand, therefore, in our Friend's words, 'that, for man's well-being, Faith is properly the one thing needful; how, with it, Martyrs, otherwise weak, can cheerfully endure the shame and the cross; and without it, worldlings puke-up their sick existence, by suicide, in the midst of luxury': to such it will be clear that, for a pure moral nature, the loss of his religious Belief was the loss of everything. Unhappy young man! All wounds, the crush of long-continued Destitution, the stab of false Friendship and of false Love, all wounds in thy so genial heart, would have healed again, had not its life-warmth been withdrawn. Well might he exclaim, in his wild way: 'Is there no God, then; but at best an absentee God, sitting idle, ever since the first Sabbath, at the outside of his Universe, and *see*ing it go? Has the word Duty no meaning; is what we call Duty no divine Messenger and Guide, but a false earthly Fantasm, made-up of Desire and Fear, of emanations from the Gallows and from Dr. Graham's Celestial-Bed? Happiness of an approving Conscience! Did not Paul of Tarsus, whom

admiring men have since named Saint, feel that *he* was
" the chief of sinners "; and Nero of Rome, jocund in
spirit (*wohlgemuth*), spend much of his time in fiddling?
Foolish Word-monger and Motive-grinder, who in thy
Logic-mill hast an earthly mechanism for the Godlike
itself, and wouldst fain grind me out Virtue from the
husks of Pleasure,—I tell thee, Nay! To the unregen-
erate Prometheus Vinctus of a man, it is ever the
bitterest aggravation of his wretchedness that he is
conscious of Virtue, that he feels himself the victim not
of suffering only, but of injustice. What then? Is the
heroic inspiration we name Virtue but some Passion;
some bubble of the blood, bubbling in the direction
others *profit* by? I know not: only this I know, If
what thou namest Happiness be our true aim, then are
we all astray. With Stupidity and sound Digestion
man may front much. But what, in these dull unim-
aginative days, are the terrors of Conscience to the
diseases of the Liver! Not on Morality, but on
Cookery, let us build our stronghold : there brandishing
our frying-pan, as censer, let us offer sweet incense to
the Devil, and live at ease on the fat things *he* has
provided for his Elect!'

Thus has the bewildered Wanderer to stand, as so
many have done, shouting question after question into
the Sibyl-cave of Destiny, and receive no Answer but
an Echo. It is all a grim Desert, this once-fair world
of his; wherein is heard only the howling of wild-beasts,
or the shrieks of despairing, hate-filled men; and no
Pillar of Cloud by day, and no Pillar of Fire by night,
any longer guides the Pilgrim. To such length has the
spirit of Inquiry carried him. ' But what boots it (*was
thut's*)?' cries he : ' it is but the common lot in this
era. Not having come to spiritual majority prior to the
Siècle de Louis Quinze, and not being born purely a
Loghead (*Dummkopf*), thou hadst no other outlook.
The whole world is, like thee, sold to Unbelief; their
old Temples of the Godhead, which for long have not
been rainproof, crumble down; and men ask now:
Where is the Godhead; our eyes never saw him?'

Pitiful enough were it, for all these wild utterances,
to call our Diogenes wicked. Unprofitable servants

as we all are, perhaps at no era of his life was he more decisively the Servant of Goodness, the Servant of God, than even now when doubting God's existence. 'One circumstance I note,' says he: 'after all the nameless woe that Inquiry, which for me, what it is not always, was genuine Love of Truth, had wrought me, I nevertheless still loved Truth, and would bate no jot of my allegiance to her. "Truth"! I cried, "though the Heavens crush me for following her: no Falsehood! though a whole celestial Lubberland were the price of Apostasy." In conduct it was the same. Had a divine Messenger from the clouds, or miraculous Handwriting on the wall, convincingly proclaimed to me *This thou shalt do*, with what passionate readiness, as I often thought, would I have done it, had it been leaping into the infernal Fire. Thus, in spite of all Motive-grinders, and Mechanical Profit-and-Loss Philosophies, with the sick ophthalmia and hallucination they had brought on, was the Infinite nature of Duty still dimly present to me: living without God in the world, of God's light I was not utterly bereft; if my as yet sealed eyes, with their unspeakable longing, could nowhere see Him, nevertheless in my heart He was present, and His heaven-written Law still stood legible and sacred there.'

Meanwhile, under all these tribulations, and temporal and spiritual destitutions, what must the Wanderer, in his silent soul, have endured! 'The painfullest feeling,' writes he, 'is that of your own Feebleness (*Unkraft*); ever, as the English Milton says, to be weak is the true misery. And yet of your Strength there is and can be no clear feeling, save by what you have prospered in, by what you have done. Between vague wavering Capability and fixed indubitable Performance, what a difference! A certain inarticulate Self-consciousness dwells dimly in us; which only our Works can render articulate and decisively discernible. Our Works are the mirror wherein the spirit first sees its natural lineaments. Hence, too, the folly of that impossible Precept, *Know thyself;* till it be translated into this partially possible one, *Know what thou canst work-at.*

'But for me, so strangely unprosperous had I been,

the net-result of my Workings amounted as yet simply
to—Nothing. How then could I believe in my Strength,
when there was as yet no mirror to see it in? Ever
did this agitating, yet, as I now perceive, quite frivolous
question, remain to me insoluble: Hast thou a certain
Faculty, a certain Worth, such even as the most have
not; or art thou the completest Dullard of these modern
times? Alas! the fearful Unbelief is unbelief in yourself; and how could I believe? Had not my first, last
Faith in myself, when even to me the Heavens seemed
laid open, and I dared to love, been all-too cruelly
belied? The speculative Mystery of Life grew ever
more mysterious to me: neither in the practical Mystery
had I made the slightest progress, but been everywhere
buffeted, foiled, and contemptuously cast-out. A feeble
unit in the middle of a threatening Infinitude, I seemed
to have nothing given me but eyes, whereby to discern
my own wretchedness. Invisible yet impenetrable
walls, as of Enchantment, divided me from all living:
was there, in the wide world, any true bosom I could
press trustfully to mine? O Heaven, No, there was
none! I kept a lock upon my lips: why should I speak
much with that shifting variety of so-called Friends,
in whose withered, vain and too-hungry souls Friendship was but an incredible tradition? In such cases,
your resource is to talk little, and that little mostly from
the Newspapers. Now when I look back, it was a
strange isolation I then lived in. The men and women
around me, even speaking with me, were but Figures;
I had, practically, forgotten that they were alive, that
they were not merely automatic. In midst of their
crowded streets and assemblages, I walked solitary;
and (except as it was my own heart, not another's, that
I kept devouring) savage also, as the tiger in his jungle.
Some comfort it would have been, could I, like a Faust,
have fancied myself tempted and tormented of the
Devil; for a Hell, as I imagine, without Life, though
only diabolic Life, were more frightful: but in our age
of Down-pulling and Disbelief, the very Devil has been
pulled down, you cannot so much as believe in a Devil.
To me the Universe was all void of Life, of Purpose,
of Volition, even of Hostility: it was one huge, dead,

immeasurable Steam-engine, rolling on, in its dead indifference, to grind me limb from limb. O, the vast, gloomy, solitary Golgotha, and Mill of Death! Why was the Living banished thither companionless, conscious? Why, if there is no Devil; nay, unless the Devil is your God'?

A prey incessantly to such corrosions, might not, moreover, as the worst aggravation to them, the iron constitution even of a Teufelsdröckh threaten to fail? We conjecture that he has known sickness; and, in spite of his locomotive habits, perhaps sickness of the chronic sort. Hear this, for example: ' How beautiful to die of broken-heart, on Paper! Quite another thing in practice; every window of your Feeling, even of your Intellect, as it were, begrimed and mud-bespattered, so that no pure ray can enter; a whole Drugshop in your inwards; the fordone soul drowning slowly in quagmires of Disgust!'

Putting all which external and internal miseries together, may we not find in the following sentences, quite in our Professor's still vein, significance enough? ' From Suicide a certain aftershine (*Nachschein*) of Christianity withheld me: perhaps also a certain indolence of character; for, was not that a remedy I had at any time within reach? Often, however, was there a question present to me: Should some one now, at the turning of that corner, blow thee suddenly out of Space, into the other World, or other No-World, by pistol-shot,—how were it? On which ground, too, I have often, in sea-storms and sieged cities and other death-scenes, exhibited an imperturbability, which passed, falsely enough, for courage.'

' So had it lasted,' concludes the Wanderer, ' so had it lasted, as in bitter protracted Death-agony, through long years. The heart within me, unvisited by any heavenly dewdrop, was smouldering in sulphurous, slow-consuming fire. Almost since earliest memory I had shed no tear; or once only when I, murmuring half-audibly, recited Faust's Deathsong, that wild *Selig der den er im Siegesglanze findet* (Happy whom *he* finds in Battle's splendour), and thought that of this last Friend even I was not forsaken, that Destiny itself could not doom me not to die. Having no hope, neither had I any definite fear, were it of Man or of Devil : nay, I often felt as if it might be solacing, could the Arch-Devil himself, though in Tartarean terrors, but rise to me, that I might tell him a little of my mind. And yet, strangely enough, I lived in a continual, indefinite, pining fear; tremulous, pusillanimous, apprehensive of I knew not what : it seemed as if all things in the Heavens above and the Earth beneath would hurt me; as if the Heavens and the Earth were but boundless jaws of a devouring monster, wherein I, palpitating, waited to be devoured.

' Full of such humour, and perhaps the miserablest man in the whole French Capital or Suburbs, was I, one sultry Dog-day, after much perambulation, toiling along the dirty little *Rue Saint-Thomas de l'Enfer*, among civic rubbish enough, in a close atmosphere, and over pavements hot as Nebuchadnezzar's Furnace; whereby doubtless my spirits were little cheered; when, all at once, there rose a Thought in me, and I asked myself : " What *art* thou afraid of? Wherefore, like a coward, dost thou forever pip and whimper, and go cowering and trembling? Despicable biped ! what is the sum-total of the worst that lies before thee? Death? Well, Death; and say the pangs of Tophet too, and all that the Devil and Man may, will or can do against thee ! Hast thou not a heart; canst thou not suffer whatsoever it be; and, as a Child of Freedom, though outcast, trample Tophet itself under thy feet, while it consumes thee? Let it come, then; I will meet it and defy it !" And as I so thought, there rushed like a stream of fire over my whole soul; and I shook base Fear away from me forever. I was strong, of unknown strength; a spirit, almost a god. Ever from that time, the temper of my misery was changed : not Fear or whining Sorrow was it, but Indignation and grim fire-eyed Defiance.

' Thus had the EVERLASTING No (*das ewige Nein*) pealed authoritatively through all the recesses of my Being, of my ME; and then was it that my whole ME stood up, in native God-created majesty, and with emphasis recorded its Protest. Such a Protest, the

F 278

most important transaction in Life, may that same
Indignation and Defiance, in a psychological point of
view, be fitly called. The Everlasting No had said :
" Behold, thou are fatherless, outcast, and the Universe
is mine (the Devil's)"; to which my whole Me now
made answer : " *I* am not thine, but Free, and forever
hate thee !"

' It is from this hour that I incline to date my
Spiritual New-birth, or Baphometic Fire-baptism;
perhaps I directly thereupon began to be a Man.'

CHAPTER VIII

CENTRE OF INDIFFERENCE

THOUGH, after this ' Baphometic Fire-baptism ' of
his, our Wanderer signifies that his Unrest was but
increased; as, indeed, ' Indignation and Defiance,'
especially against things in general, are not the most
peaceable inmates; yet can the Psychologist surmise
that it was no longer a quite hopeless Unrest; that
henceforth it had at least a fixed centre to revolve round.
For the fire-baptised soul, long so scathed and thunder-
riven, here feels its own Freedom, which feeling is its
Baphometic Baptism : the citadel of its whole kingdom
it has thus gained by assault, and will keep inexpugnable ; outwards from which the remaining dominions,
not indeed without hard battling, will doubtless by
degrees be conquered and pacificated. Under another
figure, we might say, if in that great moment, in the *Rue
Saint-Thomas de l'Enfer*, the old inward Satanic School
was not yet thrown out of doors, it received peremptory
judicial notice to quit;—whereby, for the rest, its howl-
chantings, Ernulphus-cursings, and rebellious gnash-
ings of teeth, might, in the meanwhile, become only the
more tumultuous, and difficult to keep secret.

Accordingly, if we scrutinise these Pilgrimings well,
there is perhaps discernible henceforth a certain incipient method in their madness. Not wholly as a
Spectre does Teufelsdröckh now storm through the

world; at worst as a spectre-fighting Man, nay who will one day be a Spectre-queller. If pilgriming restlessly to so many ' Saints' Wells,' and ever without quenching of his thirst, he nevertheless finds little secular wells, whereby from time to time some alleviation is ministered. In a word, he is now, if not ceasing, yet intermitting to ' eat his own heart '; and clutches round him outwardly on the NOT-ME for wholesomer food. Does not the following glimpse exhibit him in a much more natural state?

' Towns also and Cities, especially the ancient, I failed not to look upon with interest. How beautiful to see thereby, as through a long vista, into the remote Time; to have, as it were, an actual section of almost the earliest Past brought safe into the Present, and set before your eyes ! There, in that old City, was a live ember of Culinary Fire put down, say only two thousand years ago; and there, burning more or less triumphantly, with such fuel as the region yielded, it has burnt, and still burns, and thou thyself seest the very smoke thereof. Ah ! and the far more mysterious live ember of Vital Fire was then also put down there; and still miraculously burns and spreads; and the smoke and ashes thereof (in these Judgment-Halls and Churchyards), and its bellows-engines (in these Churches), thou still seest; and its flame, looking out from every kind countenance, and every hateful one, still warms thee or scorches thee.

' Of Man's Activity and Attainment the chief results are aeriform, mystic, and preserved in Tradition only : such are his Forms of Government, with the Authority they rest on; his Customs, or Fashions both of Cloth-habits and of Soul-habits; much more his collective stock of Handicrafts, the whole Faculty he has acquired of manipulating Nature : all these things, as indispensable and priceless as they are, cannot in any way be fixed under lock and key, but must flit, spirit-like, on impalpable vehicles, from Father to Son; if you demand sight of them, they are nowhere to be met with. Visible Ploughmen and Hammermen there have been, ever from Cain and Tubalcain downwards : but where does your accumulated Agricultural, Metallurgic, and other

Manufacturing SKILL lie warehoused? It transmits
itself on the atmospheric air, on the sun's rays (by
Hearing and by Vision); it is a thing aeriform, impalpable, of quite spiritual sort. In like manner, ask me
not, Where are the LAWS; where is the GOVERNMENT?
In vain wilt thou go to Schönbrunn, to Downing Street,
to the Palais Bourbon: thou findest nothing there but
brick or stone houses, and some bundles of Papers tied
with tape. Where, then, is that same cunningly-
devised almighty GOVERNMENT of theirs to be laid
hands on? Everywhere, yet nowhere: seen only in its
works, this too is a thing aeriform, invisible; or if
you will, mystic and miraculous. So spiritual (*geistig*)
is our whole daily Life: all that we do springs out of
Mystery, Spirit, invisible Force; only like a little Cloud-
image, or Armida's Palace, air-built, does the Actual
body itself forth from the great mystic Deep.

'Visible and tangible products of the Past, again,
I reckon-up to the extent of three: Cities, with their
Cabinets and Arsenals; then tilled Fields, to either or
to both of which divisions Roads with their Bridges
may belong; and thirdly —— Books. In which third
truly, the last invented, lies a worth far surpassing that
of the two others. Wondrous indeed is the virtue of
a true Book. Not like a dead city of stones, yearly
crumbling, yearly needing repair; more like a tilled
field, but then a spiritual field: like a spiritual tree, let
me rather say, it stands from year to year, and from
age to age (we have Books that already number some
hundred-and-fifty human ages); and yearly comes its
new produce of leaves (Commentaries, Deductions,
Philosophical, Political Systems; or were it only
Sermons, Pamphlets, Journalistic Essays), every one of
which is talismanic and thaumaturgic, for it can persuade men. O thou who art able to write a Book,
which once in the two centuries or oftener there is a
man gifted to do, envy not him whom they name City-
builder, and inexpressibly pity him whom they name
Conqueror or City-burner! Thou too art a Conqueror
and Victor: but of the true sort, namely over the Devil:
thou too hast built what will outlast all marble and
metal, and be a wonder-bringing City of the Mind, a

Temple and Seminary and Prophetic Mount, whereto all kindreds of the Earth will pilgrim.—Fool! why journeyest thou wearisomely, in thy antiquarian fervour, to gaze on the stone pyramids of Geeza, or the clay ones of Sacchara? These stand there, as I can tell thee, idle and inert, looking over the Desert, foolishly enough, for the last three-thousand years: but canst thou not open thy Hebrew BIBLE, then, or even Luther's Version thereof?'

No less satisfactory is his sudden appearance not in Battle, yet on some Battle-field; which, we soon gather, must be that of Wagram; so that here, for once, is a certain approximation to distinctness of date. Omitting much, let us impart what follows:

'Horrible enough! A whole Marchfeld strewed with shell-splinters, cannon-shot, ruined tumbrils, and dead men and horses; stragglers still remaining not so much as buried. And those red mould heaps: ay, there lie the Shells of Men, out of which all the Life and Virtue has been blown; and now are they swept together, and crammed-down out of sight, like blown Egg-shells!—Did Nature, when she bade the Donau bring down his mould-cargoes from the Carinthian and Carpathian Heights, and spread them out here into the softest, richest level,—intend thee, O Marchfeld, for a corn-bearing Nursery, whereon her children might be nursed; or for a Cockpit, wherein they might the more commodiously be throttled and tattered? Were thy three broad Highways, meeting here from the ends of Europe, made for Ammunition-wagons, then? Were thy Wagrams and Stillfrieds but so many ready-built Casemates, wherein the house of Hapsburg might batter with artillery, and with artillery be battered? König Ottokar, amid yonder hillocks, dies under Rodolf's truncheon; here Kaiser Franz falls a-swoon under Napoleon's: within which five centuries, to omit the others, how has thy breast, fair Plain, been defaced and defiled! The greensward is torn-up and trampled-down; man's fond care of it, his fruit-trees, hedge-rows, and pleasant dwellings, blown-away with gun-powder; and the kind seedfield lies a desolate, hideous Place of Sculls.—Nevertheless, Nature is at work;

neither shall these Powder-Devilkins with their utmost devilry gainsay her : but all that gore and carnage will be shrouded-in, absorbed into manure ; and next year the Marchfeld will be green, nay greener. Thrifty unwearied Nature, ever out of our great waste educing some little profit of thy own,—how dost thou, from the very carcass of the Killer, bring Life for the Living !

'What, speaking in quite unofficial language, is the net-purport and upshot of war? To my own know-ledge, for example, there dwell and toil, in the British village of Dumdrudge, usually some five-hundred souls. From these, by certain "Natural Enemies" of the French, there are successively selected, during the French war, say thirty able-bodied men : Dumdrudge, at her own expense, has suckled and nursed them : she has, not without difficulty and sorrow, fed them up to manhood, and even trained them to crafts, so that one can weave, another build, another hammer, and the weakest can stand under thirty stone avoirdupois. Nevertheless, amid much weeping and swearing, they are selected ; all dressed in red ; and shipped away, at the public charges, some two-thousand miles, or say only to the south of Spain ; and fed there till wanted. And now to that same spot, in the south of Spain, are thirty similar French artisans, from a French Dum-drudge, in like manner wending : till at length, after infinite effort, the two parties come into actual juxta-position ; and Thirty stands fronting Thirty, each with a gun in his hand. Straightway the word " Fire !" is given : and they blow the souls out of one another ; and in place of sixty brisk useful craftsmen, the world has sixty dead carcasses, which it must bury, and anew shed tears for. Had these men any quarrel? Busy as the Devil is, not the smallest ! They lived far enough apart ; were the entirest strangers ; nay, in so wide a Universe, there was even, unconsciously, by Commerce, some mutual helpfulness between them. How then? Simpleton ! their Governors had fallen-out ; and, instead of shooting one another, had the cunning to make these poor blockheads shoot.—Alas, so is it in Deutschland, and hitherto in all other lands ; still as of old, " what devilry soever Kings do, the Greeks must pay the piper!"—In that fiction of the English Smollet, it is true, the final Cessation of War is perhaps prophetically shadowed forth; where the two Natural Enemies, in person, take each a Tobacco-pipe, filled with Brimstone; light the same, and smoke in one another's faces, till the weaker gives in : but from such predicted Peace-Era, what blood-filled trenches, and contentious centuries, may still divide us !'

Thus can the Professor, at least in lucid intervals, look away from his own sorrows, over the many-coloured world, and pertinently enough note what is passing there. We may remark, indeed, that for the matter of spiritual culture, if for nothing else, perhaps few periods of his life were richer than this. Internally, there is the most momentous instructive Course of Practical Philosophy, with Experiments, going on; towards the right comprehension of which his Peripatetic habits, favourable to Meditation, might help him rather than hinder. Externally, again, as he wanders to and fro, there are, if for the longing heart little substance, yet for the seeing eye sights enough : in these so boundless Travels of his, granting that the Satanic School was even partially kept down, what an incredible knowledge of our Planet, and its Inhabitants and their Works, that is to say, of all knowable things, might not Teufelsdröckh acquire !

'I have read in most Public Libraries,' says he, 'including those of Constantinople and Samarcand : in most Colleges, except the Chinese Mandarin ones, I have studied, or seen that there was no studying. Unknown Languages have I oftenest gathered from their natural repertory, the Air, by my organ of Hearing; Statistics, Geographics, Topographics came, through the Eye, almost of their own accord. The ways of Man, how he seeks food, and warmth, and protection for himself, in most regions, are ocularly known to me. Like the great Hadrian, I meted-out much of the terraqueous Globe with a pair of Compasses that belonged to myself only.

'Of great Scenes why speak? Three summer days, I lingered reflecting, and even composing (*dichtete*), by the Pinechasms of Vaucluse; and in that clear Lakelet moistened my bread. I have sat under the Palm-trees of Tadmor; smoked a pipe among the ruins of Babylon. The great Wall of China I have seen; and can testify that it is of gray brick, coped and covered with granite, and shows only second-rate masonry.—Great Events, also, have not I witnessed? Kings sweated-down (*ausgemergelt*) into Berlin-and-Milan Customhouse-Officers; the World well won, and the World well lost; oftener than once a hundred-thousand individuals shot (by each other) in one day. All kindreds and peoples and nations dashed together, and shifted and shovelled into heaps, that they might ferment there, and in time unite. The birth-pangs of Democracy, wherewith convulsed Europe was groaning in cries that reached Heaven, could not escape me.

'For great Men I have ever had the warmest predilection; and can perhaps boast that few such in this era have wholly escaped me. Great Men are the inspired (speaking and acting) Texts of that divine BOOK OF REVELATIONS, whereof a Chapter is completed from epoch to epoch, and by some named HISTORY; to which inspired Texts your numerous talented men, and your innumerable untalented men, are the better or worse exegetic Commentaries, and wagonload of too-stupid, heretical or orthodox, weekly Sermons. For my study the inspired Texts themselves! Thus did not I, in very early days, having disguised me as tavern-waiter, stand behind the field-chairs, under that shady Tree at Treisnitz by the Jena Highway; waiting upon the great Schiller and greater Goethe; and hearing what I have not forgotten. For——'

——But at this point the Editor recalls his principle of caution, some time ago laid down, and must suppress much. Let not the sacredness of Laurelled, still more, of Crowned Heads, be tampered with. Should we, at a future day, find circumstances altered, and the time come for Publication, then may these glimpses into the privacy of the Illustrious be conceded; which for the present were little better than treacherous, perhaps traitorous Eavesdroppings. Of Lord Byron, therefore, of Pope Pius, Emperor Tarakwang, and the 'White Water-roses' (Chinese Carbonari) with their mysteries, no notice here! Of Napoleon himself we shall only, glancing from afar, remark that Teufelsdröckh's relation to him seems to have been of very varied character. At first we find our poor Professor on the point of being shot as a spy; then taken into private conversation, even pinched on the ear, yet presented with no money; at last indignantly dismissed, almost thrown out of doors, as an 'Ideologist.' 'He himself,' says the Professor, 'was among the completest Ideologists, at least Ideopraxists : in the Idea (*in der Idee*) he lived, moved and fought. The man was a Divine Missionary, though unconscious of it; and preached, through the cannon's throat, that great doctrine, *La carrière ouverte aux talens* (The Tools to him that can handle them), which is our ultimate Political Evangel, wherein alone can liberty lie. Madly enough he preached, it is true, as Enthusiasts and first Missionaries are wont, with imperfect utterance, amid much frothy rant; yet as articulately perhaps as the case admitted. Or call him, if you will, an American Backwoodsman, who had to fell unpenetrated forests, and battle with innumerable wolves, and did not entirely forbear strong liquor, rioting, and even theft; whom, notwithstanding, the peaceful Sower will follow, and, as he cuts the boundless harvest, bless.'

More legitimate and decisively authentic is Teufelsdröckh's appearance and emergence (we know not well whence) in the solitude of the North Cape, on that June Midnight. He has 'a light-blue Spanish cloak' hanging round him, as his 'most commodious, principal, indeed sole upper garment'; and stands there, on the World-promontory, looking over the infinite Brine, like a little blue Belfry (as we figure), now motionless indeed, yet ready, if stirred, to ring quaintest changes.

'Silence as of death,' writes he; 'for Midnight, even in the Arctic latitudes, has its character : nothing but the granite cliffs ruddy-tinged, the peaceable gurgle of that slow-heaving Polar Ocean, over which in the utmost North the great Sun hangs low and lazy, as if he too were slumbering. Yet is his cloud-couch wrought of crimson and cloth-of-gold; yet does his light stream over the mirror of waters, like a tremulous fire-pillar, shooting downwards to the abyss, and hide itself under my feet. In such moments, Solitude also is invaluable; for who would speak, or be looked on, when behind him lies all Europe and Africa, fast asleep, except the watchmen; and before him the silent Immensity, and Palace of the Eternal, whereof our Sun is but a porch-lamp?

' Nevertheless, in this solemn moment comes a man, or monster, scrambling from among the rock-hollows; and, shaggy, huge as the Hyperborean Bear, hails me in Russian speech: most probably, therefore, a Russian Smuggler. With courteous brevity, I signify my indifference to contraband trade, my humane intentions, yet strong wish to be private. In vain: the monster, counting doubtless on his superior stature, and minded to make sport for himself, or perhaps profit, were it with murder, continues to advance; ever assailing me with his importunate train-oil breath; and now has advanced, till we stand both on the verge of the rock, the deep Sea rippling greedily down below. What argument will avail? On the thick Hyperborean, cherubic reasoning, seraphic eloquence were lost. Prepared for such extremity, I, deftly enough, whisk aside one step; draw out, from my interior reservoirs, a sufficient Birmingham Horse-pistol, and say, " Be so obliging as retire, Friend (*Er ziehe sich zurück, Freund*), and with promptitude!" This logic even the Hyperborean understands; fast enough, with apologetic, petitionary growl, he sidles off; and, except for suicidal as well as homicidal purposes, need not return.

' Such I hold to be the genuine use of Gunpowder: that it makes all men alike tall. Nay, if thou be cooler, cleverer than I, if thou have more *Mind*, though all but no Body whatever, then canst thou kill me first, and art the taller. Hereby, at last, is the Goliath powerless, and the David resistless; savage Animalism is nothing, inventive Spiritualism is all.

' With respect to Duels, indeed, I have my own ideas. Few things, in this so surprising world, strike me with more surprise. Two little visual Spectra of men, hovering with insecure enough cohesion in the midst of the

UNFATHOMABLE, and to dissolve therein, at any rate, very soon,—make pause at the distance of twelve paces asunder; whirl round; and, simultaneously by the cunningest mechanism, explode one another into Dissolution; and off-hand become Air, and Non-extant! Deuce on it (*verdammt*), the little spitfires!—Nay, I think with old Hugo von Trimberg: " God must needs laugh outright, could such a thing be, to see his wondrous Manikins here below." '

But amid these specialties, let us not forget the great generality, which is our chief quest here: How prospered the inner man of Teufelsdröckh under so much outward shifting? Does Legion still lurk in him, though repressed; or has he exorcised that Devil's Brood? We can answer that the symptoms continue promising. Experience is the grand spiritual Doctor; and with him Teufelsdröckh has now been long a patient, swallowing many a bitter bolus. Unless our poor Friend belong to the numerous class of Incurables, which seems not likely, some cure will doubtless be effected. We should rather say that Legion, or the Satanic School, was now pretty well extirpated and cast out, but next to nothing introduced in its room; whereby the heart remains, for the while, in a quiet but no comfortable state.

' At length, after so much roasting,' thus writes our Autobiographer, ' I was what you might name calcined. Pray only that it be not rather, as is the more frequent issue, reduced to a *caput-mortuum!* But in any case, by mere dint of practice, I had grown familiar with many things. Wretchedness was still wretched; but I could now partly see through it, and despise it. Which highest mortal, in this inane Existence, had I not found a Shadow-hunter, or Shadow-hunted; and, when I looked through his brave garnitures, miserable enough? Thy wishes have all been sniffed aside, thought I: but what, had they even been all granted! Did not the Boy Alexander weep because he had not two Planets to conquer; or a whole Solar System; or after that, a whole Universe? *Ach Gott,* when I gazed into these Stars, have they not looked down on me as

if with pity, from their serene spaces; like Eyes glisten-
ing with heavenly tears over the little lot of man!
Thousands of human generations, all as noisy as our
own, have been swallowed-up of Time, and there remains
no wreck of them any more; and Arcturus and Orion
and Sirius and the Pleiades are still shining in their
courses, clear and young, as when the Shepherd first
noted them in the plain of Shinar. Pshaw! what is
this paltry little Dog-cage of an Earth; what art thou
that sittest whining there? Thou art still Nothing,
Nobody: true; but who, then, is Something, Somebody? For thee the Family of Man has no use; it
rejects thee; thou art wholly as a dissevered limb: so
be it; perhaps it is better so!'

Too-heavy-laden Teufelsdröckh! Yet surely his
bands are loosening; one day he will hurl the burden
far from him, and bound forth free and with a second
youth.

'This,' says our Professor, 'was the CENTRE OF
INDIFFERENCE I had now reached; through which whoso
travels from the Negative Pole to the Positive must
necessarily pass.'

CHAPTER IX

THE EVERLASTING YEA

'TEMPTATIONS in the Wilderness!' exclaims Teufelsdröckh: 'Have we not all to be tried with such?
Not so easily can the old Adam, lodged in us by birth,
be dispossessed. Our Life is compassed round with
Necessity; yet is the meaning of Life itself no other
than Freedom, than Voluntary Force: thus have we a
warfare; in the beginning, especially, a hard-fought
battle. For the God-given mandate, *Work thou in
Welldoing*, lies mysteriously written, in Promethean
Prophetic Characters, in our hearts; and leaves us no
rest, night or day, till it be deciphered and obeyed; till
it burn forth, in our conduct, a visible, acted Gospel of
Freedom. And as the clay-given mandate, *Eat thou*

and be filled, at the same time persuasively proclaims itself through every nerve,—must not there be a confusion, a contest, before the better Influence can become the upper?

' To me nothing seems more natural than that the Son of Man, when such God-given mandate first prophetically stirs within him, and the Clay must now be vanquished, or vanquish,—should be carried of the spirit into grim Solitudes, and there fronting the Tempter do grimmest battle with him; defiantly setting him at naught, till he yield and fly. Name it as we choose: with or without visible Devil, whether in the natural Desert of rocks and sands, or in the populous moral Desert of selfishness and baseness,—to such Temptation are we all called. Unhappy if we are not! Unhappy if we are but Half-men, in whom that divine handwriting has never blazed forth, all-subduing, in true sun-splendour; but quivers dubiously amid meaner lights: or smoulders, in dull pain, in darkness, under earthly vapours!—Our Wilderness is the wide World in an Atheistic Century; our Forty Days are long years of suffering and fasting: nevertheless, to these also comes an end. Yes, to me also was given, if not Victory, yet the consciousness of Battle, and the resolve to persevere therein while life or faculty is left. To me also, entangled in the enchanted forests, demon-peopled, doleful of sight and of sound, it was given, after weariest wanderings, to work out my way into the higher sunlit slopes—of that Mountain which has no summit, or whose summit is in Heaven only !'

He says elsewhere, under a less ambitious figure; as figures are, once for all, natural to him: ' Has not thy Life been that of most sufficient men (*tüchtigen Männer*) thou hast known in this generation? An out-flush of foolish young Enthusiasm, like the first fallow-crop, wherein are as many weeds as valuable herbs: this all parched away, under the Droughts of practical and spiritual Unbelief, as Disappointment, in thought and act, often-repeated gave rise to Doubt, and Doubt gradually settled into Denial! If I have had a second-crop, and now see the perennial greensward, and sit under umbrageous cedars, which defy all Drought (and

Doubt); herein too, be the Heavens praised, I am not
without examples, and even exemplars.'

So that, for Teufelsdröckh also, there has been a
'glorious revolution': these mad shadow-hunting
and shadow-hunted Pilgrimings of his were but some
purifying 'Temptation in the Wilderness,' before his
Apostolic work (such as it was) could begin; which
Temptation is now happily over, and the Devil once
more worsted! Was 'that high moment in the *Rue
de l'Enfer,*' then, properly the turning-point of the
battle; when the Fiend said, *Worship me or be torn
in shreds;* and was answered valiantly with an *Apage
Satana?*—Singular Teufelsdröckh, would thou hadst
told thy singular story in plain words! But it is fruitless to look there, in those Paper-bags, for such. Nothing but innuendoes, figurative crotchets: a typical
Shadow, fitfully wavering, prophetico-satiric; no clear
logical Picture. 'How paint to the sensual eye,' asks
he once, 'what passes in the Holy-of-Holies of Man's
Soul; in what words, known to these profane times,
speak even afar-off of the unspeakable?' We ask in
turn: Why perplex these times, profane as they are,
with needless obscurity, by omission and by commission?
Not mystical only is our Professor, but whimsical; and
involves himself, now more than ever, in eye-bewilder-
ing *chiaroscuro.* Successive glimpses, here faithfully
imparted, our more gifted readers must endeavour to
combine for their own behoof.

He says: 'The hot Harmattan wind had raged itself
out; its howl went silent within me; and the long-
deafened soul could now hear. I paused in my wild
wanderings; and sat me down to wait, and consider;
for it was as if the hour of change drew nigh. I seemed
to surrender, to renounce utterly, and say: Fly, then,
false shadows of Hope; I will chase you no more, I
will believe you no more. And ye too, haggard spectres
of Fear, I care not for you; ye too are all shadows and
a lie. Let me rest here: for I am way-weary and life-
weary; I will rest here, were it but to die: to die or
to live is alike to me; alike insignificant.'—And again:
'Here, then, as I lay in that CENTRE OF INDIFFERENCE;
cast, doubtless by benignant upper Influence, into a

healing sleep, the heavy dreams rolled gradually away, and I awoke to a new Heaven and a new Earth. The first preliminary moral Act, Annihilation of Self (*Selbst-tödtung*), had been happily accomplished; and my mind's eyes were now unsealed, and its hands ungyved.'

Might we not also conjecture that the following passage refers to his Locality, during this same ' healing sleep '; that his Pilgrim-staff lies cast aside here, on ' the high table-land '; and indeed that the repose is already taking wholesome effect on him? If it were not that the tone, in some parts, has more of riancy, even of levity, than we could have expected ! However, in Teufelsdröckh, there is always the strangest Dualism : light dancing, with guitar-music, will be going on in the fore-court, while by fits from within comes the faint whimpering of woe and wail. We transcribe the piece entire :

' Beautiful it was to sit there, as in my skyey Tent, musing and meditating; on the high table-land, in front of the Mountains; over me, as roof, the azure Dome, and around me, for walls, four azure-flowing curtains, —namely, of the Four azure winds, on whose bottom-fringes also I have seen gilding. And then to fancy the fair Castles that stood sheltered in these Mountain hollows; with their green flower-lawns, and white dames and damosels, lovely enough : or better still, the straw-roofed Cottages, wherein stood many a Mother baking bread, with her children round her :—all hidden and protectingly folded-up in the valley-folds; yet there and alive, as sure as if I beheld them. Or to see, as well as fancy, the nine Towns and Villages, that lay round my mountain-seat, which, in still weather, were wont to speak to me (by their steeple-bells) with metal tongue; and, in almost all weather, proclaimed their vitality by repeated Smoke-clouds; whereon, as on a culinary horologe, I might read the hour of the day. For it was the smoke of cookery, as kind housewives at morning, midday, eventide, were boiling their husbands' kettles; and ever a blue pillar rose up into the air, successively or simultaneously, from each of the nine, saying, as plainly as smoke could say : Such and such a meal is getting ready here. Not uninteresting ! For

you have the whole Borough, with all its love-makings
and scandal-mongeries, contentions and contentments,
as in miniature, and could cover it all with your hat.
—If, in my wide Wayfarings, I had learned to look into
the business of the World in its details, here perhaps
was the place for combining it into general propositions,
and deducing inferences therefrom.

' Often also could I see the black Tempest marching
in anger through the Distance : round some Schreckhorn, as yet grim-blue, would the eddying vapour
gather, and there tumultuously eddy, and flow down
like a mad witch's hair; till, after a space, it vanished,
and, in the clear sunbeam, your Schreckhorn stood
smiling grim-white, for the vapour had held snow.
How thou fermentest and elaboratest, in thy great fermenting-vat and laboratory of an Atmosphere, of a
World, O Nature!—Or what is Nature? Ha! why
do I not name thee GOD? Art not thou the " Living
Garment of God "? O Heavens, is it, in very deed,
HE, then, that ever speaks through thee; that lives
and loves in thee, that lives and loves in me?

' Fore-shadows, call them rather fore-splendours, of
that Truth, and Beginning of Truths, fell mysteriously
over my soul. Sweeter than Dayspring to the Shipwrecked in Nova Zembla ; ah, like the mother's voice
to her little child that strays bewildered, weeping, in
unknown tumults; like soft streamings of celestial
music to my too-exasperated heart, came that Evangel.
The Universe is not dead and demoniacal, a charnel-
house with spectres ; but godlike, and my Father's !

' With other eyes, too, could I now look upon my
fellow man ; with an infinite Love, an infinite Pity.
Poor, wandering, wayward man ! Art thou not tired,
and beaten with stripes, even as I am? Ever, whether
thou bear the royal mantle or the beggar's gabardine,
art thou not so weary, so heavy-laden ; and thy Bed of
Rest is but a Grave. O my Brother, my Brother, why
cannot I shelter thee in my bosom, and wipe away all
tears from thy eyes ! Truly, the din of many-voiced
Life, which, in this solitude, with the mind's organ, I
could hear, was no longer a maddening discord, but a
melting one ; like inarticulate cries, and sobbings of

a dumb creature, which in the ear of Heaven are prayers. The poor Earth, with her poor joys, was now my needy Mother, not my cruel Stepdame; Man, with his so mad Wants and so mean Endeavours, had become the dearer to me; and even for his sufferings and his sins, I now first named him Brother. Thus was I standing in the porch of that "*Sanctuary of Sorrow;*" by strange, steep ways had I too been guided thither; and ere long its sacred gates would open, and the "*Divine Depth of Sorrow*" lie disclosed to me.'

The Professor says, he here first got eye on the Knot that had been strangling him, and straightway could unfasten it, and was free. 'A vain interminable controversy,' writes he, 'touching what is at present called Origin of Evil, or some such thing, arises in every soul, since the beginning of the world; and in every soul, that would pass from idle Suffering into actual Endeavouring, must first be put an end to. The most, in our time, have to go content with a simple, incomplete enough Suppression of this controversy; to a few some Solution of it is indispensable. In every new era, too, such Solution comes-out in different terms; and ever the Solution of the last era has become obsolete, and is found unserviceable. For it is man's nature to change his Dialect from century to century; he cannot help it though he would. The authentic *Church-Catechism* of our present century has not yet fallen into my hands: meanwhile, for my own private behoof, I attempt to elucidate the matter so. Man's Unhappiness, as I construe, comes of his Greatness; it is because there is an Infinite in him, which with all his cunning he cannot quite bury under the Finite. Will the whole Finance Ministers and Upholsterers and Confectioners of modern Europe undertake, in jointstock company, to make one Shoeblack HAPPY? They cannot accomplish it, above an hour or two; for the Shoeblack also has a Soul quite other than his Stomach; and would require, if you consider it, for his permanent satisfaction and saturation, simply this allotment, no more, and no less: *God's infinite Universe altogether to himself,* therein to enjoy infinitely, and fill every wish as fast as it rose. Oceans of Hochheimer, a Throat like that of Ophiuchus: speak not of them; to the infinite Shoeblack they are as nothing. No sooner is your ocean filled, than he grumbles that it might have been of better vintage. Try him with half of a Universe, of an Omnipotence, he sets to quarrelling with the proprietor of the other half, and declares himself the most maltreated of men.—Always there is a black spot in our sunshine: it is even as I said, the *Shadow of Ourselves*.

'But the whim we have of Happiness is somewhat thus. By certain valuations, and averages, of our own striking, we come upon some sort of average terrestrial lot; this we fancy belongs to us by nature, and of indefeasible right. It is simple payment of our wages, of our deserts; requires neither thanks nor complaint; only such *overplus* as there may be do we account Happiness; any *deficit* again is Misery. Now consider that we have the valuation of our own deserts ourselves, and what a fund of Self-conceit there is in each of us,—do you wonder that the balance should so often dip the wrong way, and many a Blockhead cry: See there, what a payment; was ever worthy gentleman so used!—I tell thee, Blockhead, it all comes of thy Vanity; of what thou *fanciest* those same deserts of thine to be. Fancy that thou deservest to be hanged (as is most likely), thou wilt feel it happiness to be only shot: fancy that thou deservest to be hanged in a hair-halter, it will be a luxury to die in hemp.

'So true is it, what I then say, that *the Fraction of Life can be increased in value not so much by increasing your Numerator as by lessening your Denominator*. Nay, unless my Algebra deceive me, *Unity* itself divided by *Zero* will give *Infinity*. Make thy claim of wages a zero, then; thou hast the world under thy feet. Well did the Wisest of our time write: "It is only with Renunciation (*Entsagen*) that Life, properly speaking, can be said to begin."

'I asked myself: What is this that, ever since earliest years, thou hast been fretting and fuming, and lamenting and self-tormenting, on account of? Say it in a word: is it not because thou art not HAPPY? Because the THOU (sweet gentleman) is not sufficiently honoured, nourished, soft-bedded, and lovingly cared for? Foolish soul! What Act of Legislature was there that *thou* shouldst be Happy? A little while ago thou hadst no right to *be* at all. What if thou wert born and predestined not to be Happy, but to be Unhappy! Art thou nothing other than a Vulture, then, that fliest through the Universe seeking after somewhat to *eat;* and shrieking dolefully because carrion enough is not given thee? Close thy *Byron;* open thy *Goethe.*'

'*Es leuchtet mir ein,* I see a glimpse of it!' cries he elsewhere: 'there is in man a Higher than Love of Happiness: he can do without Happiness, and instead thereof find Blessedness! Was it not to preach-forth this same Higher that sages and martyrs, the Poet and the Priest, in all times, have spoken and suffered; bearing testimony, through life and through death, of the Godlike that is in Man, and how in the Godlike only has he Strength and Freedom? Which God-inspired Doctrine art thou also honoured to be taught; O Heavens! and broken with manifold merciful Afflictions, even till thou become contrite, and learn it! O, thank thy Destiny for these; thankfully bear what yet remain: thou hadst need of them; the Self in thee needed to be annihilated. By benignant fever-paroxysms is Life rooting out the deep-seated chronic Disease, and triumphs over Death. On the roaring billows of Time, thou art not engulfed, but borne aloft into the azure of Eternity. Love not Pleasure; love God. This is the Everlasting Yea, wherein all contradiction is solved: wherein whoso walks and works, it is well with him.'

And again: 'Small is it that thou canst trample the Earth with its injuries under thy feet, as old Greek Zeno trained thee: thou canst love the Earth while it injures thee, and even because it injures thee; for this a Greater than Zeno was needed, and he too was sent. Knowest thou that " *Worship of Sorrow* "? The Temple thereof, founded some eighteen centuries ago, now lies in ruins, overgrown with jungle, the habitation of doleful creatures: nevertheless, venture forward; in a low crypt, arched out of falling fragments, thou findest the Altar still there, and its sacred Lamp perennially burning.'

Without pretending to comment on which strange utterances, the Editor will only remark, that there lies beside them much of a still more questionable character; unsuited to the general apprehension; nay wherein he himself does not see his way. Nebulous disquisitions on Religion, yet not without bursts of splendour; on the 'perennial continuance of Inspiration;' on Prophecy; that there are 'true Priests, as well as Baal-Priests, in our own day:' with more of the like sort. We select some fractions, by way of finish to this farrago.

'Cease, my much-respected Herr von Voltaire,' thus apostrophises the Professor: 'shut thy sweet voice; for the task appointed thee seems finished. Sufficiently hast thou demonstrated this proposition, considerable or otherwise: That the Mythus of the Christian Religion looks not in the eighteenth century as it did in the eighth. Alas, were thy six-and-thirty quartos, and the six-and-thirty thousand other quartos and folios, and flying sheets or reams, printed before and since on the same subject, all needed to convince us of so little! But what next? Wilt thou help us to embody the divine Spirit of that Religion in a new Mythus, in a new vehicle and vesture, that our Souls, otherwise too like perishing, may live? What! thou hast no faculty in that kind? Only a torch for burning, no hammer for building? Take our thanks, then, and——thyself away.

'Meanwhile what are antiquated Mythuses to me? Or is the God present, felt in my own heart, a thing which Herr von Voltaire will dispute out of me; or dispute into me? To the " *Worship of Sorrow* " ascribe what origin and genesis thou pleasest, *has* not that Worship originated, and been generated; is it not *here?* Feel it in thy heart, and then say whether it is of God! This is Belief; all else is Opinion,—for which latter whoso will let him worry and be worried.'

'Neither,' observes he elsewhere, 'shall ye tear-out one another's eyes, struggling over "Plenary Inspiration," and suchlike: try rather to get a little even Partial Inspiration, each of you for himself. One BIBLE I know, of whose Plenary Inspiration doubt is not so much as possible; nay with my own eyes I saw the God's-Hand writing it: thereof all other Bibles are but leaves,—say, in Picture-Writing to assist the weaker faculty.'

Or, to give the wearied reader relief, and bring it to an end, let him take the following perhaps more intelligible passage:

'To me, in this our life,' says the Professor, 'which is an internecine warfare with the Time-spirit, other warfare seems questionable. Hast thou in any way a Contention with thy brother, I advise thee, think well what the meaning thereof is. If thou gauge it to the bottom, it is simply this: "Fellow, see! thou art taking more than thy share of Happiness in the world, something from *my* share: which, by the Heavens, thou shalt not; nay I will fight thee rather."—Alas, and the whole lot to be divided is such a beggarly matter, truly a "feast of shells," for the substance has been spilled out: not enough to quench one Appetite; and the collective human species clutching at them!—Can we not, in all such cases, rather say: "Take it, thou too-ravenous individual; take that pitiful additional fraction of a share, which I reckoned mine, but which thou so wantest; take it with a blessing: would to Heaven I had enough for thee!"—If Fichte's *Wissenschaftslehre* be, "to a certain extent, Applied Christianity," surely to a still greater extent, so is this. We have here not a Whole Duty of Man, yet a Half Duty, namely the Passive half: could we but do it, as we can demonstrate it!

'But indeed Conviction, were it never so excellent, is worthless till it convert itself into Conduct. Nay properly Conviction is not possible till then; inasmuch as all Speculation is by nature endless, formless, a vortex amid vortices: only by a felt indubitable certainty of Experience does it find any centre to revolve round, and so fashion itself into a system. Most true is it, as a wise man teaches us, that "Doubt of any sort cannot be removed except by Action." On which ground, too, let him who gropes painfully in darkness or uncertain light, and prays vehemently that the dawn may ripen into day, lay this other precept well to heart, which to me was of invaluable service : " *Do the Duty which lies nearest thee,*" which thou knowest to be a Duty ! Thy second Duty will already have become clearer.

' May we not say, however, that the hour of Spiritual Enfranchisement is even this : When your Ideal World, wherein the whole man has been dimly struggling and inexpressibly languishing to work, becomes revealed, and thrown open; and you discover, with amazement enough, like the Lothario in *Wilhelm Meister*, that your " America is here or nowhere "? The Situation that has not its Duty, its Ideal, was never yet occupied by man. Yes here, in this poor, miserable, hampered, despicable Actual, wherein thou even now standest, here or nowhere is thy Ideal : work it out therefrom ; and working, believe, live, be free. Fool ! the Ideal is in thyself, the impediment too is in thyself : thy Condition is but the stuff thou art to shape that same Ideal out of : what matters whether such stuff be of this sort or that, so the Form thou give it be heroic, be poetic? O thou that pinest in the imprisonment of the Actual, and criest bitterly to the gods for a kingdom wherein to rule and create, know this of a truth : the thing thou seekest is already with thee, " here or nowhere," couldst thou only see !

' But it is with man's Soul as it was with Nature : the beginning of Creation is—Light. Till the eye have vision, the whole members are in bonds. Divine moment, when over the tempest-tost Soul, as once over the wild-weltering Chaos, it is spoken : Let there be Light ! Ever to the greatest that has felt such moment, is it not miraculous and God-announcing ; even as, under simpler figures, to the simplest and least. The mad primeval Discord is hushed ; the rudely-jumbled conflict-ing elements bind themselves into separate Firmaments : deep silent rock-foundations are built beneath ; and the skyey vault with its everlasting Luminaries above : in-stead of a dark wasteful Chaos, we have a blooming, fertile, heaven-encompassed World.

' I too could now say to myself : Be no longer a Chaos, but a World, or even Worldkin. Produce ! Produce ! Were it but the pitifullest infinitesimal fraction of a Product, produce it, in God's name ! 'Tis

the utmost thou hast in thee : out with it, then.   Up,
up ! Whatsoever thy hand findeth to do, do it with
thy whole might.   Work while it is called Today; for
the Night cometh, wherein no man can work.'

CHAPTER X

PAUSE

THUS have we, as closely and perhaps satisfactorily
as, in such circumstances, might be, followed Teufelsdröckh through the various successive states and stages
of Growth, Entanglement, Unbelief, and almost Reprobation, into a certain clearer state of what he himself
seems to consider as Conversion. ' Blame not the
word,' says he; ' rejoice rather that such a word,
signifying such a thing, has come to light in our modern
Era, though hidden from the wisest Ancients.   The Old
World knew nothing of Conversion; instead of an *Ecce
Homo*, they had only some *Choice of Hercules*. It was
a new-attained progress in the Moral Development of
man : hereby has the Highest come home to the bosoms
of the most Limited; what to Plato was but a hallucination, and to Socrates a chimera, is now clear and certain
to your Zinzendorfs, your Wesleys, and the poorest of
their Pietists and Methodists.'

It is here, then, that the spiritual majority of Teufelsdröckh commences : we are henceforth to see him ' work
in well-doing,' with the spirit and clear aims of a Man.
He has discovered that the Ideal Workshop he so panted
for is even this same Actual ill-furnished Workshop
he has so long been stumbling in.   He can say to himself : ' Tools?   Thou hast no Tools?   Why, there is
not a Man, or a Thing, now alive but has tools.   The
basest of created animalcules, the Spider itself, has a
spinning-jenny, and warping-mill, and power-loom within its head : the stupidest of Oysters has a Papin's-
Digester, with stone-and-lime house to hold it in : every
being that can live can do something : this let him
do.—Tools?   Hast thou not a Brain, furnished, furnish-

able with some glimmerings of Light; and three fingers
to hold a Pen withal? Never since Aaron's Rod went
out of practice, or even before it, was there such a
wonder-working Tool: greater than all recorded
miracles have been performed by Pens. For strangely
in this so solid-seeming World, which nevertheless is in
continual restless flux, it is appointed that *Sound*, to
appearance the most fleeting, should be the most continuing of all things. The WORD is well said to be
omnipotent in this world; man, thereby divine, can
create as by a *Fiat*. Awake, arise! Speak forth what
is in thee; what God has given thee, what the Devil
shall not take away. Higher task than that of Priesthood was allotted to no man: wert thou but the meanest
in that sacred Hierarchy, is it not honour enough therein
to spend and be spent?

‘ By this Art, which whoso will may sacrilegiously
degrade into a handicraft,’ adds Teufelsdröckh, ‘ have
I thenceforth abidden. Writings of mine, not indeed
known as mine (for what am *I*?), have fallen, perhaps
not altogether void, into the mighty seed-field of
Opinion; fruits of my unseen sowing gratifyingly meet
me here and there. I thank the Heavens that I have
now found my Calling; wherein, with or without perceptible result, I am minded diligently to persevere.

‘ Nay how knowest thou,’ cries he, ‘ but this and
the other pregnant Device, now grown to be a world-
renowned far-working Institution; like a grain of right
mustard-seed once cast into the right soil, and now
stretching-out strong boughs to the four winds, for the
birds of the air to lodge in,—may have been properly
my doing? Some one’s doing, it without doubt was;
from some Idea, in some single Head, it did first of all
take beginning: why not from some Idea in mine?’
Does Teufelsdröckh here glance at that ‘ SOCIETY FOR
THE CONSERVATION OF PROPERTY (*Eigenthums-conser-
virende Gesellschaft*),’ of which so many ambiguous
notices glide spectre-like through these inexpressible
Paper-bags? ‘ An Institution,’ hints he, ‘ not unsuitable to the wants of the time; as indeed such sudden
extension proves: for already can the Society number,
among its office-bearers or corresponding members, the

highest Names, if not the highest Persons, in Germany, England, France; and contributions, both of money and of meditation, pour-in from all quarters; to, if possible, enlist the remaining Integrity of the world, and, defensively and with forethought, marshal it round this Palladium.' Does Teufelsdröckh mean, then, to give himself out as the originator of that so notable *Eigenthums - conservirende* (' Owndom - conserving ') *Gesellschaft;* and if so, what, in the Devil's name, is it? He again hints : ' At a time when the divine Commandment, *Thou shalt not steal,* wherein truly, if well understood, is comprised the whole Hebrew Decalogue, with Solon's and Lycurgus's Constitutions, Justinian's Pandects, the Code Napoléon, and all Codes, Catechisms, Divinities, Moralities whatsoever, that man has hitherto devised (and enforced with Altar-fire and Gallows-ropes) for his social guidance : at a time, I say, when this divine Commandment has all-but faded away from the general remembrance; and, with little disguise, a new opposite Commandment, *Thou shalt steal,* is everywhere promulgated,—it perhaps behoved, in this universal dotage and deliration, the sound portion of mankind to bestir themselves and rally. When the widest and wildest violations of that divine right of Property, the only divine right now extant or conceivable, are sanctioned and recommended by a vicious Press, and the world has lived to hear it asserted that *we have no Property in our very Bodies, but only an accidental Possession and Life-rent,* what is the issue to be looked for? Hangmen and Catchpoles may, by their noose-gins and baited fall-traps, keep-down the smaller sort of vermin; but what, except perhaps some such Universal Association, can protect us against whole meat-devouring and man-devouring hosts of Boa-constrictors? If, therefore, the more sequestered Thinker have wondered, in his privacy, from what hand that perhaps not ill-written *Program* in the Public Journals, with its high *Prize-Questions* and so liberal *Prizes,* could have proceeded,—let him now cease such wonder; and, with undivided faculty, betake himself to the *Concurrenz* (Competition).'

We ask : Has this same ' perhaps not ill-written

Program,' or any other authentic Transaction of that Property-conserving Society, fallen under the eye of the British Reader, in any Journal foreign or domestic? If so, what are those *Prize-Questions;* what are the terms of Competition, and when and where? No printed Newspaper-leaf, no farther light of any sort, to be met with in these Paper-bags! Or is the whole business one other of those whimsicalities and perverse inexplicabilities, whereby Herr Teufelsdröckh, meaning much or nothing, is pleased so often to play fast-and-loose with us?

Here, indeed, at length, must the Editor give utterance to a painful suspicion, which, through late Chapters, has begun to haunt him; paralysing any little enthusiasm that might still have rendered his thorny Biographical task a labour of love. It is a suspicion grounded perhaps on trifles, yet confirmed almost into certainty by the more and more discernible humoristico-satirical tendency of Teufelsdröckh, in whom underground humours and intricate sardonic rogueries, wheel within wheel, defy all reckoning: a suspicion, in one word, that these Autobiographical Documents are partly a mystification! What if many a so-called Fact were little better than a Fiction; if here we had no direct Camera-obscura Picture of the Professor's History; but only some more or less fantastic Adumbration, symbolically, perhaps significantly enough, shadowing-forth the same! Our theory begins to be that, in receiving as literally authentic what was but hieroglyphically so, Hofrath Heuschrecke, whom in that case we scruple not to name Hofrath Nose-of-Wax, was made a fool of, and set adrift to make fools of others. Could it be expected, indeed, that a man so known for impenetrable reticence as Teufelsdröckh, would all at once frankly unlock his private citadel to an English Editor and a German Hofrath; and not rather deceptively *in*lock both Editor and Hofrath in the labyrinthic tortuosities and covered-ways of said citadel (having enticed them thither), to see, in his half-devilish way, how the fools would look?

Of one fool, however, the Herr Professor will per-

haps find himself short. On a small slip, formerly
thrown aside as blank, the ink being all-but invisible,
we lately notice, and with effort decipher, the following :
'What are your historical Facts; still more your biographical? Wilt thou know a Man, above all a Mankind, by stringing-together beadrolls of what thou
namest Facts? The Man is the spirit he worked in;
not what he did, but what he became. Facts are
engraved Hierograms, for which the fewest have the
key. And then how your Blockhead (*Dummkopf*)
studies not their Meaning; but simply whether they
are well or ill cut, what he calls Moral or Immoral!
Still worse is it with your Bungler (*Pfuscher*): such I
have seen reading some Rousseau, with pretences of
interpretation; and mistaking the ill-cut Serpent-of-
Eternity for a common poisonous reptile.' Was the
Professor apprehensive lest an Editor, selected as the
present boasts himself, might mistake the Teufelsdröckh Serpent-of-Eternity in like manner? For which
reason it was to be altered, not without underhand satire,
into a plainer Symbol? Or is this merely one of his
half-sophisms, half-truisms, which if he can but set on
the back of a Figure, he cares not whither it gallop?
We say not with certainty; and indeed, so strange is
the Professor, can never say. If our suspicion be
wholly unfounded, let his own questionable ways, not
our necessary circumspectness, bear the blame.

But be this as it will, the somewhat exasperated and
indeed exhausted Editor determines here to shut these
Paper-bags for the present. Let it suffice that we know
of Teufelsdröckh, so far, if ' not what he did, yet what
he became :' the rather, as his character has now taken
its ultimate bent, and no new revolution, of importance, is to be looked for. The imprisoned Chrysalis is
now a winged Psyche : and such, wheresoever be its
flight, it will continue. To trace by what complex
gyrations (flights or involuntary waftings) through the
mere external Life element, Teufelsdröckh reaches his
University Professorship, and the Psyche clothes herself
in civic Titles, without altering her now fixed nature,—
would be comparatively an unproductive task, were we
even unsuspicious of its being, for us at least, a false

and impossible one. His outward Biography, therefore, which, at the Blumine Lover's-Leap, we saw churned utterly into spray-vapour, may hover in that condition, for aught that concerns us here. Enough that by survey of certain 'pools and plashes,' we have ascertained its general direction; do we not already know that, by one way and other, it *has* long since raineddown again into a stream; and even now, at Weissnichtwo, flows deep and still, fraught with the *Philosophy of Clothes*, and visible to whoso will cast eye thereon? Over much invaluable matter, that lies scattered, like jewels among quarry-rubbish, in those Paper-catacombs we may have occasion to glance back, and somewhat will demand insertion at the right place: meanwhile be our tiresome diggings therein suspended.

If now, before reopening the great *Clothes-Volume,* we ask what our degree of progress, during these Ten Chapters, has been, towards right understanding of the *Clothes-Philosophy,* let not our discouragement become total. To speak in that old figure of the Hellgate Bridge over Chaos, a few flying pontoons have perhaps been added, though as yet they drift straggling on the Flood; how far they will reach, when once the chains are straightened and fastened, can, at present, only be matter of conjecture.

So much we already calculate: Through many a little loop-hole, we have had glimpses into the internal world of Teufelsdröckh; his strange mystic, almost magic Diagram of the Universe, and how it was gradually drawn, is not henceforth altogether dark to us. Those mysterious ideas on TIME, which merit consideration, and are not wholly unintelligible with such, may by and by prove significant. Still more may his somewhat peculiar view of Nature, the decisive Oneness he ascribes to Nature. How all Nature and Life are but one *Garment*, a 'Living Garment,' woven and ever a-weaving in the ' Loom of Time;' is not here, indeed, the outline of a whole *Clothes-Philosophy;* at least the arena it is to work in? Remark, too, that the Character of the Man, nowise without meaning in such a matter, becomes less enigmatic: amid so much tumultuous obscurity, almost like diluted madness, do not a certain

indomitable Defiance and yet a boundless Reverence
seem to loom-forth, as the two mountain-summits, on
whose rock-strata all the rest were based and built?

Nay further, may we not say that Teufelsdröckh's
Biography, allowing it even, as suspected, only a hieroglyphical truth, exhibits a man, as it were preappointed
for Clothes-Philosophy? To look through the Shows
of things into Things themselves he is led and compelled. The ' Passivity ' given him by birth is fostered
by all turns of his fortune. Everywhere cast out, like
oil out of water, from mingling in any Employment, in
any public Communion, he has no portion but Solitude,
and a life of Meditation. The whole energy of his existence is directed, through long years, on one task : that
of enduring pain, if he cannot cure it. Thus everywhere
do the Shows of things oppress him, withstand him,
threaten him with fearfullest destruction : only by
victoriously penetrating into Things themselves can he
find peace and a stronghold. But is not this same looking through the Shows, or Vestures, into the Things,
even the first preliminary to a *Philosophy of Clothes?*
Do we not, in all this, discern some beckonings towards
the true higher purport of such a Philosophy; and what
shape it must assume with such a man, in such an era?

Perhaps in entering on Book Third, the courteous
Reader is not utterly without guess whither he is bound :
nor, let us hope, for all the fantastic Dream-Grottoes
through which, as is our lot with Teufelsdröckh, he
must wander, will there be wanting between whiles some
twinkling of a steady Polar Star.

BOOK THIRD

CHAPTER I

INCIDENT IN MODERN HISTORY

As a wonder-loving and wonder-seeking man, Teufelsdröckh, from an early part of this Clothes-Volume, has more and more exhibited himself. Striking it was, amid all his perverse cloudiness, with what force of vision and of heart he pierced into the mystery of the World; recognising in the highest sensible phenomena, so far as Sense went, only fresh or faded Raiment; yet ever, under this, a celestial Essence thereby rendered visible: and while, on the one hand, he trod the old rags of Matter, with their tinsels, into the mire, he on the other everywhere exalted Spirit above all earthly principalities and powers, and worshipped it, though under the meanest shapes, with a true Platonic Mysticism. What the man ultimately purposed by thus casting his Greek-fire into the general Wardrobe of the Universe; what such, more or less complete, rending and burning of Garments throughout the whole compass of Civilized Life and Speculation, should lead to; the rather as he was no Adamite, in any sense, and could not, like Rousseau, recommend either bodily or intellectual Nudity, and a return to the savage state: all this our readers are now bent to discover; this is, in fact, properly the gist and purport of Professor Teufelsdröckh's Philosophy of Clothes.

Be it remembered, however, that such purport is here not so much evolved, as detected to lie ready for evolving. We are to guide our British Friends into the new Gold-country, and show them the mines; nowise to dig-out and exhaust its wealth, which indeed remains for all time inexhaustible. Once there, let each dig for his own behoof, and enrich himself.

Neither, in so capricious inexpressible a Work as this of the Professor's can our course now more than formerly be straightforward, step by step, but at best leap by leap. Significant Indications stand-out here and there; which for the critical eye, that looks both widely and narrowly, shape themselves into some ground-scheme of a Whole: to select these with judgment, so that a leap from one to the other be possible, and (in our old figure) by chaining them together, a passable Bridge be effected: this, as heretofore, continues our only method. Among such light-spots, the following, floating in much wild matter about *Perfectibility,* has seemed worth clutching at:

'Perhaps the most remarkable incident in Modern History,' says Teufelsdröckh, 'is not the Diet of Worms, still less the Battle of Austerlitz, Waterloo, Peterloo, or any other Battle; but an incident passed carelessly over by most Historians, and treated with some degree of ridicule by others: namely, George Fox's making to himself a suit of Leather. This man, the first of the Quakers, and by trade a Shoemaker, was one of those, to whom, under ruder or purer form, the Divine Idea of the Universe is pleased to manifest itself; and, across all the hulls of Ignorance and earthly Degradation, shine through, in unspeakable Awfulness, unspeakable Beauty, on their souls: who therefore are rightly accounted Prophets, God-possessed; or even Gods, as in some periods it has chanced. Sitting in his stall; working on tanned hides, amid pincers, pastehorns, rosin, swine-bristles, and a nameless flood of rubbish, this youth had, nevertheless, a Living Spirit belonging to him; also an antique Inspired Volume, through which, as through a window, it could look upwards, and discern its celestial Home. The task of a daily pair of shoes, coupled even with some prospect of victuals, and an honourable Mastership in Cordwainery, and perhaps the post of Thirdborough in his hundred, as the crown of long faithful sewing,—was nowise satisfaction enough to such a mind: but ever amid the boring and hammering came tones from that far country, came Splendours and Terrors; for this poor Cordwainer, as we said, was a Man; and the Temple of Immensity, wherein as Man he had been sent to minister, was full of holy mystery to him.

'The Clergy of the neighbourhood, the ordained Watchers and Interpreters of that same holy mystery, listened with unaffected tedium to his consultations, and advised him, as the solution of such doubts, to "drink beer and dance with the girls." Blind leaders of the blind! For what end were their tithes levied and eaten; for what were their shovel-hats scooped-out, and their surplices and cassock-aprons girt-on; and such a church-repairing, and chaffering, and organing, and other racketing, held over that spot of God's Earth,—if Man were but a Patent Digester, and the Belly with its adjuncts the grand Reality? Fox turned from them, with tears and a sacred scorn, back to his Leather-parings and his Bible. Mountains of encumbrance, higher than Ætna, had been heaped over that Spirit: but it was a Spirit, and would not lie buried there. Through long days and nights of silent agony, it struggled and wrestled, with a man's force, to be free: how its prison-mountains heaved and swayed tumultuously, as the giant spirit shook them to this hand and that, and emerged into the light of Heaven! That Leicester shoe-shop, had men known it, was a holier place than any Vatican or Loretto-shrine.—" So bandaged, and hampered, and hemmed in," groaned he, "with thousand requisitions, obligations, straps, tatters, and tagrags, I can neither see nor move: not my own am I, but the World's; and Time flies fast, and Heaven is high, and Hell is deep: Man! bethink thee, if thou hast power of Thought! Why not; what binds me here? Want, want!—Ha, of what? Will all the shoe-wages under the Moon ferry me across into that far Land of Light? Only Meditation can, and devout Prayer to God. I will to the woods: the hollow of a tree will lodge me, wild-berries feed me; and for Clothes, cannot I stitch myself one perennial suit of Leather!"

'Historical Oil-painting,' continues Teufelsdröckh, 'is one of the Arts I never practised; therefore shall I not decide whether this subject were easy of execution on the canvas. Yet often has it seemed to me as if such first outflashing of man's Freewill, to lighten, more and more into Day, the Chaotic Night that threatened to engulf him in its hindrances and its horrors, were properly the only grandeur there is in History. Let some living Angelo or Rosa, with seeing eye and understanding heart, picture George Fox on that morning, when he spreads-out his cutting-board for the last time, and cuts cowhides by unwonted patterns, and stitches them together into one continuous all-including Case, the farewell service of his awl! Stitch away, thou noble Fox: every prick of that little instrument is pricking into the heart of Slavery, and World-worship, and the Mammon-god. Thy elbows jerk, and in strong swimmer-strokes, and every stroke is bearing thee across the Prison-ditch, within which Vanity holds her Work-house and Ragfair, into lands of true Liberty; were the work done, there is in broad Europe one Free Man, and thou art he!

'Thus from the lowest depth there is a path to the loftiest height; and for the Poor also a Gospel has been published. Surely if, as D'Alembert asserts, my illustrious namesake, Diogenes, was the greatest man of Antiquity, only that he wanted Decency, then by stronger reason is George Fox the greatest of the Moderns; and greater than Diogenes himself: for he too stands on the adamantine basis of his Manhood, casting aside all props and shoars; yet not, in half-savage Pride, undervaluing the Earth; valuing it rather, as a place to yield him warmth and food, he looks Heavenward from his Earth, and dwells in an element of Mercy and Worship, with a still Strength, such as the Cynic's Tub did nowise witness. Great, truly, was that Tub; a temple from which man's dignity and divinity was scornfully preached abroad: but greater is the Leather Hull, for the same sermon was preached there, and not in Scorn but in Love.'

George Fox's 'perennial suit,' with all that it held, has been worn quite into ashes for nigh two centuries: why, in a discussion on the *Perfectibility of Society,* reproduce it now? Not out of blind sectarian partisanship: Teufelsdröckh himself is no Quaker; with all his pacific tendencies, did not we see him, in that scene at the North Cape, with the Archangel Smuggler, exhibit fire-arms?

For us, aware of his deep Sansculottism, there is more meant in this passage than meets the ear. At the same time, who can avoid smiling at the earnestness and Bœotian simplicity (if indeed there be not an underhand satire in it), with which that ' Incident ' is here brought forward; and, in the Professor's ambiguous way, as clearly perhaps as he durst in Weissnichtwo, recommended to imitation ! Does Teufelsdröckh anticipate that, in this age of refinement, any considerable class of the community, by way of testifying against the ' Mammon-god,' and escaping from what he calls ' Vanity's Workhouse and Ragfair,' where doubtless some of them are toiled and whipped and hoodwinked sufficiently,—will sheathe themselves in close-fitting cases of Leather ? The idea is ridiculous in the extreme. Will Majesty lay aside its robes of state, and Beauty its frills and train-gowns, for a second-skin of tanned hide ? By which change Huddersfield and Manchester, and Coventry and Paisley, and the Fancy-Bazaar, were reduced to hungry solitudes; and only Day and Martin could profit. For neither would Teufelsdröckh's mad daydream, here as we presume covertly intended, of levelling Society (*levelling* it indeed with a vengeance, into one huge drowned marsh !), and so attaining the political effects of Nudity without its frigorific or other consequences,—be thereby realised. Would not the rich man purchase a waterproof suit of Russia Leather; and the high-born Belle step-forth in red or azure morocco, lined with shamoy : the black cowhide being left to the Drudges and Gibeonites of the world; and so all the old Distinctions be re-established ?

Or has the Professor his own deeper intention; and laughs in his sleeve at our strictures and glosses, which indeed are but a part thereof ?

CHAPTER II

CHURCH-CLOTHES

NOT less questionable is his Chapter on *Church-Clothes*, which has the farther distinction of being the shortest in the Volume. We here translate it entire :

' By Church-Clothes, it need not be premised that I mean infinitely more than Cassocks and Surplices ; and do not at all mean the mere haberdasher Sunday Clothes that men go to Church in. Far from it ! Church-Clothes are, in our vocabulary, the Forms, the *Vestures,* under which men have at various periods embodied and represented for themselves the Religious Principle ; that is to say, invested The Divine Idea of the World with a sensible and practically active Body, so that it might dwell among them as a living and life-giving WORD.

' These are unspeakably the most important of all the vestures and garnitures of Human Existence. They are first spun and woven, I may say, by that wonder of wonders, SOCIETY ; for it is still only when " two or three are gathered together," that Religion, spiritually exist-ent, and indeed indestructible, however latent, in each, first outwardly manifests itself (as with " cloven tongues of fire "), and seeks to be embodied in a visible Com-munion and Church Militant. Mystical, more than magical, is that Communing of Soul with Soul, both looking heavenward : here properly Soul first speaks with Soul ; for only in looking heavenward, take it in what sense you may, not in looking earthward, does what we can call Union, mutual Love, Society, begin to be possible. How true is that of Novalis : " It is certain my Belief gains quite *infinitely* the moment I can convince another mind thereof " ! Gaze thou in the face of thy Brother, in those eyes where plays the lam-bent fire of Kindness, or in those where rages the lurid conflagration of Anger ; feel how thy own so quiet Soul is straightway involuntarily kindled with the like, and ye blaze and reverberate on each other, till it is all one limitless confluent flame (of embracing Love, or of

deadly-grappling Hate); and then say what miraculous
virtue goes out of man into man. But if so, through
all the thick-plied hulls of our Earthly Life; how much
more when it is of the Divine Life we speak, and inmost
ME is, as it were, brought into contact with inmost ME !

'Thus was it that I said, the Church-Clothes are
first spun and woven by Society; outward Religion
originates by Society, Society becomes possible by
Religion. Nay, perhaps, every conceivable Society,
past and present, may well be figured as properly and
wholly a Church, in one or other of these three predica-
ments : an audibly preaching and prophesying Church,
which is the best; second, a Church that struggles to
preach and prophesy, but cannot as yet, till its Pentecost
come; and third and worst, a Church gone dumb with
old age, or which only mumbles delirium prior to dissolution. Whoso fancies that by Church is here meant
Chapterhouses and Cathedrals, or by preaching and
prophesying, mere speech and chanting, let him,' says
the oracular Professor, 'read on, light of heart (*getrosten
Muthes*).

'But with regard to your Church proper, and the
Church-Clothes specially recognised as Church-Clothes,
I remark, fearlessly enough, that without such Vestures
and sacred Tissues Society has not existed, and will
not exist. For if Government is, so to speak, the outward SKIN of the Body Politic, holding the whole
together and protecting it; and all your Craft-Guilds,
and Associations for Industry, of hand or of head, are
the Fleshly Clothes, the muscular and osseous Tissues
(lying *under* such SKIN), whereby Society stands and
works ;—then is Religion the inmost Pericardial and
Nervous Tissue, which ministers Life and warm Circulation to the whole. Without which Pericardial Tissue
the Bones and Muscles (of Industry) were inert, or
animated only by a Galvanic vitality; the SKIN would
become a shrivelled pelt, or fast-rotting raw-hide; and
Society itself a dead carcass,—deserving to be buried.
Men were no longer Social, but Gregarious; which
latter state also could not continue, but must gradually
issue in universal selfish discord, hatred, savage isolation, and dispersion ;—whereby, as we might continue to

say, the very dust and dead body of Society would have evaporated and become abolished. Such, and so all-important, all-sustaining, are the Church-Clothes to civilised or even to rational men.

'Meanwhile, in our era of the World, those same Church-Clothes have gone sorrowfully out-at-elbows; nay, far worse, many of them have become mere hollow Shapes, or Masks, under which no living Figure or Spirit any longer dwells; but only spiders and unclean beetles, in horrid accumulation, drive their trade; and the mask still glares on you with its glass-eyes, in ghastly affectation of Life,—some generation-and-half after Religion has quite withdrawn from it, and in un-noticed nooks is weaving for herself new Vestures, wherewith to reappear, and bless us, or our sons or grandsons. As a Priest, or Interpreter of the Holy, is the noblest and highest of all men, so is a Sham-priest (*Schein-priester*) the falsest and basest; neither is it doubtful that his Canonicals, were they Popes' Tiaras, will one day be torn from him, to make bandages for the wounds of mankind; or even to burn into tinder, for general scientific or culinary purposes.

'All which, as out of place here, falls to be handled in my Second Volume, *On the Palingenesia, or New-birth of Society;* which volume, as treating practically of the Wear, Destruction, and Retexture of Spiritual Tissues, or Garments, forms, properly speaking, the Transcendental or ultimate Portion of this my work *on Clothes,* and is already in a state of forwardness.'

And herewith, no farther exposition, note, or com-mentary being added, does Teufelsdröckh, and must his Editor now, terminate the singular chapter on Church-Clothes!

CHAPTER III

SYMBOLS

PROBABLY it will elucidate the drift of these foregoing obscure utterances, if we here insert somewhat of our Professor's speculations on *Symbols*. To state his whole doctrine, indeed, were beyond our compass : nowhere is he more mysterious, impalpable, than in this of 'Fantasy being the organ of the God-like;' and how 'Man thereby, though based, to all seeming, on the small Visible, does nevertheless extend down into the infinite deeps of the Invisible, of which Invisible, indeed, his Life is properly the bodying forth.' Let us, omitting these high transcendental aspects of the matter, study to glean (whether from the Paper-bags or the Printed Volume) what little seems logical and practical, and cunningly arrange it into such degree of coherence as it will assume. By way of proem, take the following not injudicious remarks :

'The benignant efficacies of Concealment,' cries our Professor, 'who shall speak or sing? SILENCE and SECRECY ! Altars might still be raised to them (were this an altar-building time) for universal worship. Silence is the element in which great things fashion themselves together ; that at length they may emerge, full-formed and majestic, into the daylight of Life, which they are thenceforth to rule. Not William the Silent only, but all the considerable men I have known, and the most undiplomatic and unstrategic of these, forbore to babble of what they were creating and projecting. Nay, in thy own mean perplexities, do thou thyself but *hold thy tongue for one day*: on the morrow, how much clearer are thy purposes and duties ; what wreck and rubbish have those mute workmen within thee swept away, when intrusive noises were shut out ! Speech is too often not, as the Frenchman defined it, the art of concealing Thought; but of quite stifling and suspending Thought, so that there is none to conceal. Speech too is great, but not the greatest. As the Swiss Inscription says : *Sprechen ist silbern, Schweigen ist golden* (Speech is silvern, Silence is golden); or as I might rather express it : Speech is of Time, Silence is of Eternity.

'Bees will not work except in darkness ; Thought will not work except in Silence ; neither will Virtue work except in Secrecy. Let not thy left hand know what thy right hand doeth ! Neither shalt thou prate even to thy own heart of " those secrets known to all." Is

not Shame (*Schaam*) the soil of all Virtue, of all good
manners and good morals? Like other plants, Virtue
will not grow unless its root be hidden, buried from the
eye of the sun. Let the sun shine on it, nay do but
look at it privily thyself, the root withers, and no flower
will glad thee. O my Friends, when we view the fair
clustering flowers that over-wreathe, for example, the
Marriage-bower, and encircle man's life with the fragrance and hues of Heaven, what hand will not smite the
foul plunderer that grubs them up by the roots, and
with grinning, grunting satisfaction, shows us the dung
they flourish in! Men speak much of the Printing-
Press with its Newspapers: *du Himmel!* what are these
to Clothes and the Tailor's Goose?'

'Of kin to the so incalculable influences of Concealment, and connected with still greater things, is the
wondrous agency of *Symbols*. In a Symbol there is
concealment and yet revelation: here therefore, by
Silence and by Speech acting together, comes a double
significance. And if both the Speech be itself high, and
the Silence fit and noble, how expressive will their union
be! Thus in many a painted Device, or simple Seal-
emblem, the commonest Truth stands-out to us proclaimed with quite new emphasis.

'For it is here that Fantasy with her mystic wonder-
land plays into the small prose domain of Sense, and
becomes incorporated therewith. In the Symbol proper,
what we can call a Symbol, there is ever, more or less
distinctly and directly, some embodiment and revelation
of the Infinite; the Infinite is made to blend itself with
the Finite, to stand visible, and as it were, attainable
there. By Symbols, accordingly, is man guided and
commanded, made happy, made wretched. He everywhere finds himself encompassed with Symbols, recognised as such or not recognised: the Universe is but
one vast Symbol of God; nay if thou wilt have it, what
is man himself but a Symbol of God; is not all that he
does symbolical; a revelation to Sense of the mystic
god-given force that is in him; a "Gospel of Freedom,"
which he, the "Messias of Nature," preaches, as he can,
by act and word? Not a Hut he builds but is the visible
embodiment of a Thought; but bears visible record

of invisible things; but is, in the transcendental sense, symbolical as well as real.'

'Man,' says the Professor elsewhere, in quite antipodal contrast with these high-soaring delineations, which we have here cut short on the verge of the inane, ' Man is by birth somewhat of an owl. Perhaps, too, of all the owleries that ever possessed him, the most owlish, if we consider it, is that of your actually existing Motive-Millwrights. Fantastic tricks enough man has played, in his time; has fancied himself to be most things, down even to an animated heap of Glass; but to fancy himself a dead Iron-Balance for weighing Pains and Pleasures on, was reserved for this his latter era. There stands he, his Universe one huge Manger, filled with hay and thistles to be weighed against each other; and looks long-eared enough. Alas, poor devil! spectres are appointed to haunt him: one age he is hag-ridden, bewitched; the next, priestridden, befooled; in all ages, bedevilled. And now the Genius of Mechanism smothers him worse than any Nightmare did; till the Soul is nigh choked out of him, and only a kind of Digestive, Mechanic life remains. In Earth and in Heaven he can see nothing but Mechanism; has fear for nothing else, hope in nothing else: the world would indeed grind him to pieces; but cannot he fathom the Doctrine of Motives, and cunningly compute these, and mechanise them to grind the other way?

' Were he not, as has been said, purblinded by enchantment, you had but to bid him open his eyes and look. In which country, in which time, was it hitherto that man's history, or the history of any man, went-on by calculated or calculable " Motives "? What make ye of your Christianities, and Chivalries, and Reformations, and Marseillese Hymns, and Reigns of Terror? Nay, has not perhaps the Motive-grinder himself been *in Love?* Did he never stand so much as a contested Election? Leave him to Time, and the medicating virtue of Nature.'

' Yes, Friends,' elsewhere observes the Professor, ' not our Logical, Mensurative faculty, but our Imaginative one is King over us; I might say, Priest and Prophet to lead us heavenward; our Magician and

Wizard to lead us hellward. Nay, even for the basest
Sensualist, what is Sense but the implement of Fantasy;
the vessel it drinks out of? Ever in the dullest existence there is a sheen either of Inspiration or of Madness
(thou partly hast it in thy choice, which of the two), that
gleams-in from the circumambient Eternity, and colours
with its own hues our little islet of Time. The Understanding is indeed thy window, too clear thou canst not
make it; but Fantasy is thy eye, with its colour-giving
retina, healthy or diseased. Have not I myself known
five-hundred living soldiers sabred into crows'-meat for
a piece of glazed cotton, which they called their Flag;
which, had you sold it at any market-cross, would not
have brought above three groschen? Did not the whole
Hungarian Nation rise, like some tumultuous moon-
stirred Atlantic, when Kaiser Joseph pocketed their Iron
Crown; an Implement, as was sagaciously observed, in
size and commercial value little differing from a horse-
shoe? It is in and through *Symbols* that man, consciously or unconsciously, lives, works, and has his
being: those ages, moreover, are accounted the noblest
which can the best recognise symbolical worth, and prize
it the highest. For is not a Symbol ever, to him who
has eyes for it, some dimmer or clearer revelation of
the Godlike? .

' Of Symbols, however, I remark farther, that they
have both an extrinsic and intrinsic value; oftenest
the former only. What, for instance, was in that
clouted Shoe, which the Peasants bore aloft with them
as ensign in their *Bauernkrieg* (Peasants' War)? Or
in the Wallet-and-staff round which the Netherland
Gueux, glorying in that nickname of Beggars, heroically rallied and prevailed, though against King Philip
himself? Intrinsic significance these had none: only
extrinsic; as the accidental Standards of multitudes
more or less sacredly uniting together; in which union
itself, as above noted, there is ever something mystical
and borrowing of the Godlike. Under a like category,
too, stand, or stood, the stupidest heraldic Coats-of-
arms; military Banners everywhere; and generally all
national or other Sectarian Costumes and Customs: they
have no intrinsic, necessary divineness, or even worth;

but have acquired an extrinsic one. Nevertheless through all these there glimmers something of a Divine Idea; as through military Banners themselves, the Divine Idea of Duty, of heroic Daring; in some instances of Freedom, of Right. Nay, the highest ensign that men ever met and embraced under, the Cross itself, had no meaning save an accidental extrinsic one.

' Another matter it is, however, when your Symbol has intrinsic meaning, and is of itself *fit* that men should unite round it. Let but the Godlike manifest itself to Sense; let but Eternity look, more or less visibly, through the Time-Figure (*Zeitbild*)! Then is it fit that men unite there; and worship together before such Symbol; and so from day to day, and from age to age, superadd to it new divineness.

' Of this latter sort are all true works of Art: in them (if thou know a Work of Art from a Daub of Artifice) wilt thou discern Eternity looking through Time; the Godlike rendered visible. Here too may an extrinsic value gradually superadd itself: thus certain *Iliads*, and the like, have, in three-thousand years, attained quite new significance. But nobler than all in this kind, are the Lives of heroic god-inspired Men; for what other Work of Art is so divine? In Death too, in the Death of the Just, as the last perfection of a Work of Art, may we not discern symbolic meaning? In that divinely transfigured Sleep, as of Victory, resting over the beloved face which now knows thee no more, read (if thou canst for tears) the confluence of Time with Eternity, and some gleam of the latter peering through.

' Highest of all Symbols are those wherein the Artist or Poet has risen into Prophet, and all men can recognise a present God, and worship the same: I mean religious Symbols. Various enough have been such religious Symbols, what we call *Religions;* as men stood in this stage of culture or the other, and could worse or better body-forth the Godlike: some Symbols with a transient intrinsic worth; many with only an extrinsic. If thou ask to what height man has carried it in this manner, look on our divinest Symbol: on Jesus of Nazareth, and his Life, and his Biography, and what followed therefrom. Higher has the human Thought not yet reached:

this is Christianity and Christendom; a Symbol of quite perennial, infinite character: whose significance will ever demand to be anew inquired into, and anew made manifest.

'But, on the whole, as time adds much to the sacredness of Symbols, so likewise in his progress he at length defaces or even desecrates them; and Symbols, like all terrestrial Garments, wax old. Homer's Epos has not ceased to be true; yet it is no longer *our* Epos, but shines in the distance, if clearer and clearer, yet also smaller and smaller, like a receding Star. It needs a scientific telescope, it needs to be reinterpreted and artificially brought near us, before we can so much as know that it *was* a Sun. So likewise a day comes when the Runic Thor, with his Eddas, must withdraw into dimness; and many an African Mumbo-Jumbo and Indian Pawaw be utterly abolished. For all things, even Celestial Luminaries, much more atmospheric meteors, have their rise, their culmination, their decline.'

'Small is this which thou tellest me, that the Royal Sceptre is but a piece of gilt-wood; that the Pyx has become a most foolish box, and truly, as Ancient Pistol thought, "of little price." A right Conjuror might I name thee, couldst thou conjure back into these wooden tools the divine virtue they once held.'

'Of this thing, however, be certain: wouldst thou plant for Eternity, then plant into the deep infinite faculties of man, his Fantasy and Heart; wouldst thou plant for Year and Day, then plant into his shallow superficial faculties, his Self-love and Arithmetical Understanding, what will grow there. A Hierarch, therefore, and Pontiff of the World will we call him, the Poet and inspired Maker; who, Prometheus-like, can shape new Symbols, and bring new Fire from Heaven to fix it there. Such too will not always be wanting; neither perhaps now are. Meanwhile, as the average of matters goes, we account him Legislator and wise who can so much as tell when a Symbol has grown old, and gently remove it.

'When, as the last English Coronation [1] was pre-

---

[1] That of George IV.—ED.

paring,' concludes this wonderful Professor, ' I read in their Newspapers that the " Champion of England," he who has to offer battle to the Universe for his new King, had brought it so far that he could now " mount his horse with little assistance," I said to myself : Here also we have a Symbol well-nigh superannuated. Alas, move whithersoever you may, are not the tatters and rags of superannuated worn-out symbols (in this Rag-fair of a World) dropping off everywhere, to hoodwink, to halter, to tether you ; nay, if you shake them not aside, threatening to accumulate, and perhaps produce suffocation ?'

CHAPTER IV

HELOTAGE

At this point we determine on adverting shortly, or rather reverting, to a certain Tract of Hofrath Heu-schrecke's, entitled *Institute for the Repression of Population;* which lies, dishonourable enough (with torn leaves, and a perceptible smell of aloetic drugs), stuffed into the Bag *Pisces*. Not indeed for the sake of the Tract itself, which we admire little ; but of the marginal Notes, evidently in Teufelsdröckh's hand, which rather copiously fringe it. A few of these may be in their right place here.

Into the Hofrath's *Institute,* with its extraordinary schemes, and machinery of Corresponding Boards and the like, we shall not so much as glance. Enough for us to understand that Heuschrecke is a disciple of Malthus ; and so zealous for the doctrine, that his zeal almost literally eats him up. A deadly fear of Popula-tion possesses the Hofrath ; something like a fixed-idea ; undoubtedly akin to the more diluted forms of Madness. Nowhere, in that quarter of his intellectual world, is there light ; nothing but a grim shadow of Hunger ; open mouths opening wider and wider ; a world to terminate by the frightfullest consummation : by its too dense inhabitants, famished into delirium, universally

eating one another. To make air for himself in which
strangulation, choking enough to a benevolent heart,
the Hofrath founds, or proposes to found, this *Institute*
of his, as the best he can do. It is only with our Professor's comments thereon that we concern ourselves.

First, then, remark that Teufelsdröckh, as a speculative Radical, has his own notions about human
dignity; that the Zähdarm palaces and courtesies have
not made him forgetful of the Futteral cottages. On
the blank cover of Heuschrecke's Tract we find the
following indistinctly engrossed:

'Two men I honour, and no third. First, the toil-
worn Craftsman that with earth-made Implement labori-
ously conquers the Earth, and makes her man's. Venerable to me is the hard Hand; crooked, coarse; wherein
notwithstanding lies a cunning virtue, indefeasibly
royal, as of the Sceptre of this Planet. Venerable too
is the rugged face, all weather-tanned, besoiled, with
its rude intelligence; for it is the face of a Man living
manlike. O, but the more venerable for thy rudeness,
and even because we must pity as well as love thee!
Hardly-entreated Brother! For us was thy back so
bent, for us were thy straight limbs and fingers so
deformed: thou wert our Conscript, on whom the lot
fell, and fighting our battles wert so marred. For in
thee too lay a god-created Form, but it was not to be
unfolded; encrusted must it stand with the thick
adhesions and defacements of Labour: and thy body,
like thy soul, was not to know freedom. Yet toil on,
toil on: *thou* art in thy duty, be out of it who may; thou
toilest for the altogether indispensable, for daily bread.

'A second man I honour, and still more highly:
Him who is seen toiling for the spiritually indispensable; not daily bread, but the bread of Life. Is not he
too in his duty; endeavouring towards inward Harmony; revealing this, by act or by word, through all
his outward endeavours, be they high or low? Highest
of all, when his outward and his inward endeavour are
one: when we can name him Artist; not earthly Craftsman only, but inspired Thinker, who with heaven-made
Implement conquers Heaven for us! If the poor and
humble toil that we have Food, must not the high and

glorious toil for him in return, that he have Light,
have Guidance, Freedom, Immortality?—These two, in
all their degrees, I honour : all else is chaff and dust,
which let the wind blow whither it listeth.

'Unspeakably touching is it, however, when I find
both dignities united; and he that must toil outwardly
for the lowest of man's wants, is also toiling inwardly
for the highest. Sublimer in this world know I
nothing than a Peasant Saint, could such now anywhere
be met with. Such a one will take thee back to
Nazareth itself; thou wilt see the splendour of Heaven
spring forth from the humblest depths of Earth, like a
light shining in great darkness.'

And again : 'It is not because of his toils that I
lament for the poor : we must all toil, or steal (howsoever we name our stealing), which is worse; no faithful workman finds his task a pastime. The poor is
hungry and a-thirst; but for him also there is food and
drink : he is heavy-laden and weary; but for him also
the Heavens send Sleep, and of the deepest; in his
smoky cribs, a clear dewy heaven of Rest envelops him,
and fitful glitterings of cloud-skirted Dreams. But
what I do mourn over is, that the lamp of his soul
should go out; that no ray of heavenly, or even of
earthly knowledge, should visit him; but only, in the
haggard darkness, like two spectres, Fear and Indignation bear him company. Alas, while the Body stands
so broad and brawny, must the soul lie blinded, dwarfed,
stupefied, almost annihilated! Alas, was this too a
Breath of God; bestowed in Heaven, but on earth never
to be unfolded!—That there should one Man die
ignorant who had capacity for Knowledge, this I call
a tragedy, were it to happen more than twenty times in
the minute, as by some computations it does. The miserable fraction of Science which our united Mankind, in
a wide Universe of Nescience, has acquired, why is not
this, with all diligence, imparted to all?'

Quite in an opposite strain is the following : 'The
old Spartans had a wiser method; and went out and
hunted-down their Helots, and speared and spitted
them, when they grew too numerous. With our
improved fashions of hunting, Herr Hofrath, now after

the invention of fire-arms, and standing-armies, how much easier were such a hunt! Perhaps in the most thickly-peopled country, some three days annually might suffice to shoot all the able-bodied Paupers that had accumulated within the year. Let Governments think of this. The expense were trifling : nay the very carcasses would pay it. Have them salted and barrelled; could not you victual therewith, if not Army and Navy, yet richly such infirm Paupers, in workhouses and elsewhere, as enlightened Charity, dreading no evil of them, might see good to keep alive?'

'And yet,' writes he farther on, 'there must be something wrong. A full-formed Horse will, in any market, bring from twenty to as high as two-hundred Friedrichs d'or : such is his worth to the world. A full-formed Man is not only worth nothing to the world, but the world could afford him a round sum would he simply engage to go and hang himself. Nevertheless, which of the two was the more cunningly-devised article, even as an Engine? Good Heavens! A white European Man, standing on his two Legs, with his two five-fingered Hands at his shackle-bones, and miraculous Head on his shoulders, is worth, I should say, from fifty to a hundred Horses !'

'True, thou Gold-Hofrath,' cries the Professor elsewhere : 'too crowded indeed! Meanwhile, what portion of this inconsiderable terraqueous Globe have ye actually tilled and delved, till it will grow no more? How thick stands your Population in the Pampas and Savannas of America; round ancient Carthage, and in the interior of Africa; on both slopes of the Altaic chain, in the central Platform of Asia; in Spain, Greece, Turkey, Crim Tartary, the Curragh of Kildare? One man, in one year, as I have understood it, if you lend him Earth, will feed himself and nine others. Alas, where now are the Hengsts and Alarics of our still-glowing, still-expanding Europe; who, when their home is grown too narrow, will enlist, and, like Fire-pillars, guide onwards those superfluous masses of indomitable living Valour; equipped, not now with the battle-axe and war-chariot, but with the steam-engine and plough-share? Where are they?—Preserving their Game !'

CHAPTER V

THE PHŒNIX

Putting which four singular Chapters together, and alongside of them numerous hints, and even direct utterances, scattered over these Writings of his, we come upon the startling yet not quite unlooked-for conclusion, that Teufelsdröckh is one of those who consider Society, properly so called, to be as good as extinct; and that only the gregarious feelings, and old inherited habitudes, at this juncture, hold us from Dispersion, and universal national, civil, domestic and personal war! He says expressly: 'For the last three centuries, above all for the last three quarters of a century, that same Pericardial Nervous Tissue (as we named it) of Religion, where lies the Life-essence of Society, has been smote-at and perforated, needfully and needlessly; till now it is quite rent into shreds; and Society, long pining, diabetic, consumptive, can be regarded as defunct; for those spasmodic, galvanic sprawlings are not life; neither indeed will they endure, galvanise as you may, beyond two days.'

'Call ye that a Society,' cries he again, 'where there is no longer any Social Idea extant; not so much as the Idea of a common Home, but only of a common over-crowded Lodging-house? Where each, isolated, regardless of his neighbour, turned against his neighbour, clutches what he can get, and cries " Mine !" and calls it Peace, because, in the cut-purse and cut-throat Scramble, no steel knives, but only a far cunninger sort, can be employed? Where Friendship, Communion, has become an incredible tradition; and your holiest Sacramental Supper is a smoking Tavern Dinner, with Cook for Evangelist? Where your Priest has no tongue but for plate-licking: and your high Guides and Governors cannot guide; but on all hands hear it passionately proclaimed: *Laissez faire;* Leave us alone of *your* guidance, such light is darker than darkness; eat you your wages, and sleep!

'Thus, too,' continues he, 'does an observant eye discern everywhere that saddest spectacle: The Poor perishing, like neglected, foundered Draught-Cattle, of Hunger and Over-work; the Rich, still more wretchedly, of Idleness, Satiety, and Over-growth. The Highest in rank, at length, without honour from the Lowest; scarcely, with a little mouth-honour, as from tavern-waiters who expect to put it in the bill. Once-sacred Symbols fluttering as empty Pageants, whereof men grudge even the expense; a World becoming dismantled: in one word, the CHURCH fallen speechless, from obesity and apoplexy; the STATE shrunken into a Police-Office, straitened to get its pay!'

We might ask, are there many 'observant eyes,' belonging to practical men in England or elsewhere, which have descried these phenomena; or is it only from the mystic elevation of a German *Wahngasse* that such wonders are visible? Teufelsdröckh contends that the aspect of a 'deceased or expiring Society' fronts us everywhere, so that whoso runs may read. 'What, for example,' says he, 'is the universally-arrogated Virtue, almost the sole remaining Catholic Virtue, of these days? For some half century, it has been the thing you name "Independence." Suspicion of "Servility," of reverence for Superiors, the very dogleech is anxious to disavow. Fools! Were your Superiors worthy to govern, and you worthy to obey, reverence for them were even your only possible freedom. Independence, in all kinds, is rebellion; if unjust rebellion, why parade it, and everywhere prescribe it?'

But what then? Are we returning, as Rousseau prayed, to the state of Nature? 'The Soul Politic having departed,' says Teufelsdröckh, 'what can follow but that the Body Politic be decently interred, to avoid putrescence! Liberals, Economists, Utilitarians enough I see marching with its bier, and chanting loud pæans, towards the funeral-pile, where, amid wailings from some, and saturnalian revelries from the most, the venerable Corpse is to be burnt. Or, in plain words, that these men, Liberals, Utilitarians, or whatsoever they are called, will ultimately carry their point, and dissever and destroy most existing Institutions of Society, seems a thing which has some time ago ceased to be doubtful.

'Do we not see a little subdivision of the grand
Utilitarian Armament come to light even in insulated
England? A living nucleus, that will attract and grow,
does at length appear there also; and under curious
phasis; properly as the inconsiderable fag-end, and so
far in the rear of the others as to fancy itself the van.
Our European Mechanisers are a sect of boundless
diffusion, activity, and co-operative spirit: has not
Utilitarianism flourished in high places of Thought,
here among ourselves, and in every European country,
at some time or other, within the last fifty years? If
now in all countries, except perhaps England, it has
ceased to flourish, or indeed to exist, among Thinkers,
and sunk to Journalists and the popular mass,—who
sees not that, as hereby it no longer preaches, so the
reason is, it now needs no Preaching, but is in full
universal Action, the doctrine everywhere known, and
enthusiastically laid to heart? The fit pabulum, in
these times, for a certain rugged workshop intellect and
heart, nowise without their corresponding workshop
strength and ferocity, it requires but to be stated in such
scenes to make proselytes enough.—Admirably calculated for destroying, only not for rebuilding! It
spreads like a sort of Dog-madness; till the whole
World-kennel will be rabid: then woe to the Huntsmen,
with or without their whips! They should have given
the quadrupeds water,' adds he; 'the water, namely,
of Knowledge and of Life, while it was yet time.'

Thus, if Professor Teufelsdröckh can be relied on,
we are at this hour in a most critical condition;
beleaguered by that boundless 'Armament of Mechanisers' and Unbelievers, threatening to strip us bare!
'The world,' says he, 'as it needs must, is under a
process of devastation and waste, which, whether by
silent assiduous corrosion, or open quicker combustion,
as the case chances, will effectually enough annihilate
the past Forms of Society; replace them with what it
may. For the present, it is contemplated that when
man's whole Spiritual Interests are once *divested*, these
innumerable stript-off Garments shall mostly be burnt;
but the sounder Rags among them be quilted together
into one huge Irish watchcoat for the defence of the

Body only !'—This, we think, is but Job's-news to the humane reader.

'Nevertheless,' cries Teufelsdröckh, 'who can hinder it; who is there that can clutch into the wheel-spokes of Destiny, and say to the Spirit of the Time: Turn back, I command thee?—Wiser were it that we yielded to the Inevitable and Inexorable, and accounted even this the best.'

Nay, might not an attentive Editor, drawing his own inferences from what stands written, conjecture that Teufelsdröckh individually had yielded to this same ' Inevitable and Inexorable ' heartily enough; and now sat waiting the issue, with his natural diabolico-angel-ical Indifference, if not even Placidity? Did we not hear him complain that the World was a 'huge Rag-fair,' and the ' rags and tatters of old Symbols ' were raining-down everywhere, like to drift him in, and suffocate him? What with those ' unhunted Helots ' of his; and the uneven *sic-vos-non-vobis* pressure and hard-crashing collision he is pleased to discern in exist-ing things; what with the so hateful ' empty Masks,' full of beetles and spiders, yet glaring out on him, from their glass eyes, 'with a ghastly affectation of life,' —we feel entitled to conclude him even willing that much should be thrown to the Devil, so it were but done gently ! Safe himself in that ' Pinnacle of Weissnicht-wo,' he would consent, with a tragic solemnity, that the monster UTILITARIA, held back, indeed, and moder-ated by nose-rings, halters, foot-shackles, and every conceivable modification of rope, should go forth to do her work;—to tread down old ruinous Palaces and Temples with her broad hoof, till the whole were trodden down, that new and better might be built ! Remark-able in this point of view are the following sentences.

' Society,' says he, ' is not dead : that Carcass, which you call dead Society, is but her mortal coil which she has shuffled off, to assume a nobler; she herself, through perpetual metamorphoses, in fairer and fairer development, has to live till Time also merge in Eter-nity. Wheresoever two or three Living Men are gathered together, there is Society; or there it will be, with its cunning mechanisms and stupendous structures, overspreading this little Globe, and reaching upwards to Heaven and downwards to Gehenna : for always, under one or the other figure, it has two authentic Revelations, of a God and of a Devil; the Pulpit, namely, and the Gallows.'

Indeed, we already heard him speak of ' Religion, in unnoticed nooks, weaving for herself new Vestures '; —Teufelsdröckh himself being one of the loom-treadles? Elsewhere he quotes without censure that strange aphorism of Saint-Simon's, concerning which and whom so much were to be said : *L'âge d'or, qu'une aveugle tradition a placé jusqu'ici dans le passé, est devant nous ;* The golden age, which a blind tradition has hitherto placed in the Past, is Before us.'—But listen again :

' When the Phœnix is fanning her funeral pyre, will there not be sparks flying ! Alas, some millions of men, and among them such as a Napoleon, have already been licked into that high-eddying Flame, and like moths consumed there. Still also have we to fear that incautious beards will get singed.

' For the rest, in what year of grace such Phœnix-cremation will be completed, you need not ask. The law of Perseverance is among the deepest in man : by nature he hates change; seldom will he quit his old house till it has actually fallen about his ears. Thus have I seen Solemnities linger as Ceremonies, sacred Symbols as idle-Pageants, to the extent of three-hundred years and more after all life and sacredness had evaporated out of them. And then, finally, what time the Phœnix Death-Birth itself will require, depends on unseen contingencies.—Meanwhile, would Destiny offer Mankind, that after, say two centuries of convulsion and conflagration, more or less vivid, the fire-creation should be accomplished, and we too find ourselves again in a Living Society, and no longer fighting but working,—were it not perhaps prudent in Mankind to strike the bargain?'

Thus is Teufelsdröckh content that old sick Society should be deliberately burnt (alas ! with quite other fuel than spicewood); in the faith that she is a Phœnix ; and that a new heaven-born young one will rise out of

her ashes! We ourselves, restricted to the duty of
Indicator, shall forbear commentary. Meanwhile, will
not the judicious reader shake his head, and reproachfully, yet more in sorrow than in anger, say or think:
From a *Doctor utriusque Juris*, titular Professor in a
University, and man to whom hitherto, for his services,
Society, bad as she is, has given not only food and
raiment (of a kind), but books, tobacco and gukguk,
we expected more gratitude to his benefactress; and less
of a blind trust in the future, which resembles that
rather of a philosophical Fatalist and Enthusiast, than
of a solid householder paying scot-and-lot in a Christian
country.

CHAPTER VI

OLD CLOTHES

As mentioned above, Teufelsdröckh, though a sansculottist, is in practice probably the politest man extant:
his whole heart and life are penetrated and informed
with the spirit of politeness; a noble natural Courtesy
shines through him, beautifying his vagaries; like sunlight, making a rosy-fingered, rainbow-dyed Aurora
out of mere aqueous clouds; nay brightening London-
smoke itself into gold vapour, as from the crucible of
an alchemist. Hear in what earnest though fantastic
wise he expresses himself on this head:

'Shall Courtesy be done only to the rich, and only
by the rich? In Good-breeding, which differs, if at all,
from High-breeding, only as it gracefully remembers
the rights of others, rather than gracefully insists on its
own rights, I discern no special connexion with wealth
or birth: but rather that it lies in human nature itself,
and is due from all men towards all men. Of a truth,
were your Schoolmaster at his post, and worth anything
when there, this, with so much else, would be reformed.
Nay, each man were then also his neighbour's schoolmaster; till at length a rude-visaged, unmannered
Peasant could no more be met with, than a Peasant

unacquainted with botanical Physiology, or who felt
not that the clod he broke was created in Heaven.

‘ For whether thou bear a sceptre or a sledge-
hammer, art thou not ALIVE; is not this thy brother
ALIVE? “ There is but one temple in the world,” says
Novalis, “ and that temple is the Body of Man. No-
thing is holier than this high Form. Bending before
men is a reverence done to this Revelation in the Flesh.
We touch Heaven, when we lay our hands on a human
Body.”

‘ On which ground, I would fain carry it farther than
most do ; and whereas the English Johnson only bowed
to every Clergyman, or man with a shovel-hat, I would
bow to every Man with any sort of hat, or with no hat
whatever. Is not he a Temple, then ; the visible Manifestation and Impersonation of the Divinity? And yet,
alas, such indiscriminate bowing serves not. For there
is a Devil dwells in man, as well as a Divinity ; and too
often the bow is but pocketed by the *former*. It would
go to the pocket of Vanity (which is your clearest phasis
of the Devil, in these times); therefore must we with-
hold it.

‘ The gladder am I, on the other hand, to do reverence to those Shells and outer Husks of the Body,
wherein no devilish passion any longer lodges, but only
the pure emblem and effigies of Man : I mean, to Empty,
or even to Cast Clothes. Nay, is it not to Clothes that
most men do reverence : to the fine frogged broadcloth,
nowise to the “ straddling animal with bandy legs ”
which it holds, and makes a Dignitary of? Who ever
saw any Lord my-lorded in tattered blanket fastened with
wooden skewer? Nevertheless, I say, there is in such
worship a shade of hypocrisy, a practical deception : for
how often does the Body appropriate what was meant
for the Cloth only ! Whoso would avoid falsehood,
which is the essence of all Sin, will perhaps see good
to take a different course. That reverence which cannot act without obstruction and perversion when the
Clothes are full, may have free course when they are
empty. Even as, for Hindoo Worshippers, the Pagoda
is not less sacred than the God ; so do I too worship the
hollow cloth Garment with equal fervour, as when it

contained the Man : nay, with more, for I now fear no deception, of myself or of others.

'Did not King *Toomtabard*, or, in other words, John Baliol, reign long over Scotland ; the man John Baliol being quite gone, and only the " Toom Tabard " (Empty Gown) remaining? What still dignity dwells in a suit of Cast Clothes ! How meekly it bears its honours ! No haughty looks, no scornful gesture : silent and serene, it fronts the world ; neither demanding worship, nor afraid to miss it. The Hat still carries the physiognomy of its Head : but the vanity and the stupidity, and goose-speech which was the sign of these two, are gone. The Coat-arm is stretched out, but not to strike ; the Breeches, in modest simplicity, depend at ease, and now at last have a graceful flow ; the Waistcoat hides no evil passion, no riotous desire ; hunger or thirst now dwells not in it. Thus all is purged from the grossness of sense, from the carking cares and foul vices of the World ; and rides there, on its Clothes-horse ; as, on a Pegasus, might some skyey Messenger, or purified Apparition, visiting our low Earth.

'Often, while I sojourned in that monstrous tuber-osity of Civilised Life, the Capital of England ; and meditated, and questioned Destiny, under that ink-sea of vapour, black, thick, and multifarious as Spartan broth ; and was one lone soul amid those grinding millions ;—often have I turned into their Old-Clothes Market to worship. With awe-struck heart I walk through that Monmouth Street, with its empty Suits, as through a Sanhedrim of stainless Ghosts. Silent are they, but expressive in their silence : the past witnesses and instruments of Woe and Joy, of Passions, Virtues, Crimes, and all the fathomless tumult of Good and Evil in " the Prison men call Life." Friends ! trust not the heart of that man for whom Old Clothes are not vener-able. Watch, too, with reverence, that bearded Jewish High-priest, who with hoarse voice, like some Angel of Doom, summons them from the four winds ! On his head, like the Pope, he has three Hats,—a real triple tiara ; on either hand are the similitude of wings, whereon the summoned Garments come to alight ; and ever, as he slowly cleaves the air, sounds forth his deep

fateful note, as if through a trumpet he were proclaiming : " Ghosts of Life, come to Judgment !" Reck not,
ye fluttering Ghosts : he will purify you in his Purgatory, with fire and with water; and, one day, new-
created ye shall reappear. O, let him in whom the flame
of Devotion is ready to go out, who has never worshipped, and knows not what to worship, pace and
repace, with austerest thought, the pavement of Monmouth Street, and say whether his heart and his eyes
still continue dry. If Field Lane, with its long fluttering rows of yellow handkerchiefs, be a Dionysius' Ear,
where, in stifled jarring hubbub, we hear the Indictment
which Poverty and Vice bring against lazy Wealth,
that it has left them there cast-out and trodden under
foot of Want, Darkness and the Devil,—then is Monmouth Street a Mirza's Hill, where, in motley vision,
the whole Pageant of Existence passes awfully before
us; with its wail and jubilee, mad loves and mad
hatreds, church-bells and gallows-ropes, farce-tragedy,
beast-godhood,—the Bedlam of Creation !'

To most men, as it does to ourselves, all this will
seem overcharged. We too have walked through Monmouth Street; but with little feeling of ' Devotion ' :
probably in part because the contemplative process is
so fatally broken in upon by the brood of money-
changers who nestle in that Church, and importune the
worshipper with merely secular proposals. Whereas
Teufelsdröckh might be in that happy middle state,
which leaves to the Clothes-broker no hope either of
sale or of purchase, and so be allowed to linger there
without molestation.—Something we would have given
to see the little philosophical figure, with its steeple-
hat and loose flowing skirts, and eyes in a fine frenzy,
' pacing and repacing in austerest thought ' that
foolish Street; which to him was a true Delphic avenue,
and supernatural Whispering-gallery, where the
' Ghosts of Life ' rounded strange secrets in his ear.
O thou philosophic Teufelsdröckh, that listenest while
others only gabble, and with thy quick tympanum
hearest the grass grow !

At the same time, is it not strange that, in Paper-bag Documents destined for an English work, there exists nothing like an authentic diary of this his sojourn in London; and of his Meditations among the Clothes-shops only the obscurest emblematic shadows? Neither, in conversation (for, indeed, he was not a man to pester you with his Travels), have we heard him more than allude to the subject.

For the rest, however, it cannot be uninteresting that we here find how early the significance of Clothes had dawned on the now so distinguished Clothes-Professor. Might we but fancy it to have been even in Monmouth Street, at the bottom of our own English 'ink-sea,' that this remarkable Volume first took being, and shot forth its salient point in his soul,—as in Chaos did the Egg of Eros, one day to be hatched into a Universe!

CHAPTER VII

ORGANIC FILAMENTS

For us, who happen to live while the World-Phœnix is burning herself, and burning so slowly that, as Teufelsdröckh calculates, it were a handsome bargain would she engage to have done 'within two centuries,' there seems to lie but an ashy prospect. Not altogether so, however, does the Professor figure it. 'In the living subject,' says he, 'change is wont to be gradual: thus, while the serpent sheds its old skin, the new is already formed beneath. Little knowest thou of the burning of a World-Phœnix, who fanciest that she must first burn-out, and lie as a dead cinereous heap; and therefrom the young one start-up by miracle, and fly heavenward. Far otherwise! In that Fire-whirl-wind, Creation and Destruction proceed together; ever as the ashes of the Old are blown about, do organic filaments of the New mysteriously spin themselves: and amid the rushing and the waving of the Whirlwind-Element come tones of a melodious Deathsong, which end not but in tones of a more melodious Birthsong. Nay, look into the Fire-whirlwind with thy own eyes, and thou wilt see.' Let us actually look, then : to poor individuals, who cannot expect to live two centuries, those same organic filaments, mysteriously spinning themselves, will be the best part of the spectacle. First, therefore, this of Mankind in general :

'In vain thou deniest it,' says the Professor; 'thou *art* my Brother. Thy very Hatred, thy very Envy, those foolish lies thou tellest of me in thy splenetic humour : what is all this but an inverted Sympathy? Were I a Steam-engine, wouldst thou take the trouble to tell lies of me? Not thou! I should grind all unheeded, whether badly or well.

'Wondrous truly are the bonds that unite us one and all; whether by the soft binding of Love, or the iron chaining of Necessity, as we like to choose it. More than once have I said to myself, of some perhaps whimsically strutting Figure, such as provokes whimsical thoughts : '' Wert thou, my little Brotherkin, suddenly covered-up within the largest imaginable Glass-bell,— what a thing it were, not for thyself only, but for the world! Post Letters, more or fewer, from all the four winds, impinge against thy Glass walls, but have to drop unread : neither from within comes there question or response into any Postbag; thy Thoughts fall into no friendly ear or heart, thy Manufacture into no purchasing hand : thou art no longer a circulating venous-arterial Heart, that, taking and giving, circulatest through all Space and all Time : there has a Hole fallen-out in the immeasurable, universal World-tissue, which must be darned-up again !''

'Such venous-arterial circulation, of Letters, verbal Messages, paper and other Packages, going out from him and coming in, are a blood-circulation, visible to the eye : but the finer nervous circulation, by which all things, the minutest that he does, minutely influence all men, and the very look of his face blesses or curses whomso it lights on, and so generates ever new blessing or new cursing : all this you cannot see, but only imagine. I say, there is not a red Indian, hunting by Lake Winnipic, can quarrel with his squaw, but the whole world must smart for it : will not the price of beaver rise? It is a mathematical fact that the casting of this pebble from my hand alters the centre of gravity of the Universe.

' If now an existing generation of men stand so woven together, not less indissolubly does generation with generation. Hast thou ever meditated on that word, Tradition : how we inherit not Life only, but all the garniture and form of Life; and work, and speak, and even think and feel, as our Fathers, and primeval grandfathers, from the beginning, have given it us?— Who printed thee, for example, this unpretending Volume on the Philosophy of Clothes? Not the Herren Stillschweigen and Company; but Cadmus of Thebes, Faust of Mentz, and innumerable others whom thou knowest not. Had there been no Mœsogothic Ulfila, there had been no English Shakspeare, or a different one. Simpleton! it was Tubalcain that made thy very Tailor's needle, and sewed that court-suit of thine.

' Yes, truly; if Nature is one, and a living indivisible whole, much more is Mankind, the Image that reflects and creates Nature, without which Nature were not. As palpable life-streams in that wondrous Individual Mankind, among so many life-streams that are not palpable, flow on those main-currents of what we call Opinion; as preserved in Institutions, Polities, Churches, above all in Books. Beautiful it is to understand and know that a Thought did never yet die; that as thou, the originator thereof, hast gathered it and created it from the whole Past, so thou wilt transmit it to the whole Future. It is thus that the heroic heart, the seeing eye of the first times, still feels and sees in us of the latest; that the Wise Man stands ever encompassed, and spiritually embraced, by a cloud of witnesses and brothers; and there is a living, literal *Communion of Saints*, wide as the World itself, and as the History of the World.

' Noteworthy also, and serviceable for the progress of this same Individual, wilt thou find his subdivision into Generations. Generations are as the Days of toil-some Mankind : Death and Birth are the vesper and the matin bells, that summon Mankind to sleep, and to rise refreshed for new advancement. What the Father has made, the Son can make and enjoy; but has also work

of his own appointed him. Thus all things wax, and
roll onwards; Arts, Establishments, Opinions, nothing
is completed, but ever completing. Newton has learned
to see what Kepler saw; but there is also a fresh heaven-
derived force in Newton; he must mount to still higher
points of vision. So too the Hebrew Lawgiver is, in
due time, followed by an Apostle of the Gentiles. In the
business of Destruction, as this also is from time to
time a necessary work, thou findest a like sequence and
perseverance: for Luther it was as yet hot enough to
stand by that burning of the Pope's Bull; Voltaire
could not warm himself at the glimmering ashes, but
required quite other fuel. Thus likewise, I note, the
English Whig has, in the second generation, become
an English Radical; who, in the third again, it is to be
hoped, will become an English Rebuilder. Find Mankind where thou wilt, thou findest it in living movement,
in progress faster or slower: the Phœnix soars aloft,
hovers with outstretched wings, filling Earth with her
music; or, as now, she sinks, and with spheral swan-
song immolates herself in flame, that she may soar the
higher and sing the clearer.'

Let the friends of social order, in such a disastrous
period, lay this to heart, and derive from it any little
comfort they can. We subjoin another passage, concerning Titles:

'Remark, not without surprise,' says Teufelsdröckh, 'how all high Titles of Honour come hitherto
from fighting. Your *Herzog* (Duke, *Dux*) is Leader of
Armies; your Earl (*Jarl*) is Strong Man; your Marshal
cavalry Horse-shoer. A Millennium, or reign of Peace
and Wisdom, having from of old been prophesied, and
becoming now daily more and more indubitable, may it
not be apprehended that such Fighting-titles will cease
to be palatable, and new and higher need to be devised?

'The only Title wherein I, with confidence, trace
eternity, is that of King. *König* (King), anciently *Könning*, means Ken-ning (Cunning), or which is the same
thing, Can-ning. Ever must the Sovereign of Mankind be fitly entitled King.'

'Well, also,' says he elsewhere, 'was it written by
Theologians: a King rules by divine right. He carries

in him an authority from God, or man will never give
it him. Can I choose my own King? I can choose my
own King Popinjay, and play what farce or tragedy I
may with him : but he who is to be my Ruler, whose
will is to be higher than my will, was chosen for me in
Heaven. Neither except in such Obedience to the
Heaven-chosen is Freedom so much as conceivable.'

The Editor will here admit that, among all the wondrous provinces of Teufelsdröckh's spiritual world, there
is none he walks in with such astonishment, hesitation,
and even pain, as in the Political. How, with our
English love of Ministry and Opposition, and that
generous conflict of Parties, mind warming itself against
mind in their mutual wrestle for the Public Good, by
which wrestle, indeed, is our invaluable Constitution
kept warm and alive; how shall we domesticate ourselves in this spectral Necropolis, or rather City both of
the Dead and of the Unborn, where the Present seems
little other than an inconsiderable Film dividing the
Past and the Future? In those dim longdrawn
expanses, all is so immeasurable; much so disastrous,
ghastly; your very radiances and straggling light-
beams have a supernatural character. And then with
such an indifference, such a prophetic peacefulness
(accounting the inevitably coming as already here, to
him all one whether it be distant by centuries or only
by days), does he sit;—and live, you would say, rather
in any other age than in his own ! It is our painful duty
to announce, or repeat, that, looking into this man, we
discern a deep, silent, slow-burning, inextinguishable
Radicalism, such as fills us with shuddering admiration.

Thus, for example, he appears to make little even of
the Elective Franchise; at least so we interpret the
following : ' Satisfy yourselves,' he says, ' by universal, indubitable experiment, even as ye are now
doing or will do, whether FREEDOM, heavenborn and
leading heavenward, and so vitally essential for us all,
cannot peradventure be mechanically hatched and
brought to light in that same Ballot-Box of yours ; or at
worst, in some other discoverable or devisable Box,
Edifice, or Steam-mechanism. It were a mighty con-

venience; and beyond all feats of manufacture witnessed hitherto.' Is Teufelsdröckh acquainted with the British Constitution, even slightly?—He says, under another figure: 'But after all, were the problem, as indeed it now everywhere is, To rebuild your old House from the top downwards (since you must live in it the while), what better, what other, than the Representative Machine will serve your turn? Meanwhile, however, mock me not with the name of Free, " when you have but knit-up my chains into ornamental festoons." ' —Or what will any member of the Peace Society make of such an assertion as this: 'The lower people everywhere desire War. Not so unwisely; there is then a demand for lower people—to be shot!'

Gladly, therefore, do we emerge from those soul-confusing labyrinths of speculative Radicalism, into somewhat clearer regions. Here, looking round, as was our hest, for 'organic filaments,' we ask, may not this, touching 'Hero-worship,' be of the number? It seems of a cheerful character; yet so quaint, so mystical, one knows not what, or how little, may lie under it. Our readers shall look with their own eyes:

'True is it that, in these days, man can do almost all things, only not obey. True likewise that whoso cannot obey cannot be free, still less bear rule; he that is the inferior of nothing, can be the superior of nothing, the equal of nothing. Nevertheless, believe not that man has lost his faculty of Reverence; that if it slumber in him, it has gone dead. Painful for man is that same rebellious Independence, when it has become inevitable; only in loving companionship with his fellows does he feel safe; only in reverently bowing down before the Higher does he feel himself exalted.

'Or what if the character of our so troublous Era lay even in this: that man had forever cast away Fear, which is the lower; but not yet risen into perennial Reverence, which is the higher and highest?

'Meanwhile, observe with joy, so cunningly has Nature ordered it, that whatsoever man ought to obey, he cannot but obey. Before no faintest revelation of the Godlike did he ever stand irreverent; least of all, when the Godlike showed itself revealed in his fellow-

man. Thus is there a true religious Loyalty forever
rooted in his heart; nay in all ages, even in ours, it
manifests itself as a more or less orthodox *Hero-worship*. In which fact, that Hero-worship exists, has
existed, and will forever exist, universally among Man-kind, mayest thou discern the corner-stone of living-rock, whereon all Polities for the remotest time may
stand secure.'

Do our readers discern any such corner-stone, or
even so much as what Teufelsdröckh is looking at? He
exclaims, 'Or hast thou forgotten Paris and Voltaire?
How the aged, withered man, though but a Sceptic,
Mocker, and millinery Court-poet, yet because even he
seemed the Wisest, Best, could drag mankind at his
chariot-wheels, so that princes coveted a smile from
him, and the loveliest of France would have laid their
hair beneath his feet! All Paris was one vast Temple
of Hero-worship; though their Divinity, moreover, was
of feature too apish.

'But if such things,' continues he, 'were done in
the dry tree, what will be done in the green? If, in the
most parched season of Man's History, in the most
parched spot of Europe, when Parisian life was at best
but a scientific *Hortus Siccus*, bedizened with some
Italian Gumflowers, such virtue could come out of it;
what is to be looked for when Life again waves leafy
and bloomy, and your Hero-Divinity shall have nothing
apelike, but be wholly human? Know that there is in
man a quite indestructible Reverence for whatsoever
holds of Heaven, or even plausibly counterfeits such
holding. Show the dullest clodpole, show the haughtiest
featherhead, that a soul higher than himself is actually
here; were his knees stiffened into brass, he must down
and worship.'

Organic filaments, of a more authentic sort, mysteri-ously spinning themselves, some will perhaps discover
in the following passage:

'There is no Church, sayest thou? The voice of
Prophecy has gone dumb? This is even what I dis-pute: but in any case, hast thou not still Preaching
enough? A Preaching Friar settles himself in every
village; and builds a pulpit, which he calls Newspaper.

Therefrom he preaches what most momentous doctrine is in him, for man's salvation; and dost not thou listen, and believe? Look well, thou seest everywhere a new Clergy of the Mendicant Orders, some bare-footed, some almost bare-backed, fashion itself into shape, and teach and preach, zealously enough, for copper alms and the love of God. These break in pieces the ancient idols; and, though themselves too often reprobate, as idol-breakers are wont to be, mark out the sites of new Churches, where the true God-ordained, that are to follow, may find audience, and minister. Said I not, Before the old skin was shed, the new had formed itself beneath it?'

Perhaps also in the following; wherewith we now hasten to knit-up this ravelled sleeve:

' But there is no Religion?' reiterates the Professor. ' Fool! I tell thee, there is. Hast thou well considered all that lies in this immeasurable froth-ocean we name LITERATURE? Fragments of a genuine Church-*Homiletic* lie scattered there, which Time will assort: nay fractions even of a *Liturgy* could I point out. And knowest thou no Prophet, even in the vesture, environment, and dialect of this age? None to whom the Godlike had revealed itself, through all meanest and highest forms of the Common; and by him been again prophetically revealed: in whose inspired melody, even in these rag-gathering and rag-burning days, Man's Life again begins, were it but afar off, to be divine? Knowest thou none such? I know him, and name him—Goethe.

' But thou as yet standest in no Temple; joinest in no Psalm-worship; feelest well that, where there is no ministering Priest, the people perish? Be of comfort! Thou art not alone, if thou have Faith. Spake we not of a Communion of Saints, unseen, yet not unreal, accompanying and brother-like embracing thee, so thou be worthy? Their heroic Sufferings rise up melodiously together to Heaven, out of all lands, and out of all times, as a sacred *Miserere;* their heroic Actions also, as a boundless everlasting Psalm of Triumph. Neither say that thou hast now no Symbol of the Godlike. Is not God's Universe a Symbol of the Godlike; is not Immensity a Temple; is not Man's History, and Men's

History, a perpetual Evangel? Listen, and for organ-music thou wilt ever, as of old, hear the Morning Stars sing together.'

CHAPTER VIII

NATURAL SUPERNATURALISM

IT is in his stupendous Section, headed *Natural Supernaturalism*, that the Professor first becomes a Seer; and, after long effort, such as we have witnessed, finally subdues under his feet this refractory Clothes-Philosophy, and takes victorious possession thereof. Phantasms enough he has had to struggle with; 'Cloth-webs and Cob-webs,' of Imperial Mantles, Super-annuated Symbols, and what not: yet still did he courageously pierce through. Nay, worst of all, two quite mysterious, world-embracing Phantasms, TIME and SPACE, have ever hovered round him, perplexing and bewildering: but with these also he now resolutely grapples, these also he victoriously rends asunder. In a word, he has looked fixedly on Existence, till, one after the other, its earthly hulls and garnitures have all melted away; and now, to his rapt vision, the interior celestial Holy of Holies lies disclosed.

Here, therefore, properly it is that the Philosophy of Clothes attains to Transcendentalism; this last leap, can we but clear it, takes us safe into the promised land, where *Palingenesia*, in all senses, may be considered as beginning. 'Courage, then!' may our Diogenes exclaim, with better right than Diogenes the First once did. This stupendous Section we, after long painful meditation, have found not to be unintelligible; but, on the contrary, to grow clear, nay radiant, and all-illuminating. Let the reader, turning on it what utmost force of speculative intellect is in him, do his part; as we, by judicious selection and adjustment, shall study to do ours:

'Deep has been, and is, the significance of Miracles,' thus quietly begins the Professor; 'far deeper perhaps

H 278

than we imagine. Meanwhile, the question of questions were: What specially is a Miracle? To that Dutch King of Siam, an icicle had been a miracle; whoso had carried with him an air-pump, and vial of vitriolic ether, might have worked a miracle. To my Horse, again, who unhappily is still more unscientific, do not I work a miracle, and magical " *Open sesame !*" every time I please to pay twopence, and open for him an impassable *Schlagbaum*, or shut Turnpike?

' " But is not a real Miracle simply a violation of the Laws of Nature?" ask several. Whom I answer by this new question: What are the Laws of Nature? To me perhaps the rising of one from the dead were no violation of these Laws, but a confirmation; were some far deeper Law, now first penetrated into, and by Spiritual Force, even as the rest have all been, brought to bear on us with its Material Force.

' Here too may some inquire, not without astonishment: On what ground shall one, that can make Iron swim, come and declare that therefore he can teach Religion? To us, truly, of the Nineteenth Century, such declaration were inept enough; which nevertheless to our fathers, of the First Century, was full of meaning.

' " But is it not the deepest Law of Nature that she be constant?" cries an illuminated class: " Is not the Machine of the Universe fixed to move by unalterable rules?" Probable enough, good friends: nay I, too, must believe that the God, whom ancient inspired men assert to be " without variableness or shadow of turning," does indeed never change; that Nature, that the Universe, which no one whom it so pleases can be prevented from calling a Machine, does move by the most unalterable rules. And now of you, too, I make the old inquiry: What those same unalterable rules, forming the complete Statute-Book of Nature, may possibly be?

' They stand written in our Works of Science, say you; in the accumulated records of Man's Experience? —Was Man with his Experience present at the Creation, then, to see how it all went on? Have any deepest scientific individuals yet dived-down to the foundations of the Universe, and gauged everything there? Did the Maker take them into His counsel; that they read His groundplan of the incomprehensible All; and can say, This stands marked therein, and no more than this? Alas, not in anywise! These scientific individuals have been nowhere but where we also are; have seen some handbreadths deeper than we see into the Deep that is infinite, without bottom as without shore.

'Laplace's Book on the Stars, wherein he exhibits that certain Planets, with their Satellites, gyrate round our worthy Sun, at a rate and in a course, which, by greatest good fortune, he and the like of him have succeeded in detecting,—is to me as precious as to another. But is this what thou namest "Mechanism of the Heavens," and "System of the World"; this, wherein Sirius and the Pleiades, and all Herschel's Fifteenthousand Suns per minute, being left out, some paltry handful of Moons, and inert Balls, had been—looked at, nicknamed, and marked in the Zodiacal Way-bill; so that we can now prate of their Whereabout; their How, their Why, their What, being hid from us, as in the signless Inane?

'System of Nature! To the wisest man, wide as is his vision, Nature remains of quite *infinite* depth, of quite infinite expansion; and all Experience thereof limits itself to some few computed centuries and measured square-miles. The course of Nature's phases, on this our little fraction of a Planet, is partially known to us: but who knows what deeper courses these depend on; what infinitely larger Cycle (of causes) our little Epicycle revolves on? To the Minnow every cranny and pebble, and quality and accident, of its little native Creek may have become familiar: but does the Minnow understand the Ocean Tides and periodic Currents, the Trade-winds, and Monsoons, and Moon's Eclipses; by all which the condition of its little Creek is regulated, and may, from time to time (*un*miraculously enough), be quite overset and reversed? Such a Minnow is Man; his Creek this Planet Earth; his Ocean the immeasurable All; his Monsoons and periodic Currents the mysterious Course of Providence through Æons of Æons.

'We speak of the Volume of Nature: and truly a

Volume it is,—whose Author and Writer is God. To
read it! Dost thou, does man, so much as well know
the Alphabet thereof? With its Words, Sentences,
and grand descriptive Pages, poetical and philosophical,
spread out through Solar Systems, and Thousands of
Years, we shall not try thee. It is a Volume written
in celestial hieroglyphs, in the true Sacred-writing; of
which even Prophets are happy that they can read here
a line and there a line. As for your Institutes, and
Academies of Science, they strive bravely; and, from
amid the thick-crowded, inextricably intertwisted hieroglyphic writing, pick-out, by dextrous combination,
some Letters in the vulgar Character, and therefrom put
together this and the other economic Recipe, of high
avail in Practice. That Nature is more than some
boundless Volume of such Recipes, or huge, well-nigh
inexhaustible Domestic-Cookery Book, of which the
whole secret will in this manner one day evolve itself,
the fewest dream.

'Custom,' continues the Professor, 'doth make
dotards of us all. Consider well, thou wilt find that
Custom is the greatest of Weavers; and weaves air-
raiment for all the Spirits of the Universe; whereby
indeed these dwell with us visibly, as ministering
servants, in our houses and workshops; but their
spiritual nature becomes, to the most, forever hidden.
Philosophy complains that Custom has hoodwinked us,
from the first; that we do everything by Custom, even
Believe by it; that our very Axioms, let us boast of
Free-thinking as we may, are oftenest simply such
Beliefs as we have never heard questioned. Nay, what
is Philosophy throughout but a continual battle against
Custom; an ever-renewed effort to *transcend* the sphere
of blind Custom, and so become Transcendental?

'Innumerable are the illusions and legerdemain-tricks
of Custom: but of all these, perhaps the cleverest is
her knack of persuading us that the Miraculous, by
simple repetition, ceases to be Miraculous. True, it is
by this means we live; for man must work as well as
wonder: and herein is Custom so far a kind nurse,
guiding him to his true benefit. But she is a fond

foolish nurse, or rather we are false foolish nurslings,
when, in our resting and reflecting hours, we prolong
the same deception. Am I to view the Stupendous with
stupid indifference, because I have seen it twice, or two-
hundred, or two-million times? There is no reason in
Nature or in Art why I should : unless, indeed, I am a
mere Work-Machine, for whom the divine gift of
Thought were no other than the terrestrial gift of Steam
is to the Steam-engine; a power whereby Cotton might
be spun, and money and money's worth realised.

' Notable enough too, here as elsewhere, wilt thou
find the potency of Names; which indeed are but one
kind of such custom-woven, wonder-hiding Garments.
Witchcraft, and all manner of Spectre-work, and
Demonology, we have now named Madness and Diseases of the Nerves. Seldom reflecting that still the
new question comes upon us : What is Madness, what
are Nerves? Ever, as before, does Madness remain a
mysterious-terrific, altogether *infernal* boiling-up of the
Nether Chaotic Deep, through this fair-painted Vision
of Creation, which swims thereon, which we name the
Real. Was Luther's Picture of the Devil less a Reality,
whether it were formed within the bodily eye, or without it? In every the wisest Soul lies a whole world of
internal Madness, an authentic Demon Empire; out of
which, indeed, his world of Wisdom has been creatively
built together, and now rests there, as on its dark
foundations does a habitable flowery Earth-rind.

' But deepest of all illusory Appearances, for hiding
Wonder, as for many other ends, are your two grand
fundamental world-enveloping Appearances, SPACE and
TIME. These, as spun and woven for us from before
Birth itself, to clothe our celestial ME for dwelling here,
and yet to blind it,—lie all embracing, as the universal
canvas, or warp and woof, whereby all minor Illusions,
in this Phantasm Existence, weave and paint themselves. In vain, while here on Earth, shall you endeavour to strip them off; you can, at best, but rend them
asunder for moments, and look through.

' Fortunatus had a wishing Hat, which when he put
on, and wished himself Anywhere, behold he was There.

By this means had Fortunatus triumphed over Space, he had annihilated Space; for him there was no Where, but all was Here. Were a Hatter to establish himself, in the Wahngasse of Weissnichtwo, and make felts of this sort for all mankind, what a world we should have of it! Still stranger, should, on the opposite side of the street, another Hatter establish himself; and as his fellow-craftsman made Space-annihilating Hats, make Time-annihilating! Of both would I purchase, were it with my last groschen; but chiefly of this latter. To clap-on your felt, and, simply by wishing that you were Any*where*, straightway to be *There!* Next to clap-on your other felt, and, simply by wishing that you were Any*when*, straightway to be *Then!* This were indeed the grander: shooting at will from the Fire-Creation of the World to its Fire-Consummation; here historically present in the First Century, conversing face to face with Paul and Seneca; there prophetically in the Thirty-first, conversing also face to face with other Pauls and Senecas, who as yet stand hidden in the depth of that late Time!

' Or thinkest thou it were impossible, unimaginable? Is the Past annihilated, then, or only past; is the Future non-extant, or only future? Those mystic faculties of thine, Memory and Hope, already answer: already through those mystic avenues, thou the Earth-blinded summonest both Past and Future, and communest with them, though as yet darkly, and with mute beckonings. The curtains of Yesterday drop down, the curtains of Tomorrow roll up; but Yesterday and Tomorrow both *are*. Pierce through the Time-element, glance into the Eternal. Believe what thou findest written in the sanctuaries of Man's Soul, even as all Thinkers, in all ages, have devoutly read it there: that Time and Space are not God, but creations of God; that with God as it is a universal HERE, so is it an everlasting Now.

' And seest thou therein any glimpse of IMMORTALITY? —O Heaven! Is the white Tomb of our Loved One, who died from our arms, and had to be left behind us there, which rises in the distance, like a pale, mournfully receding Milestone, to tell how many toilsome uncheered miles we have journeyed on alone,—but a pale spectral Illusion! Is the lost Friend still mysteriously Here, even as we are Here mysteriously, with God!—Know of a truth that only the Time-shadows have perished, or are perishable; that the real Being of whatever was, and whatever is, and whatever will be, *is* even now and forever. This, should it unhappily seem new, thou mayest ponder at thy leisure; for the next twenty years, or the next twenty centuries: believe it thou must; understand it thou canst not.

'That the Thought-forms, Space and Time, wherein, once for all, we are sent into this Earth to live, should condition and determine our whole Practical reasonings, conceptions, and imagings or imaginings,—seems altogether fit, just, and unavoidable. But that they should, furthermore, usurp such sway over pure spiritual Meditation, and blind us to the wonder everywhere lying close on us, seems nowise so. Admit Space and Time to their due rank as Forms of Thought; nay even, if thou wilt, to their quite undue rank of Realities: and consider, then, with thyself how their thin disguises hide from us the brightest God-effulgences! Thus, were it not miraculous, could I stretch forth my hand and clutch the Sun? Yet thou seest me daily stretch forth my hand and therewith clutch many a thing, and swing it hither and thither. Art thou a grown baby, then, to fancy that the Miracle lies in miles of distance, or in pounds avoirdupois of weight; and not to see that the true inexplicable God-revealing Miracle lies in this, that I can stretch forth my hand at all; that I have free Force to clutch aught therewith? Innumerable other of this sort are the deceptions, and wonder-hiding stupefactions, which Space practises on us.

'Still worse is it with regard to Time. Your grand anti-magician, and universal wonder-hider, is this same lying Time. Had we but the Time-annihilating Hat, to put on for once only, we should see ourselves in a World of Miracles, wherein all fabled or authentic Thaumaturgy, and feats of Magic, were outdone. But unhappily we have not such a Hat; and man, poor fool that he is, can seldom and scantily help himself without one.

'Were it not wonderful, for instance, had Orpheus,

or Amphion, built the walls of Thebes by the mere sound of his Lyre? Yet tell me, Who built these walls of Weissnichtwo; summoning-out all the sandstone rocks, to dance along from the *Steinbruch* (now a huge Troglodyte Chasm, with frightful green-mantled pools); and shape themselves into Doric and Ionic pillars, squared ashlar houses and noble streets? Was it not the still higher Orpheus, or Orpheuses, who, in past centuries, by the divine Music of Wisdom, succeeded in civilising Man? Our highest Orpheus walked in Judea, eighteen hundred years ago: his sphere-melody, flowing in wild native tones, took captive the ravished souls of men; and, being of a truth sphere-melody, still flows and sounds, though now with thousandfold accompaniments, and rich symphonies, through all our hearts; and modulates, and divinely leads them. Is that a wonder, which happens in two hours; and does it cease to be wonderful if happening in two million? Not only was Thebes built by the music of an Orpheus; but without the music of some inspired Orpheus was no city ever built, no work that man glories-in ever done.

' Sweep away the Illusion of Time; glance, if thou hast eyes, from the near moving-cause to its far-distant Mover: The stroke that came transmitted through a whole galaxy of elastic balls, was it less a stroke than if the last ball only had been struck, and sent flying? O, could I (with the Time-annihilating Hat) transport thee direct from the Beginnings to the Endings, how were thy eyesight unsealed, and thy heart set flaming in the Light-sea of celestial wonder! Then sawest thou that this fair Universe, were it in the meanest province thereof, is in very deed the star-domed City of God; that through every star, through every grass-blade, and most through every Living Soul, the glory of a present God still beams. But Nature, which is the Time-vesture of God, and reveals Him to the wise, hides Him from the foolish.

' Again, could anything be more miraculous than an actual authentic Ghost? The English Johnson longed, all his life, to see one; but could not, though he went to Cock Lane, and thence to the church-vaults, and tapped on coffins. Foolish Doctor! Did he never, with the mind's eye as well as with the body's, look round him into that full tide of human Life he so loved; did he never so much as look into Himself? The good Doctor was a Ghost, as actual and authentic as heart could wish; well-nigh a million of Ghosts were travelling the streets by his side. Once more I say, sweep away the illusion of Time; compress the threescore years into three minutes: what else was he, what else are we? Are we not Spirits, that are shaped into a body, into an Appearance; and that fade-away again into air and Invisibility? This is no metaphor, it is a simple scientific *fact:* we start out of Nothingness, take figure, and are Apparitions; round us, as round the veriest spectre, is Eternity; and to Eternity minutes are as years and æons. Come there not tones of Love and Faith, as from celestial harp-strings, like the Song of beautified Souls? And again, do not we squeak and jibber (in our discordant, screech-owlish debatings and recriminatings); and glide bodeful, and feeble, and fearful; or uproar (*poltern*), and revel in our mad Dance of the Dead,—till the scent of the morning air summons us to our still Home; and dreamy Night becomes awake and Day? Where now is Alexander of Macedon : does the steel Host, that yelled in fierce battle-shouts at Issus and Arbela, remain behind him; or have they all vanished utterly, even as perturbed Goblins must? Napoleon too, and his Moscow Retreats and Austerlitz Campaigns! Was it all other than the veriest Spectre-hunt; which has now, with its howling tumult that made Night hideous, flitted away?—Ghosts! There are nigh a thousand-million walking the Earth openly at noontide; some half-hundred have vanished from it, some half-hundred have arisen in it, ere thy watch ticks once.

' O Heaven, it is mysterious, it is awful to consider that we not only carry each a future Ghost within him; but are, in very deed, Ghosts! These Limbs, whence had we them; this stormy Force; this life-blood with its burning Passion? They are dust and shadow; a Shadow-system gathered round our ME; wherein, through some moments or years, the Divine Essence is to be revealed in the Flesh. That warrior on his strong

*H 278

war-horse, fire flashes through his eyes; force dwells in his arm and heart : but warrior and war-horse are a vision; a revealed Force, nothing more. Stately they tread the Earth, as if it were a firm substance : fool! the earth is but a film; it cracks in twain, and warrior and war-horse sink beyond plummet's sounding. Plummet's? Fantasy herself will not follow them. A little while ago, they were not; a little while, and they are not, their very ashes are not.

' So has it been from the beginning, so will it be to the end. Generation after generation takes to itself the Form of a Body; and forth-issuing from Cimmerian Night, on Heaven's mission APPEARS. What Force and Fire is in each he expends : one grinding in the mill of Industry; one hunter-like climbing the giddy Alpine heights of Science; one madly dashed in pieces on the rocks of Strife, in war with his fellow :—and then the Heaven-sent is recalled; his earthly Vesture falls away, and soon even to Sense becomes a vanished Shadow. Thus, like some wild-flaming, wild-thundering train of Heaven's Artillery, does this mysterious MANKIND thunder and flame, in long-drawn, quick-succeeding grandeur, through the unknown Deep. Thus, like a God-created, fire-breathing Spirit-host, we emerge from the Inane; haste stormfully across the astonished Earth; then plunge again into the Inane. Earth's mountains are levelled, and her seas filled up, in our passage : can the Earth, which is but dead and a vision, resist Spirits which have reality and are alive? On the hardest adamant some footprint of us is stamped-in; the last Rear of the host will read traces of the earliest Van. But whence?—O Heaven, whither? Sense knows not; Faith knows not; only that it is through Mystery to Mystery, from God and to God.

" We *are such stuff*
As Dreams are made of, and our little Life
Is rounded with a sleep!" '

CHAPTER IX

CIRCUMSPECTIVE

HERE, then, arises the so momentous question : Have many British Readers actually arrived with us at the new promised country ; is the Philosophy of Clothes now at last opening around them? Long and adventurous has the journey been : from those outmost vulgar, palpable Woollen-Hulls of Man ; through his wondrous Flesh-Garments, and his wondrous Social Garnitures ; inwards to the Garments of his very Soul's Soul, to Time and Space themselves ! And now does the Spiritual, eternal Essence of Man, and of Mankind, bared of such wrappages, begin in any measure to reveal itself ? Can many readers discern, as through a glass darkly, in huge wavering outlines, some primeval rudiments of Man's Being, what is changeable divided from what is unchangeable? Does that Earth-Spirit's speech in *Faust*,—

> "'Tis thus at the roaring Loom of Time I ply,
> And weave for God the Garment thou see'st Him by' ;

or that other thousand-times repeated speech of the Magician, Shakspeare,—

> ' And like the baseless fabric of this vision,
> The cloudcapt Towers, the gorgeous Palaces,
> The solemn Temples, the great Globe itself,
> And all which it inherit, shall dissolve ;
> And like this unsubstantial pageant faded,
> Leave not a wrack behind ' ;

begin to have some meaning for us? In a word, do we at length stand safe in the far region of Poetic Creation and Palingenesia, where that Phœnix Death-Birth of Human Society, and of all Human Things, appears possible, is seen to be inevitable?

Along this most insufficient, unheard-of Bridge, which the Editor, by Heaven's blessing, has now seen himself enabled to conclude if not complete, it cannot be his sober calculation, but only his fond hope, that many have travelled without accident.   No firm arch, overspanning the Impassable with paved highway, could the Editor construct; only, as was said, some zigzag series of rafts floating tumultuously thereon. Alas, and the leaps from raft to raft were too often of a breakneck character; the darkness, the nature of the element, all was against us!

Nevertheless, may not here and there one of a thousand, provided with a discursiveness of intellect rare in our day, have cleared the passage, in spite of all? Happy few! little band of Friends! be welcome, be of courage. By degrees, the eye grows accustomed to its new Whereabout; the hand can stretch itself forth to work there: it is in this grand and indeed highest work of Palingenesia that ye shall labour, each according to ability. New labourers will arrive; new Bridges will be built; nay, may not our own poor rope-and-raft Bridge, in your passings and repassings, be mended in many a point, till it grow quite firm, passable even for the halt?

Meanwhile, of the innumerable multitude that started with us, joyous and full of hope, where now is the innumerable remainder, whom we see no longer by our side? The most have recoiled, and stand gazing afar off, in unsympathetic astonishment, at our career: not a few, pressing forward with more courage, have missed footing, or leaped short; and now swim weltering in the Chaos-flood, some towards this shore, some towards that. To these also a helping hand should be held out; at least some word of encouragement be said.

Or, to speak without metaphor, with which mode of utterance Teufelsdröckh unhappily has somewhat infected us,—can it be hidden from the Editor that many a British Reader sits reading quite bewildered in head, and afflicted rather than instructed by the present Work? Yes, long ago has many a British Reader been, as now, demanding with something like a snarl: Whereto does all this lead; or what use is in it?

In the way of replenishing thy purse, or otherwise aiding thy digestive faculty, O British Reader, it leads to nothing, and there is no use in it; but rather the reverse, for it costs thee somewhat. Nevertheless, if through this unpromising Horn-gate, Teufelsdröckh, and we by means of him, have led thee into the true Land of Dreams; and through the Clothes-screen, as through a magical *Pierre-Pertuis*, thou lookest, even for moments, into the region of the Wonderful, and seest and feelest that thy daily life is girt with Wonder, and based on Wonder, and thy very blankets and breeches are Miracles,—then art thou profited beyond money's worth; and hast a thankfulness towards our Professor; nay, perhaps in many a literary Tea-circle wilt open thy kind lips, and audibly express that same.

Nay farther, art not thou too perhaps by this time made aware that all Symbols are properly Clothes; that all Forms whereby Spirit manifests itself to sense, whether outwardly or in the imagination, are Clothes; and thus not only the parchment Magna Charta, which a Tailor was nigh cutting into measures, but the Pomp and Authority of Law, the sacredness of Majesty, and all inferior Worships (Worthships) are properly a Vesture and Raiment; and the Thirty-nine Articles themselves are articles of wearing-apparel (for the Religious Idea)? In which case, must it not also be admitted that this Science of Clothes is a high one, and may with infinitely deeper study on thy part yield richer fruit : that it takes scientific rank beside Codification, and Political Economy, and the Theory of the British Constitution; nay rather, from its prophetic height looks down on all these, as on so many weaving-shops and spinning-mills, where the Vestures which *it* has to fashion, and consecrate and distribute, are, too often by haggard hungry operatives who see no farther than their nose, mechanically woven and spun?

But omitting all this, much more all that concerns Natural Supernaturalism, and indeed whatever has reference to the Ulterior or Transcendental portion of the Science, or bears never so remotely on that promised Volume of the *Palingenesie der menschlichen Gesellschaft* (Newbirth of Society),—we humbly suggest that no province of Clothes-Philosophy, even the lowest, is without its direct value, but that innumerable inferences of a practical nature may be drawn therefrom. To say nothing of those pregnant considerations, ethical, political, symbolical, which crowd on the Clothes-Philo-

sopher from the very threshold of his Science; nothing
even of those 'architectural ideas,' which, as we have
seen, lurk at the bottom of all Modes, and will one day,
better unfolding themselves, lead to important revolutions,—let us glance for a moment, and with the
faintest light of Clothes-Philosophy, on what may be
called the Habilatory Class of our fellow-men.   Here
too overlooking, where so much were to be looked on,
the million spinners, weavers, fullers, dyers, washers,
and wringers, that puddle and muddle in their dark
recesses, to make us Clothes, and die that we may live,
—let us but turn the reader's attention upon two small
divisions of mankind, who, like moths, may be regarded
as Cloth-animals, creatures that live, move and have
their being in Cloth: we mean, Dandies and Tailors.

In regard to both which small divisions it may be
asserted without scruple, that the public feeling, unen-
lightened by Philosophy, is at fault; and even that the
dictates of humanity are violated.   As will perhaps
abundantly appear to readers of the two following
chapters.

CHAPTER X

THE DANDIACAL BODY

First, touching Dandies, let us consider, with some
scientific strictness, what a Dandy specially is.   A
Dandy is a Clothes-wearing Man, a Man whose trade,
office and existence consists in the wearing of Clothes.
Every faculty of his soul, spirit, purse and person is
heroically consecrated to this one object, the wearing
of Clothes wisely and well: so that as others dress to
live, he lives to dress.   The all-importance of Clothes,
which a German Professor of unequalled learning and
acumen, writes his enormous Volume to demonstrate,
has sprung up in the intellect of the Dandy without
effort, like an instinct of genius; he is inspired with
Cloth, a Poet of Cloth.   What Teufelsdröckh would
call a ' Divine Idea of Cloth ' is born with him; and

this, like other such Ideas, will express itself outwardly, or wring his heart asunder with unutterable throes.

But, like a generous, creative enthusiast, he fearlessly makes his Idea an Action; shows himself in peculiar guise to mankind; walks forth, a witness and living Martyr to the eternal worth of Clothes. We called him a Poet: is not his body the (stuffed) parchment-skin whereon he writes, with cunning Huddersfield dyes, a Sonnet to his mistress' eyebrow? Say, rather, an Epos, and *Clotha Virumque cano*, to the whole world, in Macaronic verses, which he that runs may read. Nay, if you grant, what seems to be admissible, that the Dandy has a Thinking-principle in him, and some notions of Time and Space, is there not in this Life-devotedness to Cloth, in this so willing sacrifice of the Immortal to the Perishable, something (though in reverse order) of that blending and identification of Eternity with Time, which, as we have seen, constitutes the Prophetic character?

And now, for all this perennial Martyrdom, and Poesy, and even Prophecy, what is it that the Dandy asks in return? Solely, we may say, that you would recognise his existence; would admit him to be a living object; or even failing this, a visual object, or thing that will reflect rays of light. Your silver or your gold (beyond what the niggardly Law has already secured him) he solicits not; simply the glance of your eyes. Understand his mystic significance, or altogether miss and misinterpret it; do but look at him, and he is contented. May we not well cry shame on an ungrateful world, which refuses even this poor boon; which will waste its optic faculty on dried Crocodiles, and Siamese Twins; and over the domestic wonderful wonder of wonders, a live Dandy, glance with hasty indifference, and a scarcely concealed contempt! Him no Zoologist classes among the Mammalia, no Anatomist dissects with care: when did we see any injected Preparation of the Dandy in our Museums; any specimen of him preserved in spirits? Lord Herringbone may dress himself in a snuff-brown suit, with snuff-brown shirt and shoes: it skills not; the undiscerning public, occupied with grosser wants, passes by regardless on the other side.

The age of Curiosity, like that of Chivalry, is indeed,
properly speaking, gone.   Yet perhaps only gone to
sleep : for here arises the Clothes-Philosophy to resus-
citate, strangely enough, both the one and the other !
Should sound views of this Science come to prevail, the
essential nature of the British Dandy, and the mystic
significance that lies in him, cannot always remain
hidden under laughable and lamentable hallucination.
The following long Extract from Professor Teufelsdröckh may set the matter, if not in its true light, yet in
the way towards such.   It is to be regretted, however,
that here, as so often elsewhere, the Professor's keen
philosophic perspicacity is somewhat marred by a certain
mixture of almost owlish purblindness, or else of some
perverse, ineffectual, ironic tendency ; our readers shall
judge which :

'In these distracted times,' writes he, ' when the
Religious Principle, driven-out of most Churches, either
lies unseen in the hearts of good men, looking and longing and silently working there towards some new Revelation ; or else wanders homeless over the world, like a
disembodied soul seeking its terrestrial organisation,—
into how many strange shapes, of Superstition and
Fanaticism, does it not tentatively and errantly cast itself !   The higher Enthusiasm of man's nature is for
the while without Exponent; yet does it continue indestructible, unweariedly active, and work blindly in the
great chaotic deep : thus Sect after Sect, and Church
after Church, bodies itself forth, and melts again into
new metamorphosis.
' Chiefly is this observable in England, which, as the
wealthiest and worst-instructed of European nations,
offers precisely the elements (of Heat, namely, and of
Darkness), in which such moon-calves and monstrosities
are best generated.   Among the newer Sects of that
country, one of the most notable, and closely connected
with our present subject, is that of the *Dandies ;* concerning which, what little information I have been able
to procure may fitly stand here.
' It is true, certain of the English Journalists, men
generally without sense for the Religious Principle, or

judgment for its manifestations, speak, in their brief
enigmatic notices, as if this were perhaps rather a
Secular Sect, and not a Religious one; nevertheless, to
the psychologic eye its devotional and even sacrificial
character plainly enough reveals itself. Whether it belongs to the class of Fetish-worships, or of Hero-
worships or Polytheisms, or to what other class, may
in the present state of our intelligence remain undecided
(*schweben*). A certain touch of Manicheism, not indeed
in the Gnostic shape, is discernible enough : also (for
human Error walks in a cycle, and reappears at intervals) a not-inconsiderable resemblance to that Superstition of the Athos Monks, who by fasting from all
nourishment, and looking intensely for a length of time
into their own navels, came to discern therein the true
Apocalypse of Nature, and Heaven Unveiled. To my
own surmise, it appears as if this Dandiacal Sect were
but a new modification, adapted to the new time, of
that primeval Superstition, *Self-worship;* which Zer-
dusht, Quangfoutchee, Mohamed, and others, strove
rather to subordinate and restrain than to eradicate; and
which only in the purer forms of Religion has been altogether rejected. Wherefore, if any one chooses to name
it revived Ahrimanism, or a new figure of Demon-Worship, I have, so far as is yet visible, no objection.

' For the rest, these people, animated with the zeal
of a new Sect, display courage and perseverance, and
what force there is in man's nature, though never so
enslaved. They affect great purity and separatism;
distinguish themselves by a particular costume (whereof
some notices were given in the earlier part of this
Volume); likewise, so far as possible, by a particular
speech (apparently some broken *Lingua-franca*, or Eng-
lish-French); and, on the whole, strive to maintain a
true Nazarene deportment, and keep themselves un-
spotted from the world.

' They have their Temples, whereof the chief, as the
Jewish Temple did, stands in their metropolis; and is
named *Almack's*, a word of uncertain etymology. They
worship principally by night; and have their Highpriests
and Highpriestesses, who, however, do not continue for
life. The rites, by some supposed to be of the Menadic

sort, or perhaps with an Eleusinian or Cabiric character, are held strictly secret. Nor are Sacred Books wanting to the Sect; these they call *Fashionable Novels*: however, the Canon is not completed, and some are canonical and others not.

' Of such Sacred Books I, not without expense, procured myself some samples; and in hope of true insight, and with the zeal which beseems an Inquirer into Clothes, set to interpret and study them. But wholly to no purpose: that tough faculty of reading, for which the world will not refuse me credit, was here for the first time foiled and set at naught. In vain that I summoned my whole energies (*mich weidlich anstrengte*), and did my very utmost; at the end of some short space, I was uniformly seized with not so much what I can call a drumming in my ears, as a kind of infinite, unsufferable, Jews-harping and scrannel-piping there; to which the frightfullest species of Magnetic Sleep soon supervened. And if I strove to shake this away, and absolutely would not yield, there came a hitherto unfelt sensation, as of *Delirium Tremens*, and a melting into total deliquium: till at last, by order of the Doctor, dreading ruin to my whole intellectual and bodily faculties, and a general breaking-up of the constitution, I reluctantly but determinedly forbore. Was there some miracle at work here; like those Fire-balls, and supernal and infernal prodigies, which, in the case of the Jewish Mysteries, have also more than once scared-back the Alien? Be this as it may, such failure on my part, after best efforts, must excuse the imperfection of this sketch; altogether incomplete, yet the completest I could give of a Sect too singular to be omitted.

' Loving my own life and senses as I do, no power shall induce me, as a private individual, to open another *Fashionable Novel*. But luckily, in this dilemma, comes a hand from the clouds; whereby if not victory, deliverance is held out to me. Round one of those Book-packages, which the *Stillschweigen'sche Buchhandlung* is in the habit of importing from England, come, as is usual, various waste printed-sheets (*Maculatur blätter*), by way of interior wrappage: into these the Clothes-Philosopher, with a certain Mohamedan reverence even for waste-paper, where curious knowledge will sometimes hover, disdains not to cast his eye. Readers may judge of his astonishment when on such a defaced stray-sheet, probably the outcast fraction of some English Periodical, such as they name *Magazine*, appears something like a Dissertation on this very subject of *Fashionable Novels!* It sets out, indeed, chiefly from a Secular point of view; directing itself, not without asperity, against some to me unknown individual named *Pelham*, who seems to be a Mystagogue, and leading Teacher and Preacher of the Sect; so that, what indeed otherwise was not to be expected in such a fugitive fragmentary sheet, the true secret, the Religious physiognomy and physiology of the Dandiacal Body, is nowise laid fully open there.   Nevertheless, scattered lights do from time to time sparkle out, whereby I have endeavoured to profit.   Nay, in one passage selected from the Prophecies, or Mythic Theogonies, or whatever they are (for the style seems very mixed) of this Mystagogue, I find what appears to be a Confession of Faith, or Whole Duty of Man, according to the tenets of that Sect. Which Confession or Whole Duty, therefore, as proceeding from a source so authentic, I shall here arrange under Seven distinct Articles, and in very abridged shape lay before the German world; therewith taking leave of this matter.   Observe also, that to avoid possibility of error, I, as far as may be, quote literally from the Original :

' ARTICLES OF FAITH.

' " 1. Coats should have nothing of the triangle about them ; at the same time, wrinkles behind should be carefully avoided.

' " 2. The collar is a very important point : it should be low behind, and slightly rolled.

' " 3. No license of fashion can allow a man of delicate taste to adopt the posterial luxuriance of a Hottentot.

' " 4. There is safety in a swallow-tail.

' " 5. The good sense of a gentleman is nowhere more finely developed than in his rings.

' " 6. It is permitted to mankind, under certain restrictions, to wear white waistcoats.

' " 7. The trousers must be exceedingly tight across the hips."

' All which Propositions I, for the present, content myself with modestly but peremptorily and irrevocably denying.

' In strange contrast with this Dandiacal Body stands another British Sect, originally, as I understand, of Ireland, where its chief seat still is; but known also in the main Island, and indeed everywhere rapidly spreading. As this Sect has hitherto emitted no Canonical Books, it remains to me in the same state of obscurity as the Dandiacal, which has published Books that the unassisted human faculties are inadequate to read. The members appear to be designated by a considerable diversity of names, according to their various places of establishment: in England they are generally called the *Drudge* Sect; also, unphilosophically enough, the *White Negroes;* and, chiefly in scorn by those of other communions, the *Ragged-Beggar* Sect. In Scotland, again, I find them entitled *Hallanshakers*, or the *Stook of Duds* Sect; any individual communicant is named *Stook of Duds* (that is, Shock of Rags), in allusion, doubtless, to their professional Costume. While in Ireland, which, as mentioned, is their grand parent hive, they go by a perplexing multiplicity of designations, such as *Bogtrotters, Redshanks, Ribbonmen, Cottiers, Peep-of-Day Boys, Babes of the Wood, Rockites, Poor-Slaves:* which last, however, seems to be the primary and generic name; whereto, probably enough, the others are only subsidiary species, or slight varieties; or, at most, propagated offsets from the parent stem, whose minute subdivisions, and shades of difference, it were here loss of time to dwell on. Enough for us to understand, what seems indubitable, that the original Sect is that of the *Poor-Slaves;* whose doctrines, practices, and fundamental characteristics pervade and animate the whole Body, howsoever denominated or outwardly diversified.

' The precise speculative tenets of this Brotherhood: how the Universe, and Man, and Man's Life, picture

themselves to the mind of an Irish Poor-Slave; with
what feelings and opinions he looks forward on the
Future, round on the Present, back on the Past, it were
extremely difficult to specify. Something Monastic
there appears to be in their Constitution : we find them
bound by the two Monastic Vows, of Poverty and
Obedience; which Vows, especially the former, it is
said, they observe with great strictness ; nay, as I have
understood it, they are pledged, and be it by any solemn
Nazarene ordination or not, irrevocably consecrated
thereto, even *before* birth. That the third Monastic
Vow, of Chastity, is rigidly enforced among them, I
find no ground to conjecture.

Caprician

‘ Furthermore, they appear to imitate the Dandiacal
Sect in their grand principle of wearing a peculiar Costume. Of which Irish Poor-Slave Costume no description will indeed be found in the present Volume; for
this reason, that by the imperfect organ of Language it
did not seem describable. Their raiment consists of
innumerable skirts, lappets and irregular wings, of all
cloths and of all colours; through the labyrinthic intri-
cacies of which their bodies are introduced by some
unknown process. It is fastened together by a multiplex
combination of buttons, thrums and skewers; to which
frequently is added a girdle of leather, of hempen or
even of straw rope, round the loins. To straw rope,
indeed, they seem partial, and often wear it by way of
sandals. In head-dress they affect a certain freedom :
hats with partial brim, without crown, or with only a
loose, hinged, or valve crown; in the former case, they
sometimes invert the hat, and wear it brim uppermost,
like a University-cap, with what view is unknown.

‘ The name Poor-Slaves seems to indicate a Slavonic,
Polish, or Russian origin : not so, however, the interior
essence and spirit of their Superstition, which rather
displays a Teutonic or Druidical character. One might
fancy them worshippers of Hertha, or the Earth : for
they dig and affectionately work continually in her
bosom; or else, shut-up in private Oratories, meditate
and manipulate the substances derived from her; seldom
looking-up towards the Heavenly Luminaries, and then
with comparative indifference. Like the Druids, on the

other hand, they live in dark dwellings; often even
breaking their glass-windows, where they find such, and
stuffing them up with pieces of raiment, or other opaque
substances, till the fit obscurity is restored. Again, like
all followers of Nature-Worship, they are liable to out-
breakings of an enthusiasm rising to ferocity; and burn
men, if not in wicker idols, yet in sod cottages.

' In respect of diet, they have also their observances.
All Poor-Slaves are Rhizophagous (or Root-eaters); a
few are Ichthyophagous, and use Salted Herrings:
other animal food they abstain from; except indeed,
with perhaps some strange inverted fragment of a
Brahminical feeling, such animals as die a natural death.
Their universal sustenance is the root named Potato,
cooked by fire alone; and generally without condiment
or relish of any kind, save an unknown condiment
named *Point*, into the meaning of which I have vainly
inquired; the victual *Potatoes-and-Point* not appearing,
at least not with specific accuracy of description, in any
European Cookery-Book whatever. For drink, they
use, with an almost epigrammatic counterpoise of taste,
Milk, which is the mildest of liquors, and *Potheen*, which
is the fiercest. This latter I have tasted, as well as
the English *Blue-Ruin*, and the Scotch *Whisky*, analogous fluids used by the Sect in those countries: it
evidently contains some form of alcohol, in the highest
state of concentration, though disguised with acrid oils;
and is, on the whole, the most pungent substance known
to me,—indeed, a perfect liquid fire. In all their Religious Solemnities, Potheen is said to be an indispensable
requisite, and largely consumed.

' An Irish Traveller, of perhaps common veracity,
who presents himself under the to me unmeaning title
of *The late John Bernard*, offers the following sketch
of a domestic establishment, the inmates whereof,
though such is not stated expressly, appear to have been
of that Faith. Thereby shall my German readers now
behold an Irish Poor-Slave, as it were with their own
eyes; and even see him at meat. Moreover, in the so-
precious waste-paper sheet above mentioned, I have
found some corresponding picture of a Dandiacal Household, painted by that same Dandiacal Mystagogue, or

Theogonist: this also, by way of counterpart and contrast, the world shall look into.

'First, therefore, of the Poor-Slave, who appears likewise to have been a species of Innkeeper. I quote from the original:

Poor-Slave Household

' "The furniture of this Caravansera consisted of a large iron Pot, two oaken Tables, two Benches, two Chairs, and a Potheen Noggin. There was a Loft above (attainable by a ladder), upon which the inmates slept; and the space below was divided by a hurdle into two Apartments; the one for their cow and pig, the other for themselves and guests. On entering the house we discovered the family, eleven in number, at dinner: the father sitting at the top, the mother at the bottom, the children on each side, of a large oaken Board, which was scooped-out in the middle, like a trough, to receive the contents of their Pot of Potatoes. Little holes were cut at equal distances to contain Salt; and a bowl of Milk stood on the table: all the luxuries of meat and beer, bread, knives and dishes were dispensed with." The Poor-Slave himself our Traveller found, as he says, broad-backed, black-browed, of great personal strength, and mouth from ear to ear. His Wife was a sun-browned but well-featured woman; and his young ones, bare and chubby, had the appetite of ravens. Of their Philosophical or Religious tenets or observances, no notice or hint.

'But now, secondly, of the Dandiacal Household; in which, truly, that often-mentional Mystagogue and inspired Penman himself has his abode:

Dandiacal Household

' "A Dressing-room splendidly furnished; violet-coloured curtains, chairs and ottomans of the same hue. Two full-length Mirrors are placed, one on each side of a table, which supports the luxuries of the Toilet. Several Bottles of Perfumes, arranged in a peculiar fashion, stand upon a smaller table of mother-of-pearl : opposite to these are placed the appurtenances of Lavation richly wrought in frosted silver. A wardrobe of Buhl is on the left; the doors of which, being partly open, discover a profusion of Clothes; Shoes of a singularly small size monopolise the lower shelves. Fronting the wardrobe a door ajar gives some slight glimpse of a Bathroom. Folding-doors in the background.— Enter the Author," our Theogonist in person, " obsequiously preceded by a French Valet, in white silk Jacket and cambric Apron.''

' Such are the two Sects which, at this moment, divide the more unsettled portion of the British People; and agitate that ever-vexed country. To the eye of the political Seer, their mutual relation, pregnant with the elements of discord and hostility, is far from consoling. These two principals of Dandiacal Self-worship or Demon-worship, and Poor-Slavish or Drudgical Earth-worship, or whatever that same Drudgism may be, do as yet indeed manifest themselves under distant and nowise considerable shapes : nevertheless, in their roots and subterranean ramifications, they extend through the entire structure of Society, and work unweariedly in the secret depths of English national Existence; striving to separate and isolate it into two contradictory, uncommunicating masses.

' In numbers, and even individual strength, the Poor-Slaves or Drudges, it would seem, are hourly increasing. The Dandiacal, again, is by nature no proselytising Sect; but it boasts of great hereditary resources, and is strong by union; whereas the Drudges, split into parties, have as yet no rallying-point; or at best only co-operate by means of partial secret affiliations. If, indeed, there were to arise a *Communion of Drudges*, as there is already a Communion of Saints, what strangest effects would follow therefrom ! Dandyism as yet affects to look-down on Drudgism : but perhaps the hour of trial, when it will be practically seen which ought to look down, and which up, is not so distant.

' To me it seems probable that the two Sects will one

day part England between them; each recruiting itself
from the intermediate ranks, till there be none left to
enlist on either side.   Those Dandiacal Manicheans,
with the host of Dandyising Christians, will form one
body : the Drudges, gathering round them whosoever
is Drudgical, be he Christian or Infidel Pagan; sweep-
ing-up likewise all manner of Utilitarians, Radicals,
refractory Potwallopers, and so forth, into their general
mass, will form another.   I could liken Dandyism and
Drudgism to two bottomless boiling Whirlpools that
had broken-out on opposite quarters of the firm land :
as yet they appear only disquieted, foolishly bubbling
wells, which man's art might cover-in; yet mark them,
their diameter is daily widening : they are hollow Cones
that boil-up from the infinite Deep, over which your
firm land is but a thin crust or rind !   Thus daily is the
intermediate land crumbling-in, daily the empire of the
two Buchan-Bullers extending; till now there is but a
foot-plank, a mere film of Land between them; this too
is washed away : and then—we have the true Hell of
Waters, and Noah's Deluge is outdeluged !

' Or better, I might call them two boundless, and
indeed unexampled Electric Machines (turned by the
" Machinery of Society "), with batteries of opposite
quality; Drudgism the Negative, Dandyism the Positive : one attracts hourly towards it and appropriates
all the Positive Electricity of the nation (namely, the
Money thereof); the other is equally busy with the
Negative (that is to say the Hunger), which is equally
potent.   Hitherto you see only partial transient sparkles
and sputters : but wait a little, till the entire nation
is in an electric state; till your whole vital Electricity,
no longer healthfully Neutral, is cut into two isolated
portions of Positive and Negative (of Money and of
Hunger); and stands there bottled-up in two World-
Batteries !   The stirring of a child's finger brings the
two together; and then—What then?   The Earth is
but shivered into impalpable smoke by that Doom's-
thunderpeal; the Sun misses one of his Planets in
Space, and thenceforth there are no eclipses of the
Moon.—Or better still, I might liken '—

Oh ! enough, enough of likenings and similitudes;

in excess of which, truly, it is hard to say whether Teufelsdröckh or ourselves sin the more.

We have often blamed him for a habit of wire-drawing and over-refining; from of old we have been familiar with his tendency to Mysticism and Religiosity, whereby in everything he was still scenting-out Religion : but never perhaps did these amaurosis-suffusions so cloud and distort his otherwise most piercing vision, as in this of the *Dandiacal Body!* Or was there something of intended satire; is the Professor and Seer not quite the blinkard he affects to be? Of an ordinary mortal we should have decisively answered in the affirmative; but with a Teufelsdröckh there ever hovers some shade of doubt. In the mean while, if satire were actually intended, the case is little better. There are not wanting men who will answer : Does your Professor take us for simpletons? His irony has overshot itself; we see through it, and perhaps through him.

CHAPTER XI

TAILORS

THUS, however, has our first Practical Inference from the Clothes-Philosophy, that which respects Dandies, been sufficiently drawn ; and we come now to the second, concerning Tailors. On this latter our opinion happily quite coincides with that of Teufelsdröckh himself, as expressed in the concluding page of his Volume, to whom, therefore, we willingly give place. Let him speak his own last words, in his own way :

' Upwards of a century,' says he, ' must elapse, and still the bleeding fight of Freedom be fought, whoso is noblest perishing in the van, and thrones be hurled on altars like Pelion on Ossa, and the Moloch of Iniquity have his victims, and the Michael of Justice his martyrs, before Tailors can be admitted to their true prerogatives of manhood, and this last wound of suffering Humanity be closed.

'If aught in the history of the world's blindness could surprise us, here might we indeed pause and wonder. An idea has gone abroad, and fixed itself down into a wide-spreading rooted error, that Tailors are a distinct species in Physiology, not Men, but fractional Parts of a Man. Call any one a *Schneider* (Cutter, Tailor), is it not, in our dislocated, hood-winked, and indeed delirious condition of Society, equivalent to defying his perpetual fellest enmity? The epithet *schneider-mässig* (tailor-like) betokens an otherwise unapproachable degree of pusillanimity: we introduce a *Tailor's-Melancholy*, more opprobrious than any Leprosy, into our Books of Medicine; and fable I know not what of his generating it by living on Cabbage. Why should I speak of Hans Sachs (himself a Shoemaker, or kind of Leather-Tailor), with his *Schneider mit dem Panier?* Why of Shakspeare, in his *Taming of the Shrew*, and elsewhere? Does it not stand on record that the English Queen Elizabeth, receiving a deputation of Eighteen Tailors, addressed them with a "Good morning, gentlemen both!" Did not the same virago boast that she had a Cavalry Regiment, whereof neither horse nor man could be injured; her Regiment, namely, of Tailors on Mares? Thus everywhere is the falsehood taken for granted, and acted-on as an indisputable fact.

'Nevertheless, need I put the question to any Physiologist, whether it is disputable or not? Seems it not at least presumable, that, under his Clothes, the Tailor has bones and viscera, and other muscles than the sartorious? Which function of manhood is the Tailor not conjectured to perform? Can he not arrest for debt? Is he not in most countries a tax-paying animal?

'To no reader of this Volume can it be doubtful which conviction is mine. Nay if the fruit of these long vigils, and almost preternatural Inquiries, is not to perish utterly, the world will have approximated towards a higher Truth; and the doctrine, which Swift, with the keen forecast of genius, dimly anticipated, will stand revealed in clear light: that the Tailor is not only a Man, but something of a Creator or Divinity. Of Franklin it was said, that "he snatched the Thunder from Heaven and the Sceptre from Kings": but which

is greater, I would ask, he that lends, or he that
snatches? For, looking away from individual cases,
and how a Man is by the Tailor new-created into a
Nobleman, and clothed not only with Wool but with
Dignity and a Mystic Dominion,—is not the fair fabric
of Society itself, with all its royal mantles and pontifical
stoles, whereby, from nakedness and dismemberment,
we are organised into Polities, into nations, and a whole
co-operating Mankind, the creation, as has here been
often irrefragably evinced, of the Tailor alone?—What
too are all Poets and moral Teachers, but a species of
Metaphorical Tailors? Touching which high Guild the
greatest living Guild-brother has triumphantly asked us :
" Nay if thou wilt have it, who but the Poet first made
Gods for men; brought them down to us; and raised
us up to them?"

' And this is he, whom sitting downcast, on the hard
basis of his Shopboard, the world treats with con-
tumely, as the ninth part of a man! Look up, thou
much-injured one, look up with the kindling eye of
hope, and prophetic bodings of a noble better time.
Too long hast thou sat there, on crossed legs, wearing
thy ankle-joints to horn; like some sacred Anchorite,
or Catholic Fakir, doing penance, drawing down
Heaven's richest blessings, for a world that scoffed at
thee. Be of hope! Already streaks of blue peer
through our clouds; the thick gloom of Ignorance is
rolling asunder, and it will be Day. Mankind will
repay with interest their long-accumulated debt : the
Anchorite that was scoffed at will be worshipped; the
Fraction will become not an Integer only, but a Square
and Cube. With astonishment the world will recognise that the Tailor is its Hierophant and Hierarch, or
even its God.

' As I stood in the Mosque of St. Sophia, and looked
upon these Four-and-Twenty Tailors, sewing and em-
broidering that rich Cloth, which the Sultan sends
yearly for the Caaba of Mecca, I thought within myself : How many other Unholies has your covering Art
made holy, besides this Arabian Whinstone !

' Still more touching was it when, turning the corner
of a lane, in the Scottish Town of Edinburgh, I came

upon a Signpost, whereon stood written that such and such a one was " Breeches-Maker to his Majesty "; and stood painted the Effigies of a Pair of Leather Breeches, and between the knees these memorable words, SIC ITUR AD ASTRA. Was not this the martyr prison-speech of a Tailor sighing indeed in bonds, yet sighing towards deliverance, and prophetically appealing to a better day? A day of justice, when the worth of Breeches would be revealed to man, and the Scissors become forever venerable.

' Neither, perhaps, may I now say, has his appeal been altogether in vain. It was in this high moment, when the soul, rent, as it were, and shed asunder, is open to inspiring influence, that I first conceived this Work on Clothes : the greatest I can ever hope to do ; which has already, after long retardations, occupied, and will yet occupy, so large a section of my Life ; and of which the Primary and simpler Portion may here find its conclusion.'

CHAPTER XII

FAREWELL

So have we endeavoured, from the enormous, amorphous Plum-pudding, more like a Scottish Haggis, which Herr Teufelsdröckh had kneaded for his fellow mortals, to pick-out the choicest Plums, and present them separately on a cover of our own. A laborious, perhaps a thankless enterprise ; in which, however, something of hope has occasionally cheered us, and of which we can now wash our hands not altogether without satisfaction. If hereby, though in barbaric wise, some morsel of spiritual nourishment have been added to the scanty ration of our beloved British world, what nobler recompense could the Editor desire? If it prove otherwise, why should he murmur? Was not this a Task which Destiny, in any case, had appointed him ; which having now done with, he sees his general Day's-work so much the lighter, so much the shorter?

Of Professor Teufelsdröckh it seems impossible to
take leave without a mingled feeling of astonishment,
gratitude and disapproval. Who will not regret that
talents, which might have profited in the higher walks
of Philosophy, or in Art itself, have been so much
devoted to a rummaging among lumber-rooms; nay
too often to a scraping in kennels, where lost rings and
diamond-necklaces are nowise the sole conquests?
Regret is unavoidable; yet censure were loss of time.
To cure him of his mad humours British Criticism would
essay in vain : enough for her if she can, by vigilance,
prevent the spreading of such among ourselves. What
a result, should this piebald, entangled, hyper-meta-
phorical style of writing, not to say of thinking, become
general among our Literary men ! As it might so easily
do. Thus has not the Editor himself, working over
Teufelsdröckh's German, lost much of his own English
purity? Even as the smaller whirlpool is sucked into
the larger, and made to whirl along with it, so has the
lesser mind, in this instance, been forced to become
portion of the greater, and like it, see all things figuratively : which habit time and assiduous effort will be
needed to eradicate.

Nevertheless, wayward as our Professor shows himself, is there any reader that can part with him in
declared enmity? Let us confess, there is that in the
wild, much-suffering, much-inflicting man, which almost
attaches us. His attitude, we will hope and believe, is
that of a man who had said to Cant, Begone; and to
Dilettantism, Here thou canst not be; and to Truth,
Be thou in place of all to me : a man who had manfully
defied the ' Time-prince,' or Devil, to his face; nay
perhaps, Hannibal-like, was mysteriously consecrated
from birth to that warfare, and now stood minded to
wage the same, by all weapons, in all places, at all
times. In such a cause, any soldier, were he but a
Polack Scythe-man, shall be welcome.

Still the question returns on us : How could a man
occasionally of keen insight, not without keen sense of
propriety, who had real Thoughts to communicate,
resolve to emit them in a shape bordering so closely
on the absurd? Which question he were wiser than

the present Editor who should satisfactorily answer. Our conjecture has sometimes been, that perhaps Necessity as well as Choice was concerned in it. Seems it not conceivable that, in a Life like our Professor's, where so much bountifully given by Nature had in Practice failed and misgone, Literature also would never rightly prosper: that striving with his characteristic vehemence to paint this and the other Picture, and ever without success, he at last desperately dashes his sponge, full of all colours, against the canvas, to try whether it will paint Foam? With all his stillness, there were perhaps in Teufelsdröckh desperation enough for this.

A second conjecture we hazard with even less warranty. It is, that Teufelsdröckh is not without some touch of the universal feeling, a wish to proselytise. How often already have we paused, uncertain whether the basis of this so enigmatic nature were really Stoicism and Despair, or Love and Hope only seared into the figure of these! Remarkable, moreover, is this saying of his: ' How were Friendship possible? In mutual devotedness to the Good and True: otherwise impossible; except as Armed Neutrality, or hollow Commercial League. A man, be the Heavens ever praised, is sufficient for himself; yet were ten men, united in Love, capable of being and of doing what ten thousand singly would fail in. Infinite is the help man can yield to man.' And now in conjunction therewith consider this other: ' It is the Night of the World, and still long till it be Day: we wander amid the glimmer of smoking ruins, and the Sun and the Stars of Heaven are as if blotted out for a season; and two immeasurable Phantoms, HYPOCRISY and ATHEISM, with the Gowl, SENSUALITY, stalk abroad over the Earth, and call it theirs: well at ease are the Sleepers for whom Existence is a shallow Dream.'

But what of the awestruck Wakeful who find it a Reality? Should not these unite; since even an authentic Spectre is not visible to Two?—In which case were this enormous Clothes-Volume properly an enormous Pitchpan, which our Teufelsdröckh in his lone watchtower had kindled, that it might flame far and

wide through the Night, and many a disconsolately
wandering spirit be guided thither to a Brother's
bosom!—We say as before, with all his malign Indifference, who knows what mad Hopes this man may
harbour?

Meanwhile there is one fact to be stated here, which
harmonises ill with such conjecture; and, indeed, were
Teufelsdröckh made like other men, might as good as
altogether subvert it. Namely, that while the Beacon-
fire blazed its brightest, the Watchman had quitted it;
that no pilgrim could now ask him: Watchman, what
of the Night? Professor Teufelsdröckh, be it known,
is no longer visibly present at Weissnichtwo, but again
to all appearance lost in space! Some time ago, the
Hofrath Heuschrecke was pleased to favour us with
another copious Epistle; wherein much is said about
the ' Population-Institute'; much repeated in praise
of the Paper-bag Documents, the hieroglyphic nature
of which our Hofrath still seems not to have surmised;
and, lastly, the strangest occurrence communicated, to
us for the first time, in the following paragraph:

' Ew. Wohlgeboren will have seen from the public
Prints, with what affectionate and hitherto fruitless
solicitude Weissnichtwo regards the disappearance of
her Sage. Might but the united voice of Germany
prevail on him to return; nay, could we but so much
as elucidate for ourselves by what mystery he went
away! But, alas, old Lieschen experiences or affects
the profoundest deafness, the profoundest ignorance:
in the Wahngasse all lies swept, silent, sealed up; the
Privy Council itself can hitherto elicit no answer.

' It had been remarked that while the agitating news
of those Parisian Three Days flew from mouth to mouth,
and dinned every ear in Weissnichtwo, Herr Teufelsdröckh was not known, at the Gans or elsewhere, to
have spoken, for a whole week, any syllable except
once these three: Es geht an (It is beginning). Shortly
after, as Ew. Wohlgeboren knows, was the public tranquillity here, as in Berlin, threatened by a Sedition of
the Tailors. Nor did there want Evil-wishers, or perhaps mere desperate Alarmists, who asserted that the
closing Chapter of the Clothes-Volume was to blame.

In this appalling crisis, the serenity of our Philosopher was indescribable; nay, perhaps through one humble individual, something thereof might pass into the *Rath* (Council) itself, and so contribute to the country's deliverance. The Tailors are now entirely pacificated.—

' To neither of these two incidents can I attribute our loss: yet still comes there the shadow of a suspicion out of Paris and its Politics. For example, when the *Saint-Simonian Society* transmitted its Propositions hither, and the whole *Gans* was one vast cackle of laughter, lamentation and astonishment, our Sage sat mute; and at the end of the third evening said merely: " Here also are men who have discovered, not without amazement, that Man is still Man; of which high, long-forgotten Truth you already see them make a false application." Since then, as has been ascertained by examination of the Post-Director, there passed at least one Letter with its Answer between the Messieurs Bazard-Enfantin and our Professor himself; of what tenor can now only be conjectured. On the fifth night following, he was seen for the last time!

' Has this invaluable man, so obnoxious to most of the hostile Sects that convulse our Era, been spirited away by certain of their emissaries; or did he go forth voluntarily to their head-quarters to confer with them and confront them? Reason we have, at least of a negative sort, to believe the Lost still living; our widowed heart also whispers that ere long he will himself give a sign. Otherwise, indeed, his archives must, one day, be opened by Authority; where much, perhaps the *Palingenesie* itself, is thought to be reposited.'

Thus far the Hofrath; who vanishes, as is his wont, too like an Ignis Fatuus, leaving the dark still darker.

So that Teufelsdröckh's public History were not done, then, or reduced to an even, unromantic tenor; nay, perhaps the better part thereof were only beginning? We stand in a region of conjectures, where substance has melted into shadow, and one cannot be distinguished from the other. May Time, which solves or suppresses all problems, throw glad light on this also! Our own private conjecture, now amounting almost to certainty, is that, safe-moored in some stillest obscurity, not to lie always still, Teufelsdröckh is actually in London!

Here, however, can the present Editor, with an ambrosial joy as of over-weariness falling into sleep, lay down his pen. Well does he know, if human testimony be worth aught, that to innumerable British readers likewise, this is a satisfying consummation; that innumerable British readers consider him, during these current months, but as an uneasy interruption to their ways of thought and digestion; and indicate so much, not without a certain irritancy and even spoken invective. For which, as for other mercies, ought not he to thank the Upper Powers? To one and all of you, O irritated readers, he, with outstretched arms and open heart, will wave a kind farewell. Thou too, miraculous Entity, who namest thyself YORKE and OLIVER, and with thy vivacities and genialities, with thy all-too Irish mirth and madness, and odour of palled punch, makest such strange work, farewell; long as thou canst, fare-*well*! Have we not, in the course of Eternity, travelled some months of our Life-journey in partial sight of one another; have we **not** existed together, though in a state of quarrel?

APPENDIX

TESTIMONIES OF AUTHORS

THIS questionable little Book was undoubtedly written among the mountain solitudes, in 1831 ; but, owing to impediments natural and accidental, could not, for seven years more, appear as a Volume in England ;—and had at last to clip itself in pieces, and be content to struggle out, bit by bit, in some courageous *Magazine* that offered. Whereby now, to certain idly curious readers, and even to myself till I make study, the insignificant but at last irritating question, What its real history and chronology are, is, if not insoluble, considerably involved in haze.

To the first English Edition, 1838, which an American, or two American had now opened the way for, there was slightingly prefixed, under the title ' *Testimonies of Authors*,' some straggle of real documents, which, now that I find it again, sets the matter into clear light and sequence ;—and shall here, for removal of idle stumbling-blocks and nugatory guessings from the path of every reader, be reprinted as it stood. (*Author's Note of* 1868.)

TESTIMONIES OF AUTHORS

I. HIGHEST CLASS, BOOKSELLER'S TASTER

Taster to Bookseller.—"The Author of *Teufelsdröckh* is a person of talent; his work displays here and there some felicity of thought and expression, considerable fancy and knowledge: but whether or not it would take with the public seems doubtful. For a *jeu d'esprit* of that kind it is too long; it would have suited better as an essay or article than as a volume. The Author has no great tact; his wit is frequently heavy; and reminds one of the German Baron who took to leaping on tables, and answered that he was learning to be lively. *Is* the work a translation?"

Bookseller to Editor.—"Allow me to say that such a writer requires only a little more tact to produce a popular as well as an able work. Directly on receiving your permission, I sent your *MS.* to a gentleman in the highest class of men of letters, and an accomplished German scholar: I now inclose you his opinion, which, you may rely upon it, is a just one; and I have too high an opinion of your good sense to" &c. &c.—*MS. (penes nos), London, 17th September* 1831.

II. CRITIC OF THE SUN

"*Fraser's Magazine* exhibits the usual brilliancy, and also the" &c. "*Sartor Resartus* is what old Dennis used to call 'a heap of clotted nonsense,' mixed however, here and there, with passages marked by thought and striking poetic vigour. But what does the writer mean by 'Baphometic fire-baptism'? Why cannot he lay aside his pedantry, and write so as to make himself generally intelligible? We quote by way of curiosity a sentence from the *Sartor Resartus;* which may be read either backwards or forwards, for it is equally intelligible either way. Indeed, by beginning at the tail, and so working up to the head, we think the reader will stand the fairest chance of getting at its meaning: 'The fire-baptised soul, long so scathed and thunder-riven, here feels its own freedom; which feeling is its Baphometic baptism: the citadel of its whole kingdom it has thus gained by assault, and will keep inexpugnable; outwards from which the remaining dominions, not indeed without hard battering, will doubtless by degrees be conquered and pacificated.' Here is a"— . . . . . —*Sun Newspaper, 1st April* 1834.

III. NORTH-AMERICAN REVIEWER

. . . . . . "After a careful survey of the whole ground, our belief is that no such persons as Professor Teufelsdröckh or Counsellor Heuschrecke ever existed; that the six Paper-bags, with their China-ink inscriptions and multifarious contents, are a mere figment of the brain ; that the 'present Editor' is the only person who has ever written upon the Philosophy of Clothes ; and that the *Sartor Resartus* is the only treatise that has yet appeared upon that subject ;—in short, that the whole account of the origin of the work before us,—which the supposed Editor relates with so much gravity, and of which we have given a brief abstract, is, in plain English, a *hum*.

"Without troubling our readers at any great length with our reasons for entertaining these suspicions, we may remark, that the absence of all other information on the subject, except what is contained in the work, is itself a fact of a most significant character. The whole German press, as well as the particular one where the work purports to have been printed, seems to be under the control of *Stillschweigen and Co.*, —Silence and Company. If the Clothes-Philosophy and its author are making so great a sensation throughout Germany as is pretended, how happens it that the only notice we have of the fact is contained in a few numbers of a monthly Magazine published at London? How happens it that no intelligence about the matter has come out directly to this country? We pique ourselves here in New England upon knowing at least as much of what is going on in the literary way in the old Dutch Mother-land as our brethren of the fast-anchored Isle ; but thus far we have no tidings whatever of the 'extensive close-printed close-meditated volume,' which forms the subject of this pretended commentary. Again, we would respectfully inquire of the 'present Editor' upon what part of the map of Germany we are to look for the city of *Weissnichtwo*,—'Know-not-where,'—at which place the work is supposed to have been printed, and the Author to have resided. It has been our fortune to visit several portions of the German territory, and to examine pretty carefully, at different times and for various purposes, maps of the whole ; but we have no recollection of any such place. We suspect that the city of *Know-not-where* might be called, with at least as much propriety, *Nobody-knows-where*, and is to be found in the kingdom of *Nowhere*. Again, the village of *Entepfuhl*—'Duck-pond,' where the supposed Author of the work is said to have passed his youth, and that of *Hinterschlag*, where he had his education, are equally foreign to our geography. Duck-ponds enough there undoubtedly are in almost every village in Germany, as the traveller in that country knows too well to his cost, but any particular village denominated Duck-pond is to us altogether *terra incognita*. The names of the personages are not less singular than those of the places. Who can refrain from a smile at the yoking together of such a pair of appellatives as Diogenes Teufelsdröckh? The supposed bearer of this strange title is represented as admitting, in his pretended autobiography, that 'he had searched to no purpose through all the Heralds' books in and without the German empire, and through all manner of Subscribers'-lists, Militia-rolls, and other Name-catalogues,' but had nowhere been able to find the 'name Teufelsdröckh, except as appended to his own person.' We can readily believe this, and we doubt very much whether any Christian parent would think of condemning a son to carry through life the burden of so unpleasant a title. That of Counsellor Heuschrecke—'Grasshopper,' though not offensive, looks much more like a piece of fancy work than a 'fair business transaction.' The same may be said of *Blumine*—'Flower-Goddess'—the heroine of the fable ; and so of the rest.

"In short, our private opinion is, as we have remarked, that the whole story of a correspondence with Germany, a university of Nobody-knows-where, a Professor of Things in General, a Counsellor Grass-hopper, a Flower-Goddess Blumine, and so forth, has about as much foundation in truth as the late entertaining account of Sir John Herschel's discoveries in the moon. Fictions of this kind are, however, not uncommon, and ought not, perhaps, to be condemned with too much severity ; but we are not sure that we can exercise the same indulgence in regard to the attempt, which seems to be made to mislead the public as to the substance of the work before us, and its pretended German original. Both purport, as we have seen, to be upon the subject of Clothes, or dress. *Clothes, their Origin and Influence,* is the title of the supposed German treatise of Professor Teufelsdröckh, and the rather odd name of *Sartor Resartus*—the Tailor Patched,—which the present Editor has affixed to his pretended commentary, seems to look the same way. But though there is a good deal of remark through-out the work in a half-serious, half-comic style upon dress, it seems to be in reality a treatise upon the great science of Things in General, which Teufelsdröckh is supposed to have professed at the university of Nobody-knows-where. Now, without intending to adopt a too rigid standard of morals, we own that we doubt a little the propriety of offering to the public a treatise on Things in General, under the name and in the form of an Essay on Dress. For ourselves, advanced as we unfortunately are in the journey of life, far beyond the period when dress is practically a matter of interest, we have no hesitation in saying, that the real subject of the work is to us more attractive than the ostensible one. But this is probably not the case with the mass of readers. To the younger portion of the community, which constitutes everywhere the very great majority, the subject of dress is one of intense and paramount importance. An author who treats it appeals, like the poet, to the young men and maidens —*virginibus puerisque,*—and calls upon them, by all the motives which habitually operate most strongly upon their feelings, to buy his book. When, after opening their purses for this purpose, they have carried home the work in triumph, expecting to find in it some particular instruction in regard to the tying of their neckcloths, or the cut of their corsets, and meet with nothing better than a dissertation on Things in General, they will,—to use the mildest term—not be in very good humour. If the last improvements in legisla-tion, which we have made in this country, should have found their way to England, the author, we think, would stand some chance of being *Lynched*. Whether his object in this piece of *supercherie* be merely pecuniary profit, or whether he takes a malicious pleasure in quizzing the Dandies, we shall not undertake to say. In the latter part of the work, he devotes a separate chapter to this class of persons, from the tenour of which we should be disposed to conclude, that he would consider any mode of divesting them of their property very much in the nature of a spoiling of the Egyptians.

"The only thing about the work, tending to prove that it is what it purports to be, a commentary on a real German treatise, is the style, which is a sort of Babylonish dialect, not destitute, it is true, of richness, vigour, and at times a sort of singular felicity of expression, but very strongly tinged throughout with the peculiar idiom of the German language. This quality in the style, however, may be a mere result of a great familiarity with German literature, and we cannot, therefore, look upon it as in itself decisive, still less as outweighing so much evidence of an opposite character."—*North-American Review*, *No.* 89, *October* 1835.

IV. New England Editors

" The Editors have been induced, by the express desire of many persons, to collect the following sheets out of the ephemeral pamphlets[1] in which they first appeared, under the conviction that they contain in themselves the assurance of a longer date.

" The Editors have no expectation that this little Work will have a sudden and general popularity. They will not undertake, as there is no need, to justify the gay costume in which the Author delights to dress his thoughts, or the German idioms with which he has sportively sprinkled his pages. It is his humour to advance the gravest speculations upon the gravest topics in a quaint and burlesque style. If his masquerade offend any of his audience, to that degree that they will not hear what he has to say, it may chance to draw others to listen to his wisdom ; and what work of imagination can hope to please all ? But we will venture to remark that the distaste excited by these peculiarities in some readers is greatest at first, and is soon forgotten ; and that the foreign dress and aspect of the Work are quite superficial, and cover a genuine Saxon heart. We believe, no book has been published for many years, written in a more sincere style of idiomatic English, or which discovers an equal mastery over all the riches of the language. The Author makes ample amends for the occasional eccentricity of his genius, not only by frequent bursts of pure splendour, but by the wit and sense which never fail him.

" But what will chiefly commend the Book to the discerning reader is the manifest design of the work, which is, a Criticism upon the Spirit of the Age,—we had almost said, of the hour,—in which we live ; exhibiting in the most just and novel light the present aspects of Religion, Politics, Literature, Arts, and Social Life. Under all his gaiety the Writer has an earnest meaning, and discovers an insight into the manifold wants and tendencies of human nature, which is very rare among our popular authors. The philanthropy and the purity of moral sentiment, which inspire the work, will find their way to the heart of every lover of virtue."—*Preface to Sartor Resartus : Boston*, 1836, 1837.

Sunt, Fuerunt vel Fuere.

London, 30*th June* 1838.

[1] *Fraser's* (London) *Magazine*, 1833-4.

SUMMARY

BOOK I

CHAP. I. *Preliminary*

No Philosophy of Clothes yet, notwithstanding all our Science. Strangely forgotten that Man is by nature a *naked* animal. The English mind all-too practically absorbed for any such inquiry. Not so, deep-thinking Germany. Advantage of Speculation having free course. Editor receives from Professor Teufelsdröckh his new Work on Clothes (p. 1).

CHAP. II. *Editorial Difficulties*

How to make known Teufelsdröckh and his Book to English readers ; especially *such* a book ? Editor receives from the Hofrath Heuschrecke a letter promising Biographic Documents. Negotiations with Oliver Yorke. *Sartor Resartus* conceived. Editor's assurances and advice to his British reader (p. 5).

CHAP. III. *Reminiscences*

Teufelsdröckh at Weissnichtwo. Professor of Things in General at the University there : Outward aspect and character ; memorable coffee-house utterances ; domicile and watch-tower : Sights thence of City-life by day and by night ; with reflections thereon. Old 'Liza and her ways. Character of Hofrath Heuschrecke, and his relation to Teufelsdröckh (p. 9).

CHAP. IV. *Characteristics*

Teufelsdröckh and his Work on Clothes : Strange freedom of speech : transcendentalism ; force of insight and expression ; multifarious learning : Style poetic, uncouth : Comprehensiveness of his humour and moral feeling. How the Editor once saw him laugh. Different kinds of Laughter and their significance (p. 20).

CHAP. V. *The World in Clothes*

Futile cause - and - effect Philosophies. Teufelsdröckh's Orbis Vestitus. Clothes first invented for the sake of Ornament. Picture of our progenitor, the Aboriginal Savage. Wonders of growth and progress in mankind's history. Man defined as a Tool-using Animal (p. 25).

CHAP. VI. *Aprons*

Divers Aprons in the world with divers uses. The Military and Police Establishment Society's working Apron. The Episcopal Apron with its corner tucked in. The Laystall. Journalists now our only Kings and Clergy (p. 31).

Chap. VII. *Miscellaneous-Historical*

How Men and Fashions come and go. German Costume in the fifteenth century. By what strange chances do we live in History! The costume of Bolivar's Cavalry (p. 34).

Chap. VIII. *The World out of Clothes*

Teufelsdröckh's Theorem, "Society founded upon Cloth"; his Method, Intuition quickened by Experience.—The mysterious question, Who am I? Philosophic systems all at fault: A deeper meditation has always taught, here and there an individual, that all visible things are appearances only; but also emblems and revelations of God. Teufelsdröckh first comes upon the question of Clothes: Baseness to which Clothing may bring us (p. 37).

Chap. IX. *Adamatism*

The universal utility of Clothes, and their higher mystic virtue, illustrated. Conception of Mankind stripped naked; and immediate consequent dissolution of civilised Society (p. 43).

Chap. X. *Pure Reason*

A Naked World possible, nay actually exists, under the clothed one. Man, in the eye of Pure Reason, a visible God's Presence. The beginning of all wisdom, to look fixedly on Clothes till they become transparent. Wonder, the basis of Worship: Perennial in man. Modern Sciolists who cannot wonder: Teufelsdröckh's contempt for, and advice to them (p. 47).

Chap. XI. *Prospective*

Nature not an Aggregate, but a Whole. All visible things are emblems, Clothes; and exist for a time only. The grand scope of the Philosophy of Clothes.—Biographic Documents arrive. Letter from Heuschrecke on the importance of Biography. Heterogeneous character of the documents: Editor sorely perplexed; but desperately grapples with his work (p. 52).

BOOK II

Chap. I. *Genesis*

Old Andreas Futteral and Gretchen his wife: their quiet home. Advent of a mysterious stranger, who deposits with them a young infant, the future Herr Diogenes Teufelsdröckh. After-yearnings of the youth for his unknown Father. Sovereign power of Names and Naming. Diogenes a flourishing Infant (p. 61).

Chap. II. *Idyllic*

Happy Childhood! Entepfuhl: Sights, hearings and experiences of the boy Teufelsdröckh; their manifold teaching. Education; what it can do, what cannot. Obedience our universal duty and destiny. Gneschen sees the good Gretchen pray (p. 68).

CHAP. III. *Pedagogy*

Teufelsdröckh's School. His Education. How the ever-flowing Kuhbach speaks of Time and Eternity. The Hinterschlag Gymnasium; rude Boys; and pedant Professors. The need of true Teachers, and their due recognition. Father Andreas dies: and Teufelsdröckh learns the secret of his birth: His reflections thereon. The Nameless University. Statistics of Imposture much wanted. Bitter fruits of Rationalism: Teufelsdröckh's religious difficulties. The young Englishman Herr Towgood. Modern Friendship (p. 76).

CHAP. IV. *Getting under Way*

The grand thaumaturgic Art of Thought. Difficulty in fitting Capability to Opportunity, or of getting underway. The advantage of Hunger and Bread-Studies. Teufelsdröckh has to enact the stern monodrama of *No object and no rest*. Sufferings as Auscultator. Given up as a man of genius. Zähdarm House. Intolerable presumption of young men. Irony and its consequences. Teufelsdröckh's Epitaph on Count Zähdarm (p. 90).

CHAP. V. *Romance*

Teufelsdröckh gives up his Profession. The heavenly mystery of Love. Teufelsdröckh's feeling of worship towards women. First and only love. Blumine. Happy hearts and free tongues. The infinite nature of Fantasy. Love's joyful progress; sudden dissolution; and final catastrophe (p. 101).

CHAP. VI. *Sorrows of Teufelsdrockh*

Teufelsdröckh's demeanour thereupon. Turns pilgrim. A last wistful look on native Entepfuhl: Sunset amongst primitive Mountains. Basilisk-glance of the Barouche-and-four. Thoughts on View-hunting. Wanderings and Sorrowings (p. 112).

CHAP. VII. *The Everlasting No*

Loss of Hope, and of Belief. Profit-and-Loss Philosophy, Teufelsdröckh in his darkness and despair still clings to Truth and follows Duty. Inexpressible pains and fears of Unbelief. Fever-crisis: Protest against the Everlasting No: Baphometic Fire-baptism (p. 121).

CHAP. VIII. *Centre of Indifference*

Teufelsdröckh turns now outwardly to the *Not-me;* and finds wholesomer food. Ancient Cities: Mystery of their origin and growth: Invisible inheritances and possessions. Power and virtue of a true Book. Wagram Battlefield: War. Great Scenes beheld by the Pilgrim: Great Events, and Great Men. Napoleon, a divine missionary, preaching *La carrière ouverte aux talens*. Teufelsdröckh at the North Cape: Modern means of self-defence. Gunpowder and duelling. The Pilgrim, despising his miseries, reaches the Centre of Indifference (p. 128).

CHAP. IX. *The Everlasting Yea*

Temptations in the Wilderness: Victory over the Tempter. Anni-hilation of Self. Belief in God, and love to Man. The origin of Evil, a problem ever requiring to be solved anew: Teufelsdröckh's solution. Love of Happiness a vain whim: A Higher in man than Love of Happiness. The Everlasting Yea. Worship of Sorrow. Voltaire: his task now finished. Conviction worthless, impossible, without Conduct. The true Ideal, the Actual: Up and work! (p. 138).

CHAP. X. *Pause*

Conversion; a spiritual attainment peculiar to the modern Era. Teufelsdröckh accepts Authorship as his divine calling. The scope of the command *Thou shalt not steal.*—Editor begins to suspect the authenticity of the Biographical documents; and abandons them for the great Clothes volume. Result of the preceding ten Chapters: Insight into the character of Teufelsdröckh: His fundamental beliefs, and how he was forced to seek and find them (p. 149).

BOOK III

CHAP. I. *Incident in Modern History*

Story of George Fox the Quaker; and his perennial suit of Leather. A man God-possessed, witnessing for spiritual freedom and manhood (p. 156).

CHAP. II. *Church-Clothes*

Church-Clothes defined; the Forms under which the Religious principle is temporarily embodied. Outward Religion originates by Society: Society becomes possible by Religion. The condition of Church-Clothes in our time (p. 161).

CHAP. III. *Symbols*

The benignant efficacies of Silence and Secrecy. Symbols; revela-tions of the Infinite in the Finite: Man everywhere encompassed by them; lives and works by them. Theory of Motive-millwrights, a false account of human nature. Symbols of an extrinsic value; as Banners, Standards: Of intrinsic value; as Works of Art, Lives and Deaths of Heroic men. Religious Symbols; Christianity. Symbols hallowed by Time; but finally defaced and desecrated. Many super-annuated Symbols in our time, needing removal (p. 163).

CHAP. IV. *Helotage*

Heuschrecke's Malthusian Tract, and Teufelsdröckh's marginal notes thereon. The true workman, for daily bread, or spiritual bread, to be honoured; and no other. The real privation of the Poor not poverty or toil, but ignorance. Over-population: With a world like ours and wide as ours, can there be too many men? Emigration (p. 170).

Chap. V. *The Phœnix*

Teufelsdröckh considers Society as *dead;* its soul (Religion) gone, its body (existing Institutions) going. Utilitarianism, needing little farther preaching, is now in full activity of Destruction.—Teufelsdröckh would yield to the Inevitable, accounting that the best : Assurance of a fairer Living Society, arising, Phœnix-like, out of the ruins of the old dead one. Before that Phœnix death-birth is accomplished, long time, struggle, and suffering must intervene (p. 174).

Chap. VI. *Old Clothes*

Courtesy due from all men to all men : The Body of Man a Revelation in the Flesh. Teufelsdröckh's respect for Old Clothes, as the 'Ghosts of Life.' Walk in Monmouth Street, and meditations there (p. 179).

Chap. VII. *Organic Filaments*

Destruction and Creation ever proceed together ; and organic filaments of the Future are even now spinning. Wonderful connection of each man with all men ; and of each generation with all generations, before and after : Mankind is One. Sequence and progress of all human work, whether of creation or destruction, from age to age.— Titles, hitherto derived from Fighting, must give way to others. Kings will remain and their title. Political Freedom, not to be attained by any mechanical contrivance. Hero-worship, perennial amongst men ; the cornerstone of polities in the Future. Organic filaments of the New Religion : Newspapers and Literature. Let the faithful soul take courage ! (p. 183).

Chap. VIII. *Natural Supernaturalism*

Deep significance of Miracles. Littleness of human Science : Divine incomprehensibility of Nature. Custom blinds us to the miraculousness of daily-recurring miracles ; so do Names. Space and Time, appearances only ; forms of human Thought : A glimpse of Immortality. How Space hides from us the wondrousness of our commonest powers ; and Time, the divinely miraculous course of human history (p. 191).

Chap. IX. *Circumspective*

Recapitulation. Editor congratulates the few British readers who have accompanied Teufelsdröckh through all his speculations. The true use of the *Sartor Resartus*, to exhibit the Wonder of daily life and common things ; and to show that all Forms are but Clothes, and temporary. Practical inferences enough will follow (p. 201).

Chap. X. *The Dandiacal Body*

The Dandy defined. The Dandiacal Sect a new modification of the primeval superstition Self-worship : How to be distinguished. Their Sacred Books (Fashionable Novels) unreadable. Dandyism's Articles of Faith.—Brotherhood of Poor-Slaves : vowed to perpetual Poverty ; worshippers of Earth ; distinguished by peculiar costume and diet.

Picture of a Poor-Slave Household ; and of a Dandiacal. Teufelsdröckh fears these two Sects may spread, till they part all England between them, and then frightfully collide (p. 204).

Chap. XI. *Tailors*

Injustice done to Tailors, actual and metaphorical. Their rights and great services will one day be duly recognised (p. 216).

Chap. XII. *Farewvll*

Teufelsdröckh's strange manner of speech, but resolute, truthful character : His purpose seemingly to proselytise, to unite the wakeful earnest in these dark times. Letter from Hofrath Heuschrecke announcing that Teufelsdröckh has disappeared from Weissnichtwö Editor guesses he will appear again. Friendly Farewell (p. 219).

ON HEROES, HERO-WORSHIP,
AND THE HEROIC IN HISTORY

LECTURE I

THE HERO AS DIVINITY. ODIN. PAGANISM: SCANDINAVIAN MYTHOLOGY

[Tuesday, 5th May 1840]

WE have undertaken to discourse here for a little on Great Men, their manner of appearance in our world's business, how they have shaped themselves in the world's history, what ideas men formed of them, what work they did;—on Heroes, namely, and on their reception and performance; what I call Hero-worship and the Heroic in human affairs. Too evidently this is a large topic; deserving quite other treatment than we can expect to give it at present. A large topic; indeed, an illimitable one; wide as Universal History itself. For, as I take it, Universal History, the history of what man has accomplished in this world, is at bottom the History of the Great Men who have worked here. They were the leaders of men, these great ones; the modellers, patterns, and in a wide sense creators, of whatsoever the general mass of men contrived to do or to attain; all things that we see standing accomplished in the world are properly the outer material result, the practical realisation and embodiment, of Thoughts that dwelt in the Great Men sent into the world : the soul of the whole world's history, it may justly be considered, were the history of these. Too clearly it is a topic we shall do no justice to in this place !

One comfort is, that Great Men, taken up in any way, are profitable company. We cannot look, however imperfectly, upon a great man, without gaining something by him. He is the living light-fountain, which it is good and pleasant to be near. The light which enlightens, which has enlightened the darkness of the world; and this not as a kindled lamp only, but rather as a natural luminary shining by the gift of Heaven; a flowing light-fountain, as I say, of native original insight, of manhood and heroic nobleness;—in whose

239

radiance all souls feel that it is well with them.   On any terms whatsoever, you will not grudge to wander in such neighbourhood for a while.   These Six classes of Heroes, chosen out of widely-distant countries and epochs, and in mere external figure differing altogether, ought, if we look faithfully at them, to illustrate several things for us.   Could we see *them* well, we should get some glimpses into the very marrow of the world's history.   How happy, could I but, in any measure, in such times as these, make manifest to you the meanings of Heroism; the divine relation (for I may well call it such) which in all times unites a Great Man to other men; and thus, as it were, not exhaust my subject, but so much as break ground on it!   At all events, I must make the attempt.

It is well said, in every sense, that a man's religion is the chief fact with regard to him.   A man's, or a nation of men's.   By religion I do not mean here the church-creed which he professes, the articles of faith which he will sign and, in words or otherwise, assert; not this wholly, in many cases not this at all.   We see men of all kinds of professed creeds attain to almost all degrees of worth or worthlessness under each or any of them.   This is not what I call religion, this profession and assertion; which is often only a profession and assertion from the outworks of the man, from the mere argumentative region of him, if even so deep as that.   But the thing a man does practically believe (and this is often enough *without* asserting it even to himself, much less to others); the thing a man does practically lay to heart, and know for certain, concerning his vital relations to this mysterious Universe, and his duty and destiny there, that is in all cases the primary thing for him, and creatively determines all the rest.   That is his *religion;* or it may be, his mere scepticism and *no-religion:* the manner it is in which he feels himself to be spiritually related to the Unseen World or No-World; and I say, if you tell me what that is, you tell me to a very great extent what the man is, what the kind of things he will do is.   Of a man or of a nation we inquire, therefore, first of all, What religion they had? Was it Heathenism,—plurality of gods, mere sensuous representation of this Mystery of Life, and for chief recognised element therein Physical Force? Was it Christianism; faith in an Invisible, not as real only, but as the only reality; Time, through every meanest moment of it, resting on Eternity; Pagan empire of Force displaced by a nobler supremacy, that of Holiness? Was it Scepticism, uncertainty and inquiry whether there was an Unseen World, any Mystery of Life except a mad one;—doubt as to all this, or perhaps unbelief and flat denial? Answering of this question is giving us the soul of the history of the man or nation. The thoughts they had were the parents of the actions they did; their feelings were parents of their thoughts : it was the unseen and spiritual in them that determined the outward and actual;—their religion, as I say, was the great fact about them. In these Discourses, limited as we are, it will be good to direct our survey chiefly to that religious phasis of the matter. That once known well, all is known. We have chosen as the first Hero in our series, Odin the central figure of Scandinavian Paganism; an emblem to us of a most extensive province of things. Let us look for a little at the Hero as Divinity, the oldest primary form of Heroism.

Surely it seems a very strange-looking thing this Paganism; almost inconceivable to us in these days. A bewildering, inextricable jungle of delusions, confusions, falsehoods and absurdities, covering the whole field of Life ! A thing that fills us with astonishment, almost, if it were possible, with incredulity,—for truly it is not easy to understand that sane men could ever calmly, with their eyes open, believe and live by such a set of doctrines. That men should have worshipped their poor fellow-man as a God, and not him only, but stocks and stones, and all manner of animate and inanimate objects; and fashioned for themselves such a distracted chaos of hallucinations by way of Theory of the Universe : all this looks like an incredible fable. Nevertheless it is a clear fact that they did it. Such hideous inextricable jungle of misworships, misbeliefs, men, made as we are, did actually hold by, and live at home in. This is strange. Yes, we may pause in sorrow and silence over the depths of darkness that are in man; if we rejoice in the heights of purer vision he has attained to. Such things were and are in man; in all men; in us too.

Some speculators have a short way of accounting for the Pagan religion : mere quackery, priestcraft, and dupery, say they; no sane man ever did believe it,— merely contrived to persuade other men, not worthy of the name of sane, to believe it ! It will be often our duty to protest against this sort of hypothesis about men's doings and history; and I here, on the very threshold, protest against it in reference to Paganism, and to all other *isms* by which man has ever for a length of time striven to walk in this world. They have all had a truth in them, or men would not have taken them up. Quackery and dupery do abound; in religions, above all in the more advanced decaying stages of religions, they have fearfully abounded : but quackery was never the originating influence in such things; it was not the health and life of such things, but their disease, the sure precursor of their being about to die ! Let us never forget this. It seems to me a most mournful hypothesis, that of quackery giving birth to any faith even in savage men. Quackery gives birth to nothing; gives death to all things. We shall not see into the true heart of anything, or if we look merely at the quackeries of it; if we do not reject the quackeries altogether; as mere diseases, corruptions, with which our and all men's sole duty is to have done with them, to sweep them out of our thoughts as out of our practice. Man everywhere is the born enemy of lies. I find Grand Lamaism itself to have a kind of truth in it. Read the candid, clear-sighted, rather sceptical Mr Turner's *Account of his Embassy* to that country, and see. They have their belief, these poor Thibet people, that Providence sends down always an Incarnation of Himself into every generation. At bottom some belief in a kind of Pope ! At bottom still better, belief that there is a *Greatest* Man; that *he* is discoverable; that, once discovered, we ought to treat him with an obedience which knows no bounds ! This is the truth of Grand Lamaism; the 'discoverability' is the only error here. The Thibet priests have methods of their own of discovering what Man is Greatest, fit to be supreme over them. Bad methods: but are they so much worse than our methods,—of understanding him to be always the eldest born of a certain genealogy? Alas, it is a difficult thing to find good methods for !——— We shall begin to have a chance of understanding Paganism, when we first admit that to its followers it was, at one time, earnestly true. Let us consider it very certain that men did believe in Paganism; men with open eyes, sound senses, men made altogether like ourselves; that we, had we been there, should have believed in it. Ask now, What Paganism could have been?

Another theory, somewhat more respectable, attributes such things to Allegory. It was a play of poetic minds, say these theorists; a shadowing-forth, in allegorical fable, in personification and visual form, of what such poetic minds had known and felt of this Universe. Which agrees, add they, with a primary law of human nature, still everywhere observably at work, though in less important things, That what a man feels intensely, he struggles to speak-out of him, to see represented before him in visual shape, and as if with a kind of life and historical reality in it. Now doubtless there is such a law, and it is one of the deepest in human nature; neither need we doubt that it did operate fundamentally in this business. The hypothesis which ascribes Paganism wholly or mostly to this agency, I call a little more respectable; but I cannot yet call it the true hypothesis. Think, would *we* believe, and take with us as our life-guidance, an allegory, a poetic sport? Not sport but earnest is what we should require. It is a most earnest thing to be alive in this world; to die is not sport for a man. Man's life never was a sport to him; it was a stern reality, altogether a serious matter to be alive!

I find, therefore, that though these Allegory theorists are on the way towards truth in this matter, they have not reached it either. Pagan Religion is indeed an Allegory, a Symbol of what men felt and knew about the Universe; and all Religions are Symbols of that, altering always as that alters: but it seems to me a radical perversion, and even *inversion*, of the business, to put that forward as the origin and moving cause, when it was rather the result and termination. To get beautiful allegories, a perfect poetic symbol, was not the want of men; but to know what they were to believe about this Universe, what course they were to steer in it; what, in this mysterious Life of theirs, they had to hope and to fear, to do and to forbear doing. The *Pilgrim's Progress* is an Allegory, and a beautiful, just and serious one: but consider whether Bunyan's Allegory could have *preceded* the Faith it symbolises! The Faith had to be already there, standing believed by everybody;—of which the Allegory could *then* become a shadow; and, with all its seriousness, we may say a *sportful* shadow, a mere play of the Fancy, in comparison with that awful Fact and scientific certainty which it poetically strives to emblem. The Allegory is the product of the certainty, not the producer of it; not in Bunyan's, nor in any other case. For Paganism, therefore, we have still to inquire, Whence came that scientific certainty, the parent of such a bewildered heap of allegories, errors and confusions? How was it, what was it?

Surely it were a foolish attempt to pretend 'explaining,' in this place, or in any place, such a phenomenon as that far-distant distracted cloudy imbroglio of Paganism,—more like a cloudfield than a distant continent of firm land and facts! It is no longer a reality, yet it was one. We ought to understand that this seeming cloudfield was once a reality; that not poetic allegory, least of all that dupery and deception was the origin of it. Men, I say, never did believe idle songs, never risked their soul's life on allegories; men in all times, especially in early earnest times, have had an instinct for detecting quacks, for detesting quacks. Let us try if, leaving out both the quack theory and the allegory one, and listening with affectionate attention to that far-off confused rumour of the Pagan ages, we cannot ascertain so much as this at least, That there was a kind of fact at the heart of them; that they too were not mendacious and distracted, but in their own poor way true and sane!

You remember that fancy of Plato's, of a man who had grown to maturity in some dark distance, and was brought on a sudden into the upper air to see the sun rise. What would his wonder be, his rapt astonishment at the sight we daily witness with indifference! With the free open sense of a child, yet with the ripe faculty of a man, his whole heart would be kindled by that sight, he would discern it well to be Godlike, his soul would fall down in worship before it. Now, just such a child-like greatness was in the primitive nations. The first Pagan Thinker among rude men, the first man that began to think, was precisely this child-man of Plato's. Simple, open as a child, yet with the depth and strength of a man. Nature had as yet no name to him; he had not yet united under a name the infinite variety of sights, sounds, shapes and motions, which we now collectively name Universe, Nature, or the like,—and so with a name dismiss it from us. To the wild deep-hearted man all was yet new, not veiled under names or formulas; it stood naked, flashing-in on him there, beautiful, awful, unspeakable. Nature was to this man, what to the Thinker and Prophet it forever is, *preter*natural. This green flowery rock-built earth, the trees, the mountains, rivers, many-sounding seas;—that great deep sea of azure that swims overhead; the winds sweeping through it; the black cloud fashioning itself together, now pouring out fire, now hail and rain; what *is* it? Ay, what? At bottom we do not yet know; we can never know at all. It is not by our superior insight that we escape the difficulty; it is by our superior levity, our inattention, our *want* of insight. It is by *not* thinking that we cease to wonder at it. Hardened round us, encasing wholly every notion we form, is a wrappage of traditions, hearsays, mere *words*. We call that fire of the black thundercloud 'electricity,' and lecture learnedly about it, and grind the like of it out of glass and silk: but *what* is it? What made it? Whence comes it? Whither goes it? Science has done much for us; but it is a poor science that would hide from us the great deep sacred infinitude of Nescience, whither we can never penetrate, on which all science swims as a mere super-ficial film. This world, after all our science and sciences, is still a miracle; wonderful, inscrutable, *magical* and more, to whosoever will *think* of it.

That great mystery of TIME, were there no other : the illimitable, silent, never-resting thing called Time, roll-ing, rushing on, swift, silent, like an all-embracing ocean-tide, on which we and all the Universe swim like exhalations, like apparitions which *are*, and then *are not*: this is forever very literally a miracle; a thing to strike us dumb,—for we have no word to speak about it. This Universe, ah me—what could the wild man know of it; what can we yet know? That it is a Force, and thousandfold Complexity of Forces; a Force which is *not we*. That is all; it is not we, it is altogether different from *us*. Force, Force, everywhere Force; we ourselves a mysterious Force in the centre of that. ' There is not a leaf rotting on the highway but has Force in it: how else could it rot?' Nay surely, to the Atheistic Thinker, if such a one were possible, it must be a miracle too, this huge illimitable whirlwind of Force, which envelops us here; never-resting whirlwind, high as Immensity, old as Eternity. What is it? God's creation, the religious people answer; it is the Almighty God's ! Atheistic science babbles poorly of it, with scientific nomenclatures, experiments and what-not, as if it were a poor dead thing, to be bottled up in Leyden jars and sold over counters : but the natural sense of man, in all times, if he will honestly apply his sense, proclaims it to be a living thing,—ah, an unspeakable, godlike thing; towards which the best attitude for us, after never so much science, is <u>awe</u>, devout prostration and humility of soul; worship if not in words, then in silence.

But now I remark farther : What in such a time as ours it requires a Prophet or Poet to teach us, namely, the stripping-off of those poor undevout wrappages, nomenclatures and scientific hearsays,—this, the ancient earnest soul, as yet unencumbered with these things, did for itself. The world, which is now divine only to the gifted, was then divine to whosoever would turn his eye upon it. He stood bare before it face to face. ' All was Godlike or God:'—Jean Paul still finds it so; the giant Jean Paul, who has power to escape out of hearsays: but there then were no hearsays. Canopus shining-down over the desert, with its blue diamond brightness (that wild blue spirit-like brightness, far brighter than we ever witness here), would pierce into the heart of the wild Ishmaelitish man, whom it was guiding through the solitary waste there. To his wild heart, with all feelings in it, with no *speech* for any feeling, it may seem a little eye, that Canopus, glancing-out on him from the great deep Eternity; revealing the inner Splendour to him. Cannot we understand how these men *worshipped* Canopus; became what we call Sabeans, worshipping the stars? Such is to me the secret of all forms of Paganism. Worship is transcendent wonder; wonder for which there is no now no limit or measure; that is worship. To these primeval men, all things and everything they saw exist beside them were an emblem of the Godlike, of some God.

And look what perennial fibre of truth was in that. To us also, through every star, through every blade of grass, is not a God made visible, if we will open our minds and eyes? We do not worship in that way now: but is it not reckoned still a merit, proof of what we call a ' poetic nature,' that we recognise how every object has a divine beauty in it; how every object still verily is ' a window through which we may look into Infinitude itself '? He that can discern the loveliness of things, we call him Poet, Painter, Man of Genius, gifted, lovable. These poor Sabeans did even what he does,— in their own fashion. That they did it, in what fashion soever, was a merit: better than what the entirely stupid man did, what the horse and camel did,—namely, nothing !

But now if all things whatsoever that we look upon are emblems to us of the Highest God, I add that more so than any of them is man such an emblem. You have heard of St. Chrysostom's celebrated saying in reference to the Shekinah, or Ark of Testimony, visible Revelation of God, among the Hebrews : " The true Shekinah is Man !" Yes, it is even so : this is no vain phrase ; it is veritably so. The essence of our being, the mystery in

us that calls itself " I,"—ah, what words have we for
such things?—is a breath of Heaven; the Highest Being
reveals himself in man.   This body, these faculties, this
life of ours, is it not all as a vesture for that Unnamed?
'There is but one Temple in the Universe,' says the
devout Novalis, ' and that is the Body of Man.   Nothing
is holier than that high form.   Bending before men is
a reverence done to this Revelation in the Flesh.   We
touch Heaven when we lay our hand on a human body!'
This sounds much like a mere flourish of rhetoric; but it
is not so.   If well meditated, it will turn out to be a
scientific fact; the expression, in such words as can be
had, of the actual truth of the thing.   *We* are the
miracle of miracles,—the great inscrutable mystery of
God.   We cannot understand it, we know not how to
speak of it; but we may feel and know, if we like, that
it is verily so.

Well; these truths were once more readily felt than
now.   The young generations of the world, who had in
them the freshness of young children, and yet the depth
of earnest men, who did not think that they had finished-
off all things in Heaven and Earth by merely giving
them scientific names, but had to gaze direct at them
there, with awe and wonder: they felt better what of
divinity is in man and Nature;—they, without being
mad, could *worship* Nature, and man more than anything else in Nature.   Worship, that is, as I said above,
admire without limit: this, in the full use of their
faculties, with all sincerity of heart, they could do.   I
consider Hero-worship to be the grand modifying element in that ancient system of thought.   What I called
the perplexed jungle of Paganism sprang, we may say,
out of many roots: every admiration, adoration of a
star or natural object, was a root or fibre of a root; but
Hero-worship is the deepest root of all; the tap-root,
from which in a great degree all the rest were nourished
and grown.

And now if worship even of a star had some meaning
in it, how much more might that of a Hero!   Worship
of a Hero is transcendent admiration of a Great Man.
I say great men are still admirable; I say there is, at
bottom, nothing else admirable!   No nobler feeling

than this of admiration for one higher than himself
dwells in the breast of man. It is to this hour, and at
all hours, the vivifying influence in man's life. Religion
I find stand upon it; not Paganism only, but far higher
and truer religions,—all religion hitherto known. Hero-
worship, heartfelt prostrate admiration, submission,
burning, boundless, for a noblest godlike Form of Man.
—is not that the germ of Christianity itself? The
greatest of all Heroes is One—whom we do not name
here! Let sacred silence meditate that sacred matter;
you will find it the ultimate perfection of a principle
extant throughout man's whole history on earth.

Or coming into lower, less *un*speakable provinces, is
not all Loyalty akin to religious Faith also? Faith is
loyalty to some inspired Teacher, some spiritual Hero.
And what therefore is loyalty proper, the life-breath of
all society, but an effluence of Hero-worship, submissive
admiration for the truly great? Society is founded on
Hero-worship. All dignities of rank, on which human
association rests, are what we may call a *Hero*archy
(Government of Heroes),—or a Hierarchy, for it is
'sacred' enough withal! The Duke means *Dux*,
Leader; King is *Kön-ning*, *Kan-ning*, Man that *knows*
or *cans*. Society everywhere is some representation,
not *in*supportably inaccurate, of a graduated Worship
of Heroes;—reverence and obedience done to men really
great and wise. Not *in*supportably inaccurate, I say!
They are all as bank-notes, these social dignitaries, all
representing gold;—and several of them, alas, always
are *forged* notes. We can do with some forged false
notes; with a good many even; but not with all, or the
most of them forged! No: there have to come revolutions then; cries of Democracy, Liberty, and Equality,
and I know not what:—the notes being all false, and
no gold to be had for *them*, people take to crying in
their despair that there is no gold, that there never was
any!—'Gold,' Hero-worship, *is* nevertheless, as it was
always and everywhere, and cannot cease till man himself ceases.

I am well aware that in these days Hero-worship, the
thing I call Hero-worship, professes to have gone out,
and finally ceased. This, for reasons which it will be

worth while some time to inquire into, is an age that as it were denies the existence of great men; denies the desirableness of great men.   Show our critics a great man, a Luther for example, they begin to what they call ' account ' for him; not to worship him, but take the dimensions of him,—and bring him out to be a little kind of man !   He was the ' creature of the Time,' they say; the Time called him forth, the Time did everything, he nothing—but what we the little critic could have done too !   This seems to me but melancholy work.   The Time call forth?   Alas, we have known Times *call* loudly enough for their great man; but not find him when they called !   He was not there; Providence had not sent him; the Time, *calling* its loudest, had to go down to confusion and wreck because he would not come when called.

For if we will think of it, no Time need have gone to ruin, could it have *found* a man great enough, a man wise and good enough: wisdom to discern truly what the Time wanted, valour to lead it on the right road thither; these are the salvation of any Time.   But I liken common languid Times, with their unbelief, distress, perplexity, with their languid doubting characters and embarrassed circumstances, impotently crumbling-down into ever worse distress towards final ruin;—all this I liken to dry dead fuel, waiting for the lightning out of Heaven that shall kindle it.   The great man, with his free force direct out of God's own hand, is the lightning.   His word is the wise healing word which all can believe in.   All blazes round him now, when he has once struck on it, into fire like his own.   The dry mouldering sticks are thought to have called him forth.   They did want him greatly; but as to calling him forth— !—Those are critics of small vision, I think, who cry : '' See, is it not the sticks that made the fire?''   No sadder proof can be given by a man of his own littleness than disbelief in great men.   There is no sadder symptom of a generation than such general blindness to the spiritual lightning, with faith only in the heap of barren dead fuel.   It is the last consummation of unbelief.   In all epochs of the world's history, we shall find the Great Man to have been the indispensable saviour of his epoch;—the lightning, without which the fuel never would have burnt. The History of the World, I said already, was the Biography of Great Men.

Such small critics do what they can to promote unbelief and universal spiritual paralysis; but happily they cannot always completely succeed. In all times it is possible for a man to arise great enough to feel that they and their doctrines are chimeras and cobwebs. And what is notable, in no time whatever can they entirely eradicate out of living men's hearts a certain altogether peculiar reverence for Great Men; genuine admiration, loyalty, adoration, however dim and perverted it may be. Hero-worship endures for ever while man endures. Boswell venerates his Johnson, right truly even in the Eighteenth century. The unbelieving French believe in their Voltaire; and burst-out round him into very curious Hero-worship, in that last act of his life when they ' stifle him under roses.' It has always seemed to me extremely curious this of Voltaire. Truly, if Christianity be the highest instance of Hero-worship, then we may find here in Voltaireism one of the lowest! He whose life was that of a kind of Antichrist, does again on this side exhibit a curious contrast. No people ever were so little prone to admire at all as those French of Voltaire. *Persiflage* was the character of their whole mind; adoration had nowhere a place in it. Yet see! The old man of Ferney comes up to Paris; an old, tottering, infirm man of eighty-four years. They feel that he too is a kind of Hero; that he has spent his life in opposing error and injustice, delivering Calases, unmasking hypocrites in high places;—in short that *he* too, though in a strange way, has fought like a valiant man. They feel withal that, if *persiflage* be the great thing, there never was such a *persifleur*. He is the realised ideal of every one of them; the thing they are all wanting to be; of all Frenchmen the most French. *He* is properly their god,—such god as they are fit for. Accordingly all persons, from the Queen Antoinette to the Douanier at the Porte St. Denis, do they not worship him? People of quality disguise themselves as tavern-waiters. The Maître de Poste, with a broad oath,

orders his Postillion, " *Va bon train;* thou art driving
M. de Voltaire." At Paris his carriage is ' the nucleus
of a comet, whose train fills whole streets.' The ladies
pluck a hair or two from his fur, to keep it as a sacred
relic. There was nothing highest, beautifulest, noblest
in all France, that did not feel this man to be higher,
beautifuler, nobler.

Yes, from Norse Odin to English Samuel Johnson,
from the divine Founder of Christianity to the withered
Pontiff of Encyclopedism, in all times and places, the
Hero has been worshipped. It will ever be so. We all
love great men; love, venerate, and bow down submissive before great men : nay can we honestly bow down
to anything else? Ah, does not every true man feel
that he is himself made higher by doing reverence to
what is really above him? No nobler or more blessed
feeling dwells in man's heart. And to me it is very
cheering to consider that no sceptical logic, or general
triviality, insincerity and aridity of any Time and its
influences can destroy this noble inborn loyalty and
worship that is in man. In times of unbelief, which
soon have to become times of revolution, much down-
rushing, sorrowful decay and ruin is visible to everybody. For myself in these days, I seem to see in
this indestructibility of Hero-worship the everlasting
adamant lower than which the confused wreck of
revolutionary things cannot fall. The confused wreck
of things crumbling and even crashing and tumbling all
round us in these revolutionary ages, will get down so
far; *no* farther. It is an eternal corner-stone, from
which they can begin to build themselves up again. That
man, in some sense or other, worships Heroes; that we
all of us reverence and must ever reverence Great Men :
this is, to me, the living rock amid all rushings-down
whatsoever;—the one fixed point in modern revolutionary history, otherwise as if bottomless and shoreless.

So much of truth, only under an ancient obsolete
vesture, but the spirit of it still true, do I find in the
Paganism of old nations. Nature is still divine, the
revelation of the workings of God; the Hero is still
worshipable : this, under poor cramped incipient forms,

is what all Pagan religions have struggled, as they
could, to set forth. I think Scandinavian Paganism, to
us here, is more interesting than any other. It is, for
one thing, the latest; it continued in these regions of
Europe till the eleventh century : eight-hundred years
ago the Norwegians were still worshippers of Odin. It
is interesting also as the creed of our fathers; the men
whose blood still runs in our veins, whom doubtless we
still resemble in so many ways. Strange : they did
believe that, while we believe so differently. Let us
look a little at this poor Norse creed, for many reasons.
We have tolerable means to do it; for there is another
point of interest in these Scandinavian mythologies :
that they have been preserved so well.

In that strange island Iceland,—burst-up, the
geologists say, by fire from the bottom of the sea;
a wild land of barrenness and lava; swallowed many
months of every year in black tempests, yet with a wild
gleaming beauty in summer-time; towering up there,
stern and grim, in the North Ocean; with its snow
jokuls, roaring geysers, sulphur-pools and horrid volcanic
chasms, like the waste chaotic battle-field of Frost and
Fire;—where of all places we least looked for Literature or written memorials, the record of these things
was written down. On the seaboard of this wild land
is a rim of grassy country, where cattle can subsist,
and men by means of them and of what the sea yields;
and it seems they were poetic men these, men who had
deep thoughts in them, and uttered musically their
thoughts. Much would be lost, had Iceland not been
burst-up from the sea, not been discovered by the
Northmen ! The old Norse Poets were many of them
natives of Iceland.

Sæmund, one of the early Christian Priests there,
who perhaps had a lingering fondness for Paganism,
collected certain of their old Pagan songs, just about
becoming obsolete then,—Poems or Chants of a
mythic, prophetic, mostly all of a religious character :
that is what Norse critics call the *Elder* or Poetic
Edda. *Edda*, a word of uncertain etymology, is
thought to signify *Ancestress*. Snorro Sturleson, an
Iceland gentleman, an extremely notable personage,

254 On Heroes, Hero-Worship

educated by this Sæmund's grandson, took in hand next, near a century afterwards, to put together, among several other books he wrote, a kind of Prose Synopsis of the whole Mythology; elucidated by new fragments of traditionary verse. A work constructed really with great ingenuity, native talent, what one might call unconscious art; altogether a perspicuous clear work, pleasant reading still : this is the *Younger* or *Prose Edda*. By these and the numerous other *Sagas*, mostly Icelandic, with the commentaries, Icelandic or not, which go on zealously in the North to this day, it is possible to gain some direct insight even yet; and see that old Norse system of Belief, as it were, face to face. Let us forget that it is erroneous Religion; let us look at it as old Thought, and try if we cannot sympathise with it somewhat.

The primary characteristic of this old Northland Mythology I find to be Impersonation of the visible workings of Nature. Earnest simple recognition of the workings of Physical Nature, as a thing wholly miraculous, stupendous and divine. What we now lecture of as Science, they wondered at, and fell down in awe before, as Religion. The dark hostile powers of Nature they figure to themselves as '*Jötuns*,' Giants, huge shaggy beings of a demonic character. Frost, Fire, Sea-tempest; these are Jötuns. The friendly powers again, as Summer-heat, the Sun, are Gods. The empire of this Universe is divided between these two; they dwell apart, in perennial internecine feud. The Gods dwell above in Asgard, the Garden of the Asen, or Divinities; Jötunheim, a distant dark chaotic land, is the home of the Jötuns.

Curious all this; and not idle or inane, if we will look at the foundation of it! The power of *Fire*, or *Flame*, for instance, which we designate by some trivial chemical name, thereby hiding from ourselves the essential character of wonder that dwells in it as in all things, is with these old Northmen, Loke, a most swift subtle *Demon*, of the brood of the Jötuns. The savages of the Ladrones Islands too (say some Spanish voyagers) thought Fire, which they never had seen before, was a devil or god, that bit you sharply when you touched it, and that lived upon dry wood. From us too no Chemistry, if it had not Stupidity to help it, would hide that Flame is a wonder. What *is* Flame?—*Frost* the old Norse Seer discerns to be a monstrous hoary Jötun, the Giant *Thrym, Hrym:* or *Rime,* the old word now nearly obsolete here, but still used in Scotland to signify hoar-frost. *Rime* was not then as now a dead chemical thing, but a living Jötun or Devil; the monstrous Jötun *Rime* drove home his Horses at night, sat ' combing their manes,'—which Horses were *Hail-Clouds,* or fleet *Frost-Winds.* His Cows—No, not his, but a kinsman's, the Giant Hymir's Cows are *Icebergs:* this Hymir ' looks at the rocks ' with his devil-eye, and they *split* in the glance of it.

Thunder was not then mere Electricity, vitreous or resinous; it was the God Donner (Thunder) or Thor,—God also of beneficent Summer-heat. The thunder was his wrath; the gathering of the black clouds is the drawing down of Thor's angry brows; the fire-bolt bursting out of Heaven is the all-rending Hammer flung from the hand of Thor: he urges his loud chariot over the mountain-tops,—that is the peal: wrathful he ' blows in his red beard,'—that is the rustling storm-blast before the thunder begin. Balder again, the White God, the beautiful, the just and benignant (whom the early Christian Missionaries found to resemble Christ), is the Sun —beautifulest of visible things; wondrous too, and divine still, after all our Astronomies and Almanacs! But perhaps the notablest god we hear tell-of is one of whom Grimm the German Etymologist finds trace: the God *Wünsch,* or Wish. The God *Wish;* who could give us all that we *wished!* Is not this the sincerest yet rudest voice of the spirit of man? The *rudest* ideal that man ever formed; which still shows itself in the latest forms of our spiritual culture. Higher considerations have to teach us that the God *Wish* is not the true God.

Of the other Gods or Jötuns I will mention only for etymology's sake, that Sea-tempest is the Jötun *Aegir,* a very dangerous Jötun;—and now to this day, on our river Trent, as I learn, the Nottingham bargemen, when the River is in a certain flooded state (a kind of back-

water, or eddying swirl it has, very dangerous to them),
call it *Eager;* they cry out, " Have a care, there is the
Eager coming !" Curious; that word surviving, like
the peak of a submerged world ! The *oldest* Nottingham bargemen had believed in the God Aegir.   Indeed,
our English blood too in good part is Danish, Norse;
or rather, at bottom, Danish and Norse and Saxon
have no distinction, except a superficial one,—as of
Heathen and Christian, or the like.   But all over our
Island we are mingled largely with Danes proper,—
from the incessant invasions there were : and this, of
course, in a greater proportion along the east coast;
and greatest of all, as I find, in the North Country.
From the Humber upwards, all over Scotland, the
Speech of the common people is still in a singular degree
Icelandic; its Germanism has still a peculiar Norse
tinge.   They too are ' Normans,' Northmen,—if that
be any great beauty !—

Of the chief god, Odin, we shall speak by and by.
Mark at present so much; what the essence of Scandinavian and indeed of all Paganism is : a recognition
of the forces of Nature as godlike, stupendous, personal
Agencies,—as Gods and Demons.   Not inconceivable
to us.   It is the infant Thought of man opening itself,
with awe and wonder, on this ever-stupendous Universe.
To me there is in the Norse System something very
genuine, very great and manlike.   A broad simplicity,
rusticity, so very different from the light gracefulness
of the old Greek Paganism, distinguishes this Scandinavian System.   It is Thought; the genuine Thought
of deep, rude, earnest minds, fairly opened to the things
about them; a face-to-face and heart-to-heart inspection
of the things,—the first characteristic of all good
Thought in all times.   Not graceful lightness, half-
sport, as in the Greek Paganism; a certain homely
truthfulness and rustic strength, a great rude sincerity,
discloses itself here.   It is strange, after our beautiful
Apollo statues and clear smiling mythuses, to come
down upon the Norse Gods ' brewing ale ' to hold their
feast with Aegir, the Sea-Jötun; sending out Thor to
get the caldron for them in the Jötun country; Thor,
after many adventures, clapping the Pot on his head,

like a huge hat, and walking off with it,—quite lost in it, the ears of the Pot reaching down to his heels! A kind of vacant hugeness, large awkward gianthood, characterises that Norse System; enormous force, as yet altogether untutored, stalking helpless with large uncertain strides. Consider only their primary mythus of the Creation. The Gods, having got the Giant Ymer slain, a Giant made by 'warm wind,' and much confused work, out of the conflict of Frost and Fire,— determined on constructing a world with him. His blood made the sea; his flesh was the Land, the Rocks his bones; of his eyebrows they formed Asgard their Gods'-dwelling; his skull was the great blue vault of Immensity, and the brains of it became the Clouds. What a Hyper-Brobdignagian business! Untamed Thought, great, giantlike, enormous;—to be tamed in due time into the compact greatness, not giant-like, but godlike and stronger than gianthood, of the Shakspeares, the Goethes!—Spiritually as well as bodily these men are our progenitors.

I like, too, that representation they have of the Tree Igdrasil. All Life is figured by them as a Tree. Igdrasil, the Ash-tree of Existence, has its roots deep-down in the kingdoms of Hela or Death; its trunk reaches up heaven-high, spreads its boughs over the whole Universe: it is the Tree of Existence. At the foot of it, in the Death-kingdom, sit three *Nornas, Fates,*—the Past, Present, Future; watering its roots from the Sacred Well. Its 'boughs,' with their buddings and disleafings,—events, things suffered, things done, catastrophes,—stretch through all lands and times. Is not every leaf of it a biography, every fibre there an act or word? Its boughs are Histories of Nations. The rustle of it is the noise of Human Existence, onwards from of old. It grows there, the breath of Human Passion rustling through it;—or stormtost, the stormwind howling through it like the voice of all the gods. It is Igdrasil, the Tree of Existence. It is the past, the present, and the future; what was done, what is doing, what will be done; 'the infinite conjugation of the verb *To do.*' Considering how human things circulate, each inextricably in communion with all,—how the word I speak to you to-day is borrowed, not from Ulfila the Mœsogoth only, but from all men since the first man began to speak,—I find no similitude so true as this of a Tree. Beautiful; altogether beautiful and great. The '*Machine* of the Universe,'—alas, do but think of that in contrast!

Well, it is strange enough this old Norse view of Nature; different enough from what we believe of Nature. Whence it specially came, one would not like to be compelled to say very minutely! One thing we may say: It came from the thoughts of Norse men;—from the thought, above all, of the *first* Norse man who had an original power of thinking. The First Norse 'man of genius,' as we should call him! Innumerable men had passed by, across this Universe, with a dumb vague wonder, such as the very animals may feel; or with a painful, fruitlessly inquiring wonder, such as men only feel;—till the great Thinker came, the *original* man, the Seer; whose shaped spoken Thought awakes the slumbering capability of all into Thought. It is ever the way with the Thinker, the spiritual Hero. What he says, all men were not far from saying, were longing to say. The Thoughts of all start up, as from painful enchanted sleep, round his Thought; answering to it, Yes, even so! Joyful to men as the dawning of day from night; *is* it not, indeed, the awakening for them from no-being into being, from death into life? We still honour such a man; call him Poet, Genius, and so forth: but to these wild men he was a very magician, a worker of miraculous unexpected blessing for them; a Prophet, a God!—Thought once awakened does not again slumber; unfolds itself into a System of Thought; grows, in man after man, generation after generation,—till its full stature is reached, and *such* System of Thought can grow no farther, but must give place to another.

For the Norse people, the Man now named Odin, and Chief Norse God, we fancy, was such a man. A Teacher, and Captain of soul and of body; a Hero, of worth *im*measurable; admiration for whom, transcending the known bounds, became adoration. Has he not the power of articulate Thinking; and many other powers, as yet miraculous? So, with boundless gratitude, would the rude Norse heart feel. Has he not solved for them the sphinx-enigma of this Universe; given assurance to them of their own destiny there? By him they know now what they have to do here, what to look for hereafter. Existence has become articulate, melodious by him; he first has made Life alive!—We may call this Odin, the origin of Norse Mythology: Odin, or whatever name the First Norse Thinker bore while he was a man among men. His view of the Universe once promulgated, a like view starts into being in all minds; grows, keeps ever growing, while it continues credible there. In all minds it lay written, but invisibly, as in sympathetic ink; at his word it starts into visibility in all. Nay, in every epoch of the world, the great event, parent of all others, is it not the arrival of a Thinker in the world!—

One other thing we must not forget; it will explain, a little, the confusion of these Norse Eddas. They are not one coherent System of Thought; but properly the *summation* of several successive systems. All this of the old Norse Belief which is flung-out for us, in one level of distance in the Edda, like a picture painted on the same canvas, does not at all stand so in the reality. It stands rather at all manner of distances and depths, of successive generations since the Belief first began. All Scandinavian thinkers, since the first of them, contributed to the Scandinavian System of Thought; in ever-new elaboration and addition, it is the combined work of them all. What history it had, how it changed from shape to shape, by one thinker's contribution after another, till it got to the full final shape we see it under in the *Edda,* no man will now ever know: *its* Councils of Trebisond, Councils of Trent, Athanasiuses, Dantes, Luthers, are sunk without echo in the dark night! Only that it had such a history we can all know. Wheresoever a thinker appeared, there in the thing he thought-of was a contribution, accession, a change or revolution made. Alas, the grandest 'revolution' of all, the one made by the man Odin himself, is not this too sunk for us like the rest! Of Odin what history?

Strange rather to reflect that he *had* a history! That this Odin, in his wild Norse vesture, with his wild beard and eyes, his rude Norse speech and ways, was a man like us; with our sorrows, joys, with our limbs, features;—intrinsically all one as we: and did such a work! But the work, much of it, has perished; the worker, all to the name. " *Wednes*day," men will say to-morrow; Odin's day! Of Odin there exists no history; no document of it; no guess about it worth repeating.

Snorro indeed, in the quietest manner, almost in a brief business style, writes down, in his *Heimskringla,* how Odin was a heroic Prince, in the Black-Sea region, with Twelve Peers, and a great people straitened for room. How he led these *Asen* (Asiatics) of his out of Asia; settled them in the North parts of Europe, by warlike conquest; invented Letters, Poetry and so forth,—and came by and by to be worshipped as Chief God by these Scandinavians, his Twelve Peers made into Twelve Sons of his own, Gods like himself: Snorro has no doubt of this. Saxo Grammaticus, a very curious Northman of that same century, is still more unhesitating; scruples not to find out a historical fact in every individual mythus, and writes it down as a terrestrial event in Denmark or elsewhere. Torfæus, learned and cautious, some centuries later, assigns by calculation a *date* for it: Odin, he says, came into Europe about the Year 70 before Christ. Of all which, as grounded on mere uncertainties, found to be untenable now, I need say nothing. Far, very far beyond the Year 70! Odin's date, adventures, whole terrestrial history, figure and environment are sunk from us forever into unknown thousands of years.

Nay Grimm, the German Antiquary, goes so far as to deny that any man Odin ever existed. He proves it by etymology. The word *Wuotan,* which is the original form of *Odin,* a word spread, as name of their chief Divinity, over all the Teutonic Nations everywhere; this word, which connects itself, according to Grimm, with the Latin *vadere,* with the English *wade* and suchlike, —means primarily *Movement,* Source of Movement, Power; and is the fit name of the highest god, not of

any man. The word signifies Divinity, he says, among
the old Saxon, German and all Teutonic Nations ; the
adjectives formed from it all signify *divine, supreme,*
or something pertaining to the chief god. Like enough !
We must bow to Grimm in matters etymological. Let
us consider it fixed that *Wuotan* means *Wading,* force
of *Movement.* And now still, what hinders it from
being the name of a Heroic Man and *Mover,* as well
as of a god? As for the adjectives, and words formed
from it,—did not the Spaniards in their universal
admiration for Lope, get into the habit of saying ' a
Lope flower,' a ' Lope *dama,*' if the flower or woman
were of surpassing beauty? Had this lasted, *Lope*
would have grown, in Spain, to be an adjective signifying *godlike* also. Indeed, Adam Smith, in his *Essay
on Language,* surmises that all adjectives whatsoever
were formed precisely in that way : some very green
thing chiefly notable for its greenness, got the appel-
lative name *Green,* and then the next thing remarkable
for that quality, a tree for instance, was named the
green tree,—as we still say ' the *steam* coach,' ' four-
horse coach,' or the like. All primary adjectives,
according to Smith, were formed in this way ; were at
first substantives and things. We cannot annihilate a
man for etymologies like that ! Surely there was a
First Teacher and Captain ; surely there must have been
an Odin, palpable to the sense at one time ; no adjective, but a real Hero of flesh and blood ! The voice
of all tradition, history or echo of history, agrees with
all that thought will teach one about it, to assure us
of this.

How the man Odin came to be considered a *god,* the
chief god?—that surely is a question which nobody
would wish to dogmatise upon. I have said, his people
knew no *limits* to their admiration of him ; they had as
yet no scale to measure admiration by. Fancy your
own generous heart's-love of some greatest man ex-
panding till it *transcended* all bounds, till it filled and
overflowed the whole field of your thought ! Or what
if this man Odin,—since a great deep soul, with the
afflatus and mysterious tide of vision and impulse rushing on him he knows not whence, is ever an enigma,

a kind of terror and wonder to himself,—should have felt that perhaps *he* was divine; that *he* was some effluence of the ' Wuotan,' ' *Movement*,' Supreme Power and Divinity, of whom to his rapt vision all Nature was the awful Flame-image; that some effluence of *Wuotan* dwelt here in him! He was not necessarily false; he was but mistaken, speaking the truest he knew. A great soul, any sincere soul, knows not *what* he is,—alternates between the highest height and the lowest depth; can, of all things, the least measure—Himself! What others take him for, and what he guesses that he may be; these two items strangely act on one another, help to determine one another. With all men reverently admiring him; with his own wild soul full of noble ardours and affections, of whirlwind chaotic darkness and glorious new light; a divine Universe bursting all into godlike beauty round him, and no man to whom the like ever had befallen, what could he think himself to be? "Wuotan?" All men answered, "Wuotan!"—

And then consider what mere Time will do in such cases; how if a man was great while living, he becomes tenfold greater when dead. What an enormous *camera-obscura* magnifier is Tradition! How a thing grows in the human Memory, in the human Imagination, when love, worship and all that lies in the human Heart, is there to encourage it. And in the darkness, in the entire ignorance; without date or document, no book, no Arundel-marble; only here and there some dumb monumental cairn. Why, in thirty or forty years, were there no books, any great man would grow *mythic*, the contemporaries who had once seen him, being all dead. And in three-hundred years, and three-thousand years —!—To attempt *theorising* on such matters would profit little : they are matters which refuse to be *theoremed* and diagramed; which Logic ought to know that she *cannot* speak of. Enough for us to discern, far in the uttermost distance, some gleam as of a small real light shining in the centre of that enormous camera-obscura image; to discern that the centre of it all was not a madness and nothing, but a sanity and something.

This light, kindled in the great dark vortex of the

Norse mind, dark but living, waiting only for light; this is to me the centre of the whole. How such light will then shine out, and with wondrous thousandfold expansion spread itself, in forms and colours, depends not on *it,* so much as on the National Mind recipient of it. The colours and forms of your light will be those of the *cut-glass* it has to shine through.—Curious to think how, for every man, any the truest fact is modelled by the nature of the man! I said, The earnest man, speaking to his brother men, must always have stated what seemed to him a *fact,* a real Appearance of Nature. But the way in which such Appearance or fact shaped itself,—what sort of *fact* it became for him,—was and is modified by his own laws of thinking; deep, subtle, but universal, ever-operating laws. The world of Nature, for every man, is the Phantasy of Himself; this world is the multiplex 'Image of his own Dream.' Who knows to what unnameable subtleties of spiritual law all these Pagan Fables owe their shape! The number *Twelve,* divisiblest of all, which could be halved, quartered, parted into three, into six, the most remarkable number,—this was enough to determine the *Signs of the Zodiac,* the number of Odin's *Sons,* and innumerable other Twelves. Any vague rumour of number had a tendency to settle itself into Twelve. So with regard to every other matter. And quite unconsciously too,— with no notion of building-up 'Allegories'! But the fresh clear glance of those First Ages would be prompt in discerning the secret relations of things, and wholly open to obey these. Schiller finds in the *Cestus of Venus* an everlasting æsthetic truth as to the nature of all Beauty; curious :—but he is careful not to insinuate that the old Greek Mythists had any notion of lecturing about the 'Philosophy of Criticism'!——On the whole we must leave those boundless regions. Cannot we conceive that Odin was a reality? Error indeed, error enough : but sheer falsehood, idle fables, allegory aforethought,—we will not believe that our Fathers believed in these.

Odin's *Runes* are a significant feature of him. Runes, and the miracles of 'magic' he worked by them, make

*K 278

a great feature in tradition. Runes are the Scandinavian Alphabet; suppose Odin to have been the inventor
of Letters, as well as ' magic,' among that people! It
is the greatest invention man has ever made, this of
marking-down the unseen thought that is in him by
written characters. It is a kind of second speech,
almost as miraculous as the first. You remember the
astonishment and incredulity of Atahualpa the Peruvian
King; how he made the Spanish Soldier who was guarding him scratch *Dios* on his thumb-nail, that he might
try the next soldier with it, to ascertain whether such
a miracle was possible. If Odin brought Letters among
his people, he might work magic enough!

Writing by Runes has some air of being original
among the Norsemen: not a Phœnician Alphabet, but
a native Scandinavian one. Snorro tells us farther that
Odin invented Poetry; the music of human speech, as
well as that miraculous runic marking of it. Transport
yourselves into the early childhood of nations; the first
beautiful morning-light of our Europe, when all yet lay
in fresh young radiance as of a great sunrise, and our
Europe was first beginning to think, to be! Wonder,
hope; infinite radiance of hope and wonder, as of a
young child's thoughts, in the hearts of these strong
men! Strong sons of Nature; and here was not only
a wild Captain and Fighter; discerning with his wild
flashing eyes what to do, with his wild lion-heart daring
and doing it; but a Poet too, all that we mean by a
Poet, Prophet, great devout Thinker and Inventor,—
as the truly Great Man ever is. A Hero is a Hero
at all points; in the soul and thought of him first of all.
This Odin, in his rude semi-articulate way, had a word
to speak. A great heart laid open to take in this great
Universe, and man's Life here, and utter a great word
about it. A Hero, as I say, in his own rude manner;
a wise, gifted, noble-hearted man. And now, if we still
admire such a man beyond all others, what must these
wild Norse souls, first awakened into thinking, have
made of him! To them, as yet without names for it,
he was noble and noblest; Hero, Prophet, God;
Wuotan, the greatest of all. Thought is Thought,
however it speak or spell itself. Intrinsically, I con-

jecture, this Odin must have been of the same sort of stuff as the greatest kind of men. A great thought in the wild deep heart of him! The rough words he articulated, are they not the rudimental roots of those English words we still use? He worked so, in that obscure element. But he was as a *light* kindled in it; a light of Intellect, rude Nobleness of heart, the only kind of lights we have yet; a Hero, as I say: and he had to shine there, and make his obscure element a little lighter,—as is still the task of us all.

We will fancy him to be the Type Norseman; the finest Teuton whom that race had yet produced. The rude Norse heart burst-up into *boundless* admiration round him; into adoration. He is as a root of so many great things; the fruit of him is found growing, from deep thousands of years, over the whole field of Teutonic Life. Our own Wednesday, as I said, is it not still Odin's Day? Wednesbury, Wansborough, Wanstead, Wandsworth: Odin grew into England too, these are still leaves from that root! He was the Chief God to all the Teutonic Peoples; their Pattern Norseman;—in such way did *they* admire their Pattern Norseman; that was the fortune he had in the world.

Thus if the man Odin himself have vanished utterly, there is this huge Shadow of him which still projects itself over the whole History of his People. For this Odin once admitted to be God, we can understand well that the whole Scandinavian Scheme of Nature, or dim No-scheme, whatever it might before have been, would now begin to develop itself altogether differently, and grow thenceforth in a new manner. What this Odin saw into, and taught with his runes and his rhymes, the whole Teutonic People laid to heart and carried forward. His way of thought became their way of thought:—such, under new conditions, is the history of every great thinker still. In gigantic confused lineaments, like some enormous camera-obscura shadow thrown upwards from the dead deeps of the Past, and covering the whole Northern Heaven, is not that Scandinavian Mythology in some sort the Portraiture of this man Odin? The gigantic image of *his* natural face, legible or not legible there, expanded and confused in that manner! Ah, Thought, I say, is always Thought. No great man lives in vain. The History of the world is but the Biography of great men.

To me there is something very touching in this primeval figure of Heroism; in such artless, helpless, but hearty entire reception of a Hero by his fellow-men. Never so helpless in shape, it is the noblest of feelings, and a feeling in some shape or other perennial as man himself. If I could show in any measure, what I feel deeply for a long time now, That it is the vital element of manhood, the soul of man's history here in our world,—it would be the chief use of this discoursing at present. We do not now call our great men Gods, nor admire *without* limit; ah, no, *with* limit enough! But if we have no great men, or do not admire at all,— that were a still worse case.

This poor Scandinavian Hero-worship, that whole Norse way of looking at the Universe, and adjusting oneself there, has an indestructible merit for us. A rude childlike way of recognising the divineness of Nature, the divineness of Man; most rude, yet heart-felt, robust, giantlike; betokening what a giant of a man this child would grow to!—It was a truth, and is none. Is it not as the half-dumb stifled voice of the long-buried generations of our own Fathers, calling out of the depths of ages to us, in whose veins their blood still runs: "This then, this is what *we* made of the world: this is all the image and notion we could form to ourselves of this great mystery of a Life and Universe. Despise it not. You are raised high above it, to large free scope of vision; but you too are not yet at the top. No, your notion too, so much enlarged, is but a partial, imperfect one: that matter is a thing no man will ever, in time or out of time, comprehend; after thousands of years of ever-new expansion, man will find himself but struggling to comprehend again a part of it: the thing is larger than man, not to be comprehended by him; an Infinite thing!"

The essence of the Scandinavian, as indeed of all Pagan Mythologies, we found to be recognition of the divineness of Nature; sincere communion of man with the mysterious invisible Powers visibly seen at work in the world round him. This, I should say, is more sincerely done in the Scandinavian than in any Mythology I know. Sincerity is the great characteristic of it. Superior sincerity (far superior) consoles us for the total want of old Grecian grace. Sincerity, I think, is better than grace. I feel that these old Northmen were looking into Nature with open eye and soul: most earnest, honest; childlike, and yet manlike; with a great-hearted simplicity and depth and freshness, in a true, loving, admiring, unfearing way. A right valiant, true old race of men. Such recognition of Nature one finds to be the chief element of Paganism: recognition of Man, and his Moral Duty, though this too is not wanting, comes to be the chief element only in purer forms of religion. Here, indeed, is a great distinction and epoch in Human Beliefs; a great landmark in the religious development of Mankind. Man first puts himself in relation with Nature and her Powers, wonders and worships over those; not till a later epoch does he discern that all Power is Moral, that the grand point is the distinction for him of Good and Evil, of *Thou shalt* and *Thou shalt not*.

With regard to all these fabulous delineations in the *Edda,* I will remark, moreover, as indeed was already hinted, that most probably they must have been of much newer date; most probably, even from the first, were comparatively idle for the old Norsemen, and as it were a kind of Poetic sport. Allegory and Poetic Delineation, as I said above, cannot be religious Faith; the Faith itself must first be there, then Allegory enough will gather round it, as the fit body round its soul. The Norse Faith, I can well suppose, like other Faiths, was most active while it lay mainly in the silent state, and had not yet much to say about itself, still less to sing.

Among those shadowy *Edda* matters, amid all that fantastic congeries of assertions, and traditions, in their musical Mythologies, the main practical belief a man could have was probably not much more than this: of the *Valkyrs* and the *Hall of Odin;* of an inflexible *Destiny;* and that the one thing needful for a man was *to be brave.* The *Valkyrs* are Choosers of the Slain : a Destiny inexorable, which it is useless trying to bend or soften, has appointed who is to be slain ; this was a fundamental point for the Norse believer ;—as indeed it is for all earnest men everywhere, for a Mahomet, a Luther, for a Napoleon too. It lies at the basis this for every such man ; it is the woof out of which his whole system of thought is woven. The *Valkyrs;* and then that these *Choosers* lead the brave to a heavenly *Hall of Odin;* only the base and slavish being thrust elsewhither, into the realms of Hela the Death-goddess : I take this to have been the soul of the whole Norse Belief. They understood in their heart that it was indispensable to be brave; that Odin would have no favour for them, but despise and thrust them out, if they were not brave. Consider too whether there is not something in this ! It is an everlasting duty, valid in our day as in that, the duty of being brave. *Valour* is still *value.* The first duty of a man is still that of subduing *Fear.* We must get rid of Fear; we cannot act at all till then. A man's acts are slavish, not true but specious : his very thoughts are false, he thinks too as a slave and coward, till he have got Fear under his feet. Odin's creed, if we disentangle the real kernel of it, is true to this hour. A man shall and must be valiant; he must march forward, and quit himself like a man—trusting imperturbably in the appointment and *choice* of the upper Powers ; and, on the whole, not fear at all. Now and always, the completeness of his victory over Fear will determine how much of a man he is.

It is doubtless very savage that kind of valour of the old Northmen. Snorro tells us they thought it a shame and misery not to die in battle; and if natural death seemed to be coming on, they would cut wounds in their flesh, that Odin might receive them as warriors slain. Old kings, about to die, had their body laid into a ship; the ship sent forth, with sails set and slow fire burning it; that, once out at sea, it might blaze-up in flame, and in such manner bury worthily the old hero, at once in the sky and in the ocean ! Wild bloody valour; yet valour of its kind; better, I say, than none. In the old Sea-kings too, what an indomitable rugged energy! Silent, with closed lips, as I fancy them, unconscious that they were specially brave; defying the wild ocean with its monsters, and all men and things;—progenitors of our own Blakes and Nelsons! No Homer sang these Norse Sea-kings; but Agamemnon's was a small audacity, and of small fruit in the world, to some of them;—to Hrolf's of Normandy, for instance! Hrolf, or Rollo Duke of Normandy, the wild Sea-king, has a share in governing England at this hour.

Nor was it altogether nothing, even that wild sea-roving and battling, through so many generations. It needed to be ascertained which was the *strongest* kind of men; who were to be ruler over whom. Among the Northland Sovereigns, too, I find some who got the title *Wood-cutter;* Forest-felling Kings. Much lies in that. I suppose at bottom many of them were forest-fellers as well as fighters, though the Skalds talk mainly of the latter,—misleading certain critics not a little; for no nation of men could ever live by fighting alone; there could not produce enough come out of that! I suppose the right good fighter was oftenest also the right good forest-feller,—the right good improver, discerner, doer and worker in every kind; for true valour, different enough from ferocity, is the basis of all. A more legitimate kind of valour that; showing itself against the untamed Forests and dark brute Powers of Nature, to conquer Nature for us. In the same direction have not we their descendants since carried it far? May such valour last forever with us!

That the man Odin, speaking with a Hero's voice and heart, as with an impressiveness out of Heaven, told his People the infinite importance of Valour, how man thereby became a god; and that his People, feeling a response to it in their own hearts, believed this message of his, and thought it a message out of Heaven, and him a Divinity for telling it them: this seems to me the primary seed-grain of the Norse Religion, from which all manner of mythologies, symbolic practices, speculations, allegories, songs and sagas would naturally grow. Grow,—how strangely! I called it a small light shining and shaping in the huge vortex of Norse darkness. Yet the darkness itself was *alive;* consider that. It was the eager inarticulate uninstructed Mind of the whole Norse People, longing only to become articulate, to go on articulating ever farther! The living doctrine grows, grows;—like a Banyan-tree; the first *seed* is the essential thing : any branch strikes itself down into the earth, becomes a new root; and so, in endless complexity, we have a whole wood, a whole jungle, one seed the parent of it all. Was not the whole Norse Religion, accordingly, in some sense, what we called ' the enormous shadow of this man's likeness '? Critics trace some affinity in some Norse mythuses, of the Creation and suchlike, with those of the Hindoos. The Cow Adumbla, ' licking the rime from the rocks,' has a kind of Hindoo look. A Hindoo Cow, transported into frosty countries. Probably enough; indeed we may say undoubtedly, these things will have a kindred with the remotest lands, with the earliest times. Thought does not die, but only is changed. The first man that began to think in this Planet of ours, he was the beginner of all. And then the second man, and the third man :—nay, every true Thinker to this hour is a kind of Odin, teaches men *his* way of thought, spreads a shadow of his own likeness over sections of the History of the World.

Of the distinctive poetic character or merit of this Norse Mythology I have not room to speak; nor does it concern us much. Some wild Prophecies we have, as the *Völuspa* in the *Elder Edda;* of a rapt, earnest, sibylline sort. But they were comparatively an idle adjunct of the matter, men who as it were but toyed with the matter, these later Skalds; and it is *their* songs chiefly that survive. In later centuries, I suppose, they would go on singing, poetically symbolising, as our modern Painters paint, when it was no longer from the innermost heart, or not from the heart at all. This is everywhere to be well kept in mind.

Gray's fragments of Norse Lore, at any rate, will give one no notion of it;—any more than Pope will of Homer. It is no square-built gloomy palace of black ashlar marble, shrouded in awe and horror, as Gray

gives it us: no; rough as the North Rocks, as the
Iceland deserts, it is; with a heartiness, homeliness,
even a tint of good humour and robust mirth in the
middle of these fearful things. The strong old Norse
heart did not go upon theatrical sublimities; they had
not time to tremble. I like much their robust simplicity;
their veracity, directness of conception. Thor ' draws
down his brows ' in a veritable Norse rage; ' grasps his
hammer till the *knuckles grow white.*' Beautiful traits
of pity too, an honest pity. Balder ' the white God '
dies; the beautiful, benignant; he is the Sungod.
They try all Nature for a remedy; but he is dead.
Frigga, his mother, sends Hermoder to seek or see
him: nine days and nine nights he rides through gloomy
deep valleys, a labyrinth of gloom; arrives at the
Bridge with its gold roof: the Keeper says, "Yes,
Balder did pass here; but the Kingdom of the Dead
is down yonder, far towards the North." Hermoder
rides on; leaps Hell-gate, Hela's gate: does see Balder,
and speak with him: Balder cannot be delivered. Inexorable! Hela will not, for Odin or any God, give him
up. The beautiful and gentle has to remain there. His
Wife had volunteered to go with him, to die with him.
They shall forever remain there. He sends his ring to
Odin; Nanna his wife sends her *thimble* to Frigga, as
a remembrance—Ah me!—

For indeed Valour is the fountain of Pity too;—of
Truth, and all that is great and good in man. The
robust homely vigour of the Norse heart attaches one
much, in these delineations. Is it not a trait of right
honest strength, says Uhland, who has written a fine
Essay on Thor, that the Old Norse heart finds its friend
in the Thunder-god? That it is not frightened away by
his thunder; but finds that Summer-heat, the beautiful
noble summer, must and will have thunder withal! The
Norse heart *loves* this Thor and his hammer-bolt; sports
with him. Thor is Summer-heat; the god of Peaceable
Industry as well as Thunder. He is the Peasant's
friend; his true henchman and attendant is Thialfi,
Manual Labour. Thor himself engages in all manner
of rough manual work, scorns no business for its
plebeianism; is ever and anon travelling to the country

of the Jötuns, harrying those chaotic Frost-monsters,
subduing them, at least straitening and damaging them.
There is a great broad humour in some of these things.

Thor, as we saw above, goes to Jötun-land, to seek
Hymir's Caldron, that the Gods may brew beer.   Hymir
the huge Giant enters, his grey beard all full of hoar-
frost; splits pillars with the very glance of his eye;
Thor, after much rough tumult, snatches the Pot, claps
it on his head; the ' handles of it reach down to his
heels.' The Norse Skald has a kind of loving sport
with Thor.   This is the Hymir whose cattle, the critics
have discovered, are Icebergs.   Huge untutored Brobdignag genius,—needing only to be tamed-down; into
Shakspeares, Dantes, Goethes! It is all gone now,
that old Norse work,—Thor the Thunder-god changed
into Jack the Giant-killer : but the mind that made it
is here yet.   How strangely things grow, and die, and
do not die !   There are twigs of that great world-tree
of Norse Belief still curiously traceable.   This poor
Jack of the Nursery, with his miraculous shoes of swift-
ness, coat of darkness, sword of sharpness, he is one.
Hynde Etin, and still more decisively *Red Etin of
Ireland,* in the Scottish Ballads, these are both derived
from Norseland; *Etin* is evidently a *Jötun.* Nay,
Shakspeare's *Hamlet* is a twig too of this same world-
tree; there seems no doubt of that.   Hamlet, *Amleth,*
I find, is really a mythic personage; and his Tragedy,
of the poisoned Father, poisoned asleep by drops in his
ear, and the rest, is a Norse mythus !   Old Saxo, as
his wont was, made it a Danish history; Shakspeare,
out of Saxo, made it what we see.   That is a twig of
the world-tree that has *grown,* I think;—by nature or
accident that one has grown !

In fact, these old Norse songs have a *truth* in them,
an inward perennial truth and greatness,—as, indeed,
all must have that can very long preserve itself by
tradition alone.   It is a greatness not of mere body and
gigantic bulk, but a rude greatness of soul.   There is
a sublime uncomplaining melancholy traceable in these
old hearts.   A great free glance into the very deeps of
thought.   They seem to have seen, these brave old
Northmen, what Meditation has taught all men in all

ages, That this world is after all but a show,—a phenomenon or appearance, no real thing. All deep souls see
into that,—the Hindoo Mythologist, the German Philosopher,—the Shakspeare, the earnest Thinker, wherever
he may be :

'We are such stuff as Dreams are made of !'

One of Thor's expeditions, to Utgard (the *Outer*
Garden, central seat of Jötun-land), is remarkable in
this respect. Thialfi was with him, and Loke. After
various adventures they entered upon Giant-land;
wandered over plains, wild uncultivated places, among
stones and trees. At nightfall they noticed a house;
and as the door, which indeed formed one whole side
of the house, was open, they entered. It was a simple
habitation; one large hall, altogether empty. They
stayed there. Suddenly in the dead of the night loud
noises alarmed them. Thor grasped his hammer; stood
in the door, prepared for fight. His companions within
ran hither and thither in their terror, seeking some
outlet in that rude hall; they found a little closet at last,
and took refuge there. Neither had Thor any battle :
for, lo, in the morning it turned-out that the noise had
been only the *snoring* of a certain enormous but peaceable Giant, the Giant Skrymir, who lay peaceably sleeping near by; and this that they took for a house was
merely his *Glove*, thrown aside there; the door was the
Glove-wrist; the little closet they had fled into was the
Thumb ! Such a glove;—I remark too that it had not
fingers as ours have, but only a thumb, and the rest
undivided : a most ancient, rustic glove !

Skrymir now carried their portmanteau all day; Thor,
however, had his own suspicions, did not like the ways
of Skrymir; determined at night to put an end to him
as he slept. Raising his hammer, he struck down into
the Giant's face a right thunderbolt blow, of force to
rend rocks. The Giant merely awoke; rubbed his cheek,
and said, Did a leaf fall? Again Thor struck, so soon
as Skrymir again slept; a better blow than before :
but the Giant only murmured, Was that a grain of sand?
Thor's third stroke was with both his hands (the
'knuckles white' I suppose), and seemed to dint deep

into Skrymir's visage; but he merely checked his snore, and remarked, There must be sparrows roosting in this tree, I think; what is that they have dropt?—At the gate of Utgard, a place so high that you had to ' strain your neck bending back to see the top of it,' Skrymir went his ways. Thor and his companions were admitted; invited to take share in the games going on. To Thor, for his part, they handed a drinking-horn; it was a common feat, they told him, to drink this dry at one draught. Long and fiercely, three times over, Thor drank; but made hardly any impression. He was a weak child, they told him; could he lift that Cat he saw there? Small as the feat seemed, Thor with his whole godlike strength could not; he bent-up the creature's back, could not raise its feet off the ground, could at the utmost raise one foot. Why, you are no man, said the Utgard people; there is an Old Woman that will wrestle you! Thor, heartily ashamed, seized this haggard Old Woman; but could not throw her.

And now, on their quitting Utgard, the Chief Jötun, escorting them politely a little way, said to Thor: " You are beaten then :—yet be not so much ashamed; there was deception of appearance in it. That Horn you tried to drink was the *Sea:* you did make it ebb; but who could drink that, the bottomless! The Cat you would have lifted,—why, that is the *Midgard-snake,* the Great World-serpent, which, tail in mouth, girds and keeps-up the whole created world; had you torn that up, the world must have rushed to ruin! As for the Old Woman, she was *Time,* Old Age, Duration; with her what can wrestle? No man nor no god with her; gods or men, she prevails over all! And then those three strokes you struck,—look at these *three valleys;* your three strokes made these!" Thor looked at his attendant Jötun: it was Skrymir;—it was, say Norse critics, the old chaotic rocky *Earth* in person, and that glove-*house* was some Earth-cavern! But Skrymir had vanished; Utgard with its skyhigh gates, when Thor grasped his hammer to smite them, had gone to air; only the Giant's voice was heard mocking: " Better come no more to Jötunheim !"—

This is of the allegoric period, as we see, and half

play, not of the prophetic and entirely devout : but as a mythus is there not real antique Norse gold in it? More true metal, rough from the Mimerstithy, than in many a famed Greek Mythus *shaped* far better ! A great broad Brobdignag grin of true humour is in this Skrymir; mirth resting on earnestness and sadness, as the rainbow on black tempest : only a right valiant heart is capable of that.   It is the grim humour of our own Ben Jonson, rare old Ben; runs in the blood of us, I fancy; for one catches tones of it, under a still other shape, out of the American Backwoods.

That is also a very striking conception, that of the *Ragnarök*, Consummation, or *Twilight of the Gods*.   It is in the *Völuspa* Song; seemingly a very old, prophetic idea.   The Gods and Jötuns, the divine Powers and the chaotic brute ones, after long contest and partial victory by the former, meet at last in universal world-embracing wrestle and duel; World-serpent against Thor, strength against strength; mutually extinctive; and ruin, ' twilight ' sinking into darkness, swallows the created Universe.   The old Universe with its Gods is sunk; but it is not final death : there is to be a new Heaven and a new Earth; a higher supreme God, and Justice to reign among men.   Curious : this law of mutation, which also is a law written in man's inmost thought, had been deciphered by these old earnest Thinkers in their rude style; and how, though all dies, and even gods die, yet all death is but a phœnix fire-death, and new-birth into the Greater and the Better !   It is the fundamental Law of Being for a creature made of Time, living in this Place of Hope.   All earnest men have seen into it; may still see into it.

And now, connected with this, let us glance at the *last* mythus of the appearance of Thor; and end there. I fancy it to be the latest in date of all these fables; a sorrowing protest against the advance of Christianity,— set forth reproachfully by some Conservative Pagan. King Olaf has been harshly blamed for his over-zeal in introducing Christianity; surely I should have blamed him far more for an under-zeal in that !   He paid dear enough for it; he died by the revolt of his Pagan people, in battle, in the year 1033, at Stickelstad, near that

Drontheim, where the chief Cathedral of the North has now stood for many centuries, dedicated gratefully to his memory as *Saint* Olaf. The mythus about Thor is to this effect. King Olaf, the Christian Reform King, is sailing with fit escort along the shore of Norway, from haven to haven; dispensing justice, or doing other royal work : on leaving a certain haven, it is found that a stranger, of grave eyes and aspect, red beard, of stately robust figure, has stept in. The courtiers address him; his answers surprise by their pertinency and depth : at length he is brought to the King. The stranger's conversation here is not less remarkable, as they sail along the beautiful shore; but after some time, he addresses King Olaf thus : " Yes, King Olaf, it is all beautiful, with the sun shining on it there; green, fruitful, a right fair home for you, and many a sore day had Thor, many a wild fight with the rock Jötuns, before he could make it so. And now you seem minded to put away Thor. King Olaf, have a care !" said the stranger, drawing-down his brows;—and when they looked again, he was nowhere to be found.—This is the last appearance of Thor on the stage of this world !

Do we not see well enough how the Fable might arise, without unveracity on the part of any one? It is the way most Gods have come to appear among men : thus, if in Pindar's time ' Neptune was seen once at the Nemean Games,' what was this Neptune too but a ' stranger of noble grave aspect,' *fit* to be ' seen ' ! There is something pathetic, tragic for me in this last voice of Paganism. Thor is vanished, the whole Norse world has vanished; and will not return ever again. In like fashion to that pass away the highest things. All things that have been in this world, all things that are or will be in it, have to vanish, we have our sad farewell to give them.

That Norse Religion, a rude but earnest, sternly impressive *Consecration of Valour* (so we may define it), sufficed for these old valiant Northmen. Consecration of Valour is not a *bad* thing ! We will take it for good, so far as it goes. Neither is there no use in *knowing* something about this old Paganism of our Fathers. Unconsciously, and combined with higher

things, it is in *us* yet, that old Faith withal! To know
it consciously, brings us into closer and clearer relation
with the Past—with our own possessions in the Past.
For the whole Past, as I keep repeating, is the possession of the Present; the Past had always something
true, and is a precious possession.   In a different time,
in a different place, it is always some other *side* of our
common Human Nature that has been developing itself.
The actual True is the *sum* of all these; not any one of
them by itself constitutes what of Human Nature is
hitherto developed.   Better to know them all than misknow them.   " To which of these Three Religions do
you specially adhere?" inquires Meister of his Teacher.
" To all the Three!" answers the other: " To all the
Three: for they by their union first constitute the True
Religion."

LECTURE II

THE HERO AS PROPHET.   MAHOMET: ISLAM

[Friday, 8th May 1840]

FROM the first rude times of Paganism among the
Scandinavians in the North, we advance to a very
different epoch of religion, among a very different
people: Mahometanism among the Arabs.   A great
change; what a change and progress is indicated here,
in the universal condition and thoughts of men!

The Hero is not now regarded as a God among his
fellowmen; but as one God-inspired, as a prophet.   It
is the second phasis of Hero-worship; the first or oldest,
we may say, has passed away without return; in the
history of the world there will not again be any man,
never so great, whom his fellowmen will take for a god.
Nay we might rationally ask, Did any set of human
beings ever really think the man they *saw* there standing beside them a god, the maker of this world?
Perhaps not : it was usually some man they remembered,
or *had* seen.   But neither can this any more be.   The
Great Man is not recognised henceforth as a god any
more.

It was a rude gross error, that of counting the Great Man a god. Yet let us say that it is at all times difficult to know *what* he is, or how to account of him and receive him! The most significant feature in the history of an epoch is the manner it has of welcoming a Great Man. Ever, to the true instincts of men, there is something godlike in him. Whether they shall take him to be a god, to be a prophet, or what they shall take him to be? that is ever a grand question; by their way of answering that, we shall see, as through a little window, into the very heart of these men's spiritual condition. For at bottom the Great Man, as he comes from the hand of nature, is ever the same kind of thing : Odin, Luther, Johnson, Burns; I hope to make it appear that these are all originally of one stuff; that only by the world's reception of them, and the shapes they assume, are they so immeasurably diverse. The worship of Odin astonishes us—to fall prostrate before the Great Man, into *deliquium* of love and wonder over him, and feel in their hearts that he was a denizen of the skies, a god! This was imperfect enough : but to welcome, for example, a Burns as we did, was that what we can call perfect? The most precious gift that Heaven can give to the Earth; a man of ' genius ' as we call it : the Soul of a Man actually sent down from the skies with a God's-message to us—this we waste away as an idle artificial firework, sent to amuse us a little, and sink it into ashes, wreck and ineffectuality : *such* reception of a Great Man I do not call very perfect either! Looking into the heart of the thing, one may perhaps call that of Burns a still uglier phenomenon, betokening still sadder imperfections in mankind's ways, than the Scandinavian method itself! To fall into mere unreasoning *deliquium* of love and admiration, was not good; but such unreasoning, nay irrational supercilious no-love at all is perhaps still worse!—It is a thing forever changing, this of Hero-worship : different in each age, difficult to do well in any age. Indeed, the heart of the whole business of the age, one may say, is to do it well.

We have chosen Mahomet not as the most eminent Prophet, but as the one we are freest to speak of. He

is by no means the truest of Prophets; but I do esteem
him a true one. Farther, as there is no danger of our
becoming, any of us, Mahometans, I mean to say all
the good of him I justly can. It is the way to get at
his secret: let us try to understand what *he* meant with
the world; what the world meant and means with him,
will then be a more answerable question. Our current
hypotheses about Mahomet, that he was a scheming
Impostor, a Falsehood incarnate, that his religion is a
mere mass of quackery and fatuity, begins really to be
now untenable to any one. The lies, which well-mean-
ing zeal has heaped round this man, are disgraceful to
ourselves only. When Pococke inquired of Grotius,
Where the proof was of that story of the pigeon, trained
to pick peas from Mahomet's ear, and pass for an angel
dictating to him? Grotius answered that there was no
proof! It is really time to dismiss all that. The word
this man spoke has been the life-guidance now of a
hundred-and-eighty millions of men these twelve-
hundred years. These hundred-and-eighty millions were
made by God as well as we. A greater number of God's
creatures believe in Mahomet's word at this hour than
in any other word whatever. Are we to suppose that
it was a miserable piece of spiritual legerdemain, this
which so many creatures of the Almighty have lived
by and died by? I, for my part, cannot form any such
supposition. I will believe most things sooner than
that. One would be entirely at a loss what to think of
this world at all, if quackery so grew and were sanctioned here.

Alas, such theories are very lamentable. If we would
attain to knowledge of anything in God's true Creation,
let us disbelieve them wholly! They are the product
of an Age of Scepticism; they indicate the saddest
spiritual paralysis, and mere death-life of the souls of
men: more godless theory, I think, was never promulgated in this Earth. A false man found a religion?
Why, a false man cannot build a brick house! If he do
not know and follow *truly* the properties of mortar, burnt
clay and what else he works in, it is no house that he
makes, but a rubbish-heap. It will not stand for twelve
centuries, to lodge a hundred-and-eighty millions; it will

fall straightway. A man must conform himself to Nature's laws, *be* verily in communion with Nature and the truth of things, or Nature will answer him, No, not at all! Speciosities are specious—ah, me!—a Cagliostro, many Cagliostros, prominent world-leaders, do prosper by their quackery, for a day. It is like a forged bank-note; they get it passed out of *their* worthless hands: others, not they, have to smart for it. Nature bursts-up in fire-flame, French Revolutions and suchlike, proclaiming with terrible veracity that forged notes are forged.

But of a Great Man especially, of him I will venture to assert that it is incredible he should have been other than true. It seems to me the primary foundation of him, and of all that can lie in him, this. No Mirabeau, Napoleon, Burns, Cromwell, no man adequate to do anything, but is first of all in right earnest about it; what I call a sincere man. I should say *sincerity*, a deep, great, genuine sincerity, is the first characteristic of all men in any way heroic. Not the sincerity that calls itself sincere; ah, no, that is a very poor matter indeed;—a shallow braggart conscious sincerity; oftenest self-conceit mainly. The Great Man's sincerity is of the kind he cannot speak of, is not conscious of: nay, I suppose, he is conscious rather of *in*sincerity; for what man can walk accurately by the law of truth for one day? No, the Great Man does not boast himself sincere, far from that; perhaps does not ask himself if he is so: I would say rather, his sincerity does not depend on himself; he cannot help being sincere! The great Fact of Existence is great to him. Fly as he will, he cannot get out of the awful presence of this Reality. His mind is so made; he is great by that, first of all. Fearful and wonderful, real as Life, real as death, is this Universe to him. Though all men should forget its truth, and walk in a vain show, he cannot. At all moments the Flame-image glares-in upon him; undeniable, there, there!—I wish you to take this as my primary definition of a Great Man. A little man may have this, it is competent to all men that God has made: but a Great Man cannot be without it.

Such a man is what we call an *original* man: he comes

to us at first-hand. A messenger he, sent from the
Infinite Unknown with tidings to us. We may call him
Poet, Prophet, God;—in one way or other, we all feel
that the words he utters are as no other man's words.
Direct from the Inner Fact of things;—he lives, and
has to live, in daily communion with that. Hearsays
cannot hide it from him; he is blind, homeless, miserable, following hearsays; *it* glares-in upon him. Really
his utterances, are they not a kind of ' revelation;'—
what we must call such for want of some other name?
It is from the heart of the world that he comes; he is
portion of the primal reality of things. God has made
many revelations : but this man too, has not God made
him, the latest and newest of all? The ' inspiration of
the Almighty giveth *him* understanding :' we must listen
before all to him.

This Mahomet, then, we will in no wise consider as
an Inanity and Theatricality, a poor conscious ambitious
schemer; we cannot conceive him so. The rude message he delivered was a real one withal; an earnest confused voice from the unknown Deep. The man's words
were not false, nor his workings here below; no Inanity
and Simulacrum; a fiery mass of Life cast-up from the
great bosom of Nature herself. To *kindle* the world;
the world's Maker had ordered it so. Neither can the
faults, imperfections, insincerities even, of Mahomet, if
such were never so well proved against him, shake this
primary fact about him.

On the whole, we make too much of faults; the details
of the business hide the real centre of it. Faults?
The greatest of faults, I should say, is to be conscious
of none. Readers of the Bible above all, one would
think, might know better. Who is called there ' the
man according to God's own heart '? David, the
Hebrew King, had fallen into sins enough; blackest
crimes; there was no want of sins. And thereupon the
unbelievers sneer and ask, Is this your man according
to God's own heart? The sneer, I must say, seems to
me but a shallow one. What are faults, what are the
outward details of a life; if the inner secret of it, the
remorse, temptations, true, often-baffled, never-ended
struggle of it, be forgotten? ' It is not in man that

walketh to direct his steps.' Of all acts, is not, for a man, *repentance* the most divine? The deadliest sin, I say, were that same supercilious consciousness of no sin;—that is death; the heart so conscious is divorced from sincerity, humility and fact; is dead: it is ' pure ' as dead dry sand is pure.   David's life and history, as written for us in those Psalms of his, I consider to be the truest emblem ever given of a man's moral progress and warfare here below.   All earnest souls will ever discern in it the faithful struggle of an earnest human soul towards what is good and best.   Struggle often baffled, sore baffled, down as into entire wreck; yet a struggle never ended; ever, with tears, repentance, true unconquerable purpose, begun anew.   Poor human nature !   Is not a man's walking, in truth, always that : ' a succession of falls '?   Man can do no other.   In this wild element of a Life, he has to struggle onwards; now fallen, deep-abased; and ever, with tears, repentance, with bleeding heart, he has to rise again, struggle again still onwards.   That his struggle *be* a faithful unconquerable one : that is the question of questions. We will put-up with many sad details, if the soul of it were true.   Details by themselves will never teach us what it is.   I believe we misestimate Mahomet's faults even as faults : but the secret of him will never be got by dwelling there.   We will leave all this behind us ; and assuring ourselves that he did mean some true thing, ask candidly what it was or might be.

These Arabs Mahomet was born among are certainly a notable people.   Their country itself is notable ; the fit habitation for such a race.   Savage inaccessible rock-mountains, great grim deserts, alternating with beautiful strips of verdure : wherever water is, there is greenness, beauty ; odoriferous balm-shrubs, date-trees, frankincense-trees.   Consider that wide waste horizon of sand, empty, silent, like a sand-sea, dividing habitable place from habitable.   You are all alone there, left alone with the Universe ; by day a fierce sun blazing down on it with intolerable radiance ; by night the great deep Heaven with its stars.   Such a country is fit for a swift-handed, deep-hearted race of men.   There

is something most agile, active, and yet most meditative, enthusiastic in the Arab character.   The Persians
are called the French of the East, we will call the Arabs
Oriental Italians.   A gifted noble people; a people of
wild strong feelings, and of iron restraint over these :
the characteristic of noblemindedness, of genius.   The
wild Bedouin welcomes the stranger to his tent, as one
having right to all that is there; were it his worst
enemy, he will slay his foal to treat him, will serve
him with sacred hospitality for three days, will set him
fairly on his way ;—and then, by another law as sacred,
kill him if he can.   In words too, as in action.   They
are not a loquacious people, taciturn rather; but
eloquent, gifted when they do speak.   An earnest truthful kind of men.   They are, as we know, of Jewish
kindred : but with that deadly terrible earnestness of
the Jews they seem to combine something graceful,
brilliant, which is not Jewish.   They had ' Poetic con-
tests ' among them before the time of Mahomet.   Sale
says, at Ocadh, in the South of Arabia, there were
yearly fairs, and there, when the merchandising was
done, Poets sang for prizes :—the wild people gathered
to hear that.

One Jewish quality these Arabs manifest; the outcome of many or of all high qualities; what we may
call religiosity.   From of old they had been zealous
workers, according to their light.   They worshipped
the stars, as Sabeans; worshipped many natural objects,
—recognised them as symbols, immediate manifestations, of the Maker of Nature.   It was wrong; and yet
not wholly wrong.   All God's works are still in a sense
symbols of God.   Do we not, as I urged, still account
it a merit to recognise a certain inexhaustible significance, ' poetic beauty ' as we name it, in all natural
objects whatsoever?   A man is a poet, and honoured,
for doing that, and speaking or singing it,—a kind of
diluted worship.   They had many Prophets, these
Arabs; Teachers each to his tribe, each according to
the light he had.   But indeed, have we not from of old
the noblest of proofs, still palpable to every one of us,
of what devoutness and noblemindedness had dwelt in
these rustic thoughtful peoples?   Biblical critics seem

agreed that our own *Book of Job* was written in that region of the world. I call that, apart from all theories about it, one of the grandest things ever written with pen. One feels, indeed, as if it were not Hebrew; such a noble universality, different from noble patriotism or sectarianism, reigns in it. A noble Book; all men's Book! It is our first, oldest statement of the never-ending Problem,—man's destiny, and God's ways with him here in this earth. And all in such free flowing outlines; grand in its sincerity, in its simplicity; in its epic melody, and repose of reconcilement. There is the seeing eye, the mildly understanding heart. So *true* everywhere; true eyesight and vision for all things; material things no less than spiritual; the Horse,—' hast thou clothed his neck with *thunder?*'—he '*laughs* at the shaking of the spear!' Such living likenesses were never since drawn. Sublime sorrow, sublime reconciliation: oldest choral melody as of the heart of mankind; —so soft, and great; as the summer midnight, as the world with its seas and stars! There is nothing written, I think, in the Bible or out of it, of equal literary merit.—

To the idolatrous Arabs one of the most ancient universal objects of worship was that Black Stone, still kept in the building called Caabah at Mecca. Diodorus Siculus mentions this Caabah in a way not to be mistaken, as the oldest, most honoured temple in his time; that is, some half-century before our Era. Silvestre de Sacy says there is some likelihood that the Black Stone is an aerolite. In that case, some one might *see* it fall out of Heaven! It stands now beside the Well Zemzem; the Caabah is built over both. A Well is in all places a beautiful affecting object, gushing out like life from the hard earth;—still more so in these hot dry countries, where it is the first condition of being. The Well Zemzem has its name from the bubbling sound of the waters, *zem-zem*; they think it is the Well which Hagar found with her little Ishmael in the wilderness: the aerolite and it have been sacred now, and had a Caabah over them, for thousands of years. A curious object, that Caabah! There it stands at this hour, in the black cloth-covering the Sultan sends it yearly;

'twenty-seven cubits high;' with circuit, with double circuit of pillars, with festoon-rows of lamps and quaint ornaments: the lamps will be lighted again *this* night,— to glitter again under the stars. An authentic fragment of the oldest Past. It is the *Keblah* of all Moslem: from Delhi all onwards to Morocco, the eyes of innumerable praying men are turned towards *it*, five times, this day and all days: one of the notablest centres in the Habitation of Men.

It had been from the sacredness attached to this Caabah Stone and Hagar's Well, from the pilgrimings of all tribes of Arabs thither, that Mecca took its rise as a Town. A great town once, though much decayed now. It has no natural advantage for a town; stands in a sandy hollow amid bare barren hills, at a distance from the sea; its provisions, its very bread, have to be imported. But so many pilgrims needed lodgings: and then all places of pilgrimage do, from the first, become places of trade. The first day pilgrims meet, merchants have also met: where men see themselves assembled for one object, they find that they can accomplish other objects which depend on meeting together. Mecca became the Fair of all Arabia. And thereby indeed the chief staple and warehouse of whatever Commerce there was between the Indian and Western countries, Syria, Egypt, even Italy. It had at one time a population of 100,000; buyers, forwarders of those Eastern and Western products; importers for their own behoof of provisions and corn. The government was a kind of irregular aristocratic republic, not without a touch of theocracy. Ten Men of a chief tribe, chosen in some rough way, were Governors of Mecca, and Keepers of the Caabah. The Koreish were the chief tribe in Mahomet's time; his own family was of that tribe. The rest of the Nation, fractioned and cut-asunder by deserts, lived under similar rude patriarchal governments by one or several: herdsmen, carriers, traders, generally robbers too; being oftenest at war one with another, or with all: held together by no open bond, if it were not this meeting at the Caabah, where all forms of Arab Idolatry assembled in common adoration;—held mainly by the *inward* indissoluble bond of

a common blood and language. In this way had the
Arabs lived for long ages, unnoticed by the world:
a people of great qualities, unconsciously waiting for
the day when they should become notable to all the
world. Their Idolatries appear to have been in a tottering state; much was getting into confusion and fermentation among them. Obscure tidings of the most
important Event ever transacted in this world, the Life
and Death of the Divine Man in Judea, at once the
symptom and cause of immeasurable change to all people
in the world, had in the course of centuries reached
into Arabia too; and could not but, of itself, have
produced fermentation there.

It was among this Arab people, so circumstanced, in
the year 570 of our Era, that the man Mahomet was
born. He was of the family of Hashem, of the Koreish
tribe as we said; though poor, connected with the chief
persons of his country.

Almost at his birth he lost his Father; at the age
of six years his Mother too, a woman noted for her
beauty, her worth and sense: he fell to the charge of
his Grandfather, an old man, a hundred years old. A
good old man: Mahomet's Father, Abdallah, had been
his youngest favourite son. He saw in Mahomet, with
his old life-worn eyes, a century old, the lost Abdallah
come back again, all that was left of Abdallah. He
loved the little orphan Boy greatly; used to say, They
must take care of that beautiful little Boy, nothing in
their kindred was more precious than he. At his death,
while the boy was still but two years old, he left him
in charge to Abu Thaleb the eldest of the Uncles, as
to him that now was head of the house. By this Uncle,
a just and rational man as everything betokens,
Mahomet was brought-up in the best Arab way.

Mahomet, as he grew up, accompanied his Uncle on
trading journeys and suchlike; in his eighteenth year
one finds him a fighter following his Uncle in war. But
perhaps the most significant of all his journeys is one
we find noted as of some years' earlier date: a journey
to the Fairs of Syria. The young man here first came
in contact with a quite foreign world,—with one foreign

element of endless moment to him: the Christian Religion. I know not what to make of that ' Sergius, the Nestorian Monk,' whom Abu Thaleb and he are said to have lodged with; or how much any monk could have taught one still so young. Probably enough it is greatly exaggerated, this of the Nestorian Monk. Mahomet was only fourteen; had no language but his own: much in Syria must have been a strange unintelligible whirlpool to him. But the eyes of the lad were open; glimpses of many things would doubtless be taken-in, and lie very enigmatic as yet, which were to ripen in a strange way into views, into beliefs and insights one day. These journeys to Syria were probably the beginning of much to Mahomet.

One other circumstance we must not forget: that he had no school-learning; of the thing we call school-learning none at all. The art of writing was but just introduced into Arabia; it seems to be the true opinion that Mahomet never could write ! Life in the Desert, with its experiences, was all his education. What of this infinite Universe he, from his dim place, with his own eyes and thoughts, could take in, so much and no more of it was he to know. Curious, if we will reflect on it, this of having no books. Except by what he could see for himself, or hear of by uncertain rumour of speech in the obscure Arabian Desert, he could know nothing. The wisdom that had been before him or at a distance from him in the world, was in a manner as good as not there for him. Of the great brother souls, flame-beacons through so many lands and times, no one directly communicates with this great soul. He is alone there, deep down in the bosom of the Wilderness; has to grow up so,—alone with Nature and his own Thoughts.

But, from an early age, he had been remarked as a thoughtful man. His companions named him ' Al Amin, The Faithful.' A man of truth and fidelity; true in what he did, in what he spake and thought. They noted that he always meant something. A man rather taciturn in speech; silent when there was nothing to be said; but pertinent, wise, sincere, when he did speak; always throwing light on the matter. This is

L 278

the only sort of speech *worth* speaking ! Through life
we find him to have been regarded as an altogether
solid, brotherly, genuine man. A serious, sincere character ; yet amiable, cordial, companionable, jocose even ;
—a good laugh in him withal : there are men whose
laugh is as untrue as anything about them ; who cannot
laugh. One hears of Mahomet's beauty : his fine
sagacious honest face, brown florid complexion, beaming black eyes ;—I somehow like too that vein on the
brow, which swelled-up black when he was in anger :
like the ' *horse-shoe* vein ' in Scott's *Redgauntlet*. It
was a kind of feature in the Hashem family, this black
swelling vein in the brow ; Mahomet had it prominent,
as would appear. A spontaneous, passionate, yet just,
true-meaning man ! Full of wild faculty, fire and light :
of wild worth, all uncultured ; working out his life-task
in the depths of the Desert there.

How he was placed with Kadijah, a rich Widow,
as her Steward, and travelled in her business, again to
the Fairs of Syria ; how he managed all, as one can well
understand, with fidelity, adroitness ; how her gratitude,
her regard for him grew : the story of their marriage
is altogether a graceful intelligible one, as told us by
the Arab authors. He was twenty-five ; she forty,
though still beautiful. He seems to have lived in a
most affectionate, peaceable, wholesome way with this
wedded benefactress ; loving her truly, and her alone.
It goes greatly against the impostor theory, the fact that
he lived in this entirely unexceptionable, entirely quiet
and commonplace way, till the heat of his years was
done. He was forty before he talked of any mission
from Heaven. All his irregularities, real and supposed,
date from after his fiftieth year, when the good Kadijah
died. All his ' ambition,' seemingly, had been, hitherto, to live an honest life ; his ' fame,' the mere good
opinion of neighbours that knew him, had been sufficient
hitherto. Not till he was already getting old, the prurient heat of his life all burnt out, and *peace* growing to
be the chief thing this world could give him, did he
start on the ' career of ambition ;' and, belying all his
past character and existence, set-up as a wretched
empty charlatan to acquire what he could now no longer

enjoy! For my share, I have no faith whatever in that.

Ah no: this deep-hearted Son of the Wilderness, with his beaming black eyes and open social deep soul, had other thoughts in him than ambition. A silent great soul; he was one of those who cannot *but* be in earnest; whom Nature herself has appointed to be sincere. While others walk in formulas and hearsays, contented enough to dwell there, this man could not screen himself in formulas; he was alone with his own soul and the reality of things. The great Mystery of Existence, as I said, glared-in upon him, with its terrors, with its splendours; no hearsays could hide that unspeakable fact, "Here am I!" Such *sincerity,* as we named it, has in very truth something of divine. The word of such a man is a Voice direct from Nature's own Heart. Men do and must listen to that as to nothing else;—all else is wind in comparison. From of old, a thousand thoughts, in his pilgrimings and wanderings, had been in this man: What am I? What *is* this unfathomable Thing I live in, which men name Universe? What is Life; what is Death? What am I to believe? What am I to do? The grim rocks of Mount Hara, of Mount Sinai, the stern sandy solitudes answered not. The great Heaven rolling silent overhead, with its blue-glancing stars, answered not. There was no answer. The man's own soul, and what of God's inspiration dwelt there, had to answer!

It is the thing which all men have to ask themselves; which we too have to ask, and answer. This wild man felt it to be of *infinite* moment; all other things of no moment whatever in comparison. The jargon of argumentative Greek Sects, vague traditions of Jews, the stupid routine of Arab Idolatry, there was no answer in these. A Hero, as I repeat, has this first distinction, which indeed we may call first and last, the Alpha and Omega of his whole Heroism, That he looks through the shows of things into *things*. Use and wont, respectable hearsay, respectable formula: all these are good, or are not good. There is something behind and beyond all these, which all these must correspond with, be the image of, or they are—*Idolatries:* 'bits of black wood

pretending to be God;' to the earnest soul a mockery
and abomination. Idolatries never so gilded, waited
on by heads of the Koreish, will do nothing for this
man. Though all men walk by them, what good is it?
The great Reality stands glaring there upon *him*. He
there has to answer it, or perish miserably. Now, even
now, or else through all Eternity never! Answer it;
thou must find an answer.—Ambition? What could all
Arabia do for this man; with the crown of Greek Hera-
clius, of Persian Chosroes, and all crowns in the Earth;
—what could they all do for him? It was not of the
Earth he wanted to hear tell; it was of the Heaven
above and of the Hell beneath. All crowns and
sovereignties whatsoever, where would *they* in a few
brief years be? To be Sheik of Mecca or Arabia, and
have a bit of gilt wood put into your hand,—will that
be one's salvation? I decidedly think, not. We will
leave it altogether, this impostor hypothesis, as not
credible; not very tolerable even, worthy chiefly of
dismissal by us.

Mahomet had been wont to retire yearly, during the
month Ramadhan, into solitude and silence; as indeed
was the Arab custom; a praiseworthy custom, which
such a man, above all, would find natural and useful.
Communing with his own heart, in the silence of the
mountains; himself silent; open to the 'small still
voices:' it was a right natural custom! Mahomet was
in his fortieth year, when having withdrawn to a cavern
in Mount Hara, near Mecca, during this Ramadhan,
to pass the month in prayer, and meditation on those
great questions, he one day told his wife Kadijah, who
with his household was with him or near him this year,
That by the unspeakable special favour of Heaven he
had now found it all out; was in doubt and darkness
no longer, but saw it all. That all these Idols and
Formulas were nothing, miserable bits of wood; that
there was One God in and over all; and we must leave
all Idols, and look to Him. That God is great; and
that there is nothing else great! He is the Reality.
Wooden Idols are not real; He is real. He made us
at first, sustains us yet; we and all things are but the

shadow of Him; a transitory garment veiling the Eternal Splendour. ' *Allah akbar*, God is great;'—and then also ' *Islam,*' That we must *submit* to God. That our whole strength lies in resigned submission to Him, whatsoever He do to us. For this world, and for the other! The thing He sends to us, were it death and worse than death, shall be good, shall be best; we resign ourselves to God.—' If this be *Islam*,' says Goethe, ' do we not all live in *Islam?*' Yes, all of us that have any moral life; we all live so. It has ever been held the highest wisdom for a man not merely to submit to Necessity,—Necessity will make him submit,—but to know and believe well that the stern thing which Necessity had ordered was the wisest, the best, the thing wanted there. To cease his frantic pretension of scanning this great God's-World in his small fraction of a brain; to know that it *had* verily, though deep beyond his soundings, a Just Law, that the soul of it was Good;—that his part in it was to conform to the Law of the Whole, and in devout silence follow that; not questioning it, obeying it as unquestionable.

I say, this is yet the only true morality known. A man is right and invincible, virtuous and on the road towards sure conquest, precisely while he joins himself to the great deep Law of the World, in spite of all super-ficial laws, temporary appearances, profit-and-loss cal-culations; he is victorious while he coöperates with that great central Law, not victorious otherwise :—and surely his first chance of coöperating with it, or getting into the course of it, is to know with his whole soul that it *is;* that it is good, and alone good! This is the soul of Islam; it is properly the soul of Christianity;—for Islam is definable as a confused form of Christianity; had Christianity not been, neither had it been. Chris-tianity also commands us, before all, to be resigned to God. We are to take no counsel with flesh-and-blood; give ear to no vain cavils, vain sorrows and wishes: to know that we know nothing; that the worst and cruelest to our eyes is not what it seems; that we have to receive whatsoever befalls us as sent from God above, and say, It is good and wise, God is great! " Though

He slay me, yet will I trust in Him." Islam means in its way Denial of Self, Annihilation of Self. This is yet the highest Wisdom that Heaven has revealed to our Earth.

Such light had come, as it could, to illuminate the darkness of this wild Arab soul. A confused dazzling splendour as of life and Heaven, in the great darkness which threatened to be death: he called it revelation and the angel Gabriel;—who of us yet can know what to call it? It is the 'inspiration of the Almighty that giveth us understanding.' To *know*; to get into the truth of anything, is ever a mystic act,—of which the best Logics can but babble on the surface. 'Is not Belief the true god-announcing Miracle?' says Novalis. —That Mahomet's whole soul, set in flame with this grand Truth vouchsafed him, should feel as if it were important and the only important thing, was very natural. That Providence had unspeakably honoured *him* by revealing it, saving him from death and darkness; that he therefore was bound to make known the same to all creatures: this is what was meant by 'Mahomet is the Prophet of God;' this too is not without its true meaning.—

The good Kadijah, we can fancy, listened to him with wonder, with doubt: at length she answered: Yes, it was *true* this that he said. One can fancy too the boundless gratitude of Mahomet; and how of all the kindnesses she had done him, this of believing the earnest struggling word he now spoke was the greatest. 'It is certain,' says Novalis, 'my Conviction gains infinitely, the moment another soul will believe in it.' It is a boundless favour.—He never forgot this good Kadijah. Long afterwards, Ayesha his young favourite wife, a woman who indeed distinguished herself among the Moslem, by all manner of qualities, through her whole long life; this young brilliant Ayesha was, one day, questioning him: "Now am not I better than Kadijah? She was a widow; old, and had lost her looks: you love me better than you did her?"—" No, by Allah!" answered Mahomet: "No, by Allah! She believed in me when none else would believe. In the whole world I had but one friend, and she was that !''—Seid, his Slave, also believed in him; these with his young Cousin Ali, Abu Thaleb's son, were his first converts.

He spoke of his Doctrine to this man and that; but the most treated it with ridicule, with indifference; in three years, I think, he had gained but thirteen followers. His progress was slow enough. His encouragement to go on, was altogether the usual encouragement that such a man in such a case meets. After some three years of small success, he invited forty of his chief kindred to an entertainment; and there stood-up and told them what his pretension was : that he had this thing to promulgate abroad to all men; that it was the highest thing, the one thing : which of them would second him in that? Amid the doubt and silence of all, young Ali, as yet a lad of sixteen, impatient of the silence, started-up, and exclaimed in passionate fierce language, That he would! The assembly, among whom was Abu Thaleb, Ali's Father, could not be unfriendly to Mahomet; yet the sight there, of one unlettered elderly man, with a lad of sixteen, deciding on such an enterprise against all mankind, appeared ridiculous to them; the assembly broke-up in laughter. Nevertheless it proved not a laughable thing; it was a very serious thing! As for this young Ali, one cannot but like him. A noble-minded creature, as he shows himself, now and always afterwards; full of affection, of fiery daring. Something chivalrous in him; brave as a lion; yet with a grace, a truth and affection worthy of Christian knighthood. He died by assassination in the Mosque at Bagdad; a death occasioned by his own generous fairness, confidence in the fairness of others : he said, If the wound proved not unto death, they must pardon the Assassin; but if it did, then they must slay him straightway, that so they two in the same hour might appear before God, and see which side of that quarrel was the just one!

Mahomet naturally gave offence to the Koreish, Keepers of the Caabah, superintendents of the Idols. One or two men of influence had joined him : the thing spread slowly, but it was spreading. Naturally, he gave offence to everybody: Who is this that pretends

to be wiser than we all; that rebukes us all, as mere
fools and worshippers of wood! Abu Thaleb the good
Uncle spoke with him : Could he not be silent about
all that; believe it all for himself, and not trouble
others, anger the chief men, endanger himself and them
all, talking of it? Mahomet answered : If the Sun
stood on his right hand and the Moon on his left,
ordering him to hold his peace, he could not obey!
No : there was something in this Truth he had got
which was of Nature herself; equal in rank to Sun,
or Moon, or whatsoever thing Nature had made.   It
would speak itself there, so long as the Almighty
allowed it, in spite of Sun and Moon, and all Koreish
and all men and things.   It must do that, and could
do no other.   Mahomet answered so; and, they say,
' burst into tears.'   Burst into tears : he felt that Abu
Thaleb was good to him; that the task he had got
was no soft, but a stern and great one.

He went on speaking to who would listen to him;
publishing his Doctrine among the pilgrims as they
came to Mecca; gaining adherents in this place and
that.   Continual contradiction, hatred, open or secret
danger attended him.   His powerful relations protected
Mahomet himself; but by and by, on his own advice,
all his adherents had to quit Mecca, and seek refuge in
Abyssinia over the sea.   The Koreish grew ever angrier;
laid plots, and swore oaths among them, to put Mahomet to death with their own hands.   Abu Thaleb was
dead, the good Kadijah was dead.   Mahomet is not
solicitous of sympathy from us; but his outlook at this
time was one of the dismalest.   He had to hide in
caverns, escape in disguise; fly hither and thither;
homeless, in continual peril of his life.   More than once
it seemed all-over with him; more than once it turned
on a straw, some rider's horse taking fright or the like,
whether Mahomet and his Doctrine had not ended
there, and not been heard of at all.   But it was not to
end so.

In the thirteenth year of his mission, finding his
enemies all banded against him, forty sworn men, one
out of every tribe, waiting to take his life, and no continuance possible at Mecca for him any longer, Maho-

met fled to the place then called Yathreb, where he had
gained some adherents; the place they now call Medina,
or ' *Medinat al Nabi,* the City of the Prophet,' from
that circumstance. It lay some 200 miles off, through
rocks and deserts; not without great difficulty, in such
mood as we may fancy, he escaped thither, and found
welcome. The whole East dates its era from this
Flight, *Hegira* as they name it : the Year 1 of this
Hegira is 622 of our Era, the fifty-third of Mahomet's
life. He was now becoming an old man; his friends
sinking round him one by one : his path desolate, encompassed with danger : unless he could find hope in
his own heart, the outward face of things was but
hopeless for him. It is so with all men in the like
case. Hitherto Mahomet had professed to publish his
Religion by the way of preaching and persuasion alone.
But now, driven foully out of his native country, since
unjust men had not only given no ear to his earnest
Heaven's-message, the deep cry of his heart, but would
not even let him live if he kept speaking it,—the wild
Son of the Desert resolved to defend himself, like a
man and Arab. If the Koreish will have it so, they
shall have it. Tidings, felt to be of infinite moment
to them and all men, they would not listen to these;
would trample them down by sheer violence, steel and
murder : well, let steel try it then ! Ten years more
this Mahomet had : all of fighting, of breathless impetuous toil and struggle; with what result we know.

Much has been said of Mahomet's propagating his
Religion by the sword. It is no doubt far nobler what
we have to boast of the Christian Religion, that it propagated itself peaceably in the way of preaching and
conviction. Yet withal, if we take this for an argument
of the truth or falsehood of a religion, there is a radical
mistake in it. The sword indeed : but where will you
get your sword ! Every new opinion, at its starting,
is precisely in a *minority of one.* In one man's head
alone, there it dwells as yet. One man alone of the
whole world believes it; there is one man against all
men. That *he* take a sword, and try to propagate with
that, will do little for him. You must first get your
sword ! On the whole, a thing will propagate itself as

it can. We do not find, of the Christian Religion either, that it always disdained the sword, when once it had got one. Charlemagne's conversion of the Saxons was not by preaching. I care little about the sword: I will allow a thing to struggle for itself in this world, with any sword or tongue or implement it has, or can lay hold of. We will let it preach, and pamphleteer, and fight, and to the uttermost bestir itself, and do, beak and claws, whatsoever is in it; very sure that it will, in the long-run, conquer nothing which does not deserve to be conquered. What is better than itself, it cannot put away, but only what is worse. In this great Duel, Nature herself is umpire, and can do no wrong: the thing which is deepest-rooted in Nature, what we call *truest*, that thing and not the other will be found growing at last.

Here however, in reference to much that there is in Mahomet and his success, we are to remember what an umpire Nature is; what a greatness, composure of depth and tolerance there is in her. You take wheat to cast into the Earth's bosom: your wheat may be mixed with chaff, chopped straw, barn-sweepings, dust and all imaginable rubbish; no matter: you cast it into the kind just Earth; she grows the wheat,—the whole rubbish she silently absorbs, shrouds *it* in, says nothing of the rubbish. The yellow wheat is growing there; the good Earth is silent about all the rest,—has silently turned all the rest to some benefit too, and makes no complaint about it! So everywhere in Nature! She is true and not a lie; and yet so great, and just, and motherly in her truth. She requires of a thing only that it *be* genuine of heart; she will protect it if so; will not, if not so. There is a soul of truth in all the things she ever gave harbour to. Alas, is not this the history of all highest Truth that comes or ever came into the world? The *body* of them all is imperfection, an element of light *in* darkness: to us they have to come embodied in mere Logic, in some merely *scientific* Theorem of the Universe; which *cannot* be complete; which cannot but be found, one day, *in*complete, erroneous, and so die and disappear. The body of all Truth dies; and yet in all, I say, there is

a soul which never dies; which in new and ever-nobler
embodiment lives immortal as man himself! It is the
way with Nature. The genuine essence of Truth never
dies. That it be genuine, a voice from the great Deep
of Nature, there is the point at Nature's judgment-seat.
What *we* call pure or impure, is not with her the final
question. Not how much chaff is in you; but whether
you have any wheat. Pure? I might say to many a
man : Yes, you are pure; pure enough; but you are
chaff,—insincere hypothesis, hearsay, formality; you
never were in contact with the great heart of the Universe at all; you are properly neither pure nor impure;
you *are* nothing, Nature has no business with you.

Mahomet's Creed we called a kind of Christianity;
and really, if we look at the wild rapt earnestness with
which it was believed and laid to heart, I should say
a better kind than that of those miserable Syrian Sects,
with their vain janglings about *Homoiousion* and
Homoousion, the head full of worthless noise, the heart
empty and dead! The truth of it is embedded in portentous error and falsehood; but the truth of it makes
it be believed, not the falsehood: it succeeded by its
truth. A bastard kind of Christianity, but a living
kind; with a heart-life in it : not dead, chopping barren
logic merely! Out of all that rubbish of Arab idolatries, argumentative theologies, traditions, subtleties,
rumours and hypotheses of Greeks and Jews, with their
idle wire-drawings, this wild man of the Desert, with
his wild sincere heart, earnest as death and life, with
his great flashing natural eyesight, had seen into the
kernel of the matter. Idolatry is nothing : these
Wooden Idols of yours, ' ye rub them with oil and
wax, and the flies stick on them,'—these are wood, I
tell you! They can do nothing for you; they are an
impotent blasphemous pretence; a horror and abomination, if ye knew them. God alone is; God alone has
power; He made us, He can kill us and keep us alive :
' *Allah akbar*, God is great.' Understand that His will
is the best for you; that howsoever sore to flesh-and-
blood, you will find it the wisest, best : you are bound
to take it so; in this world and in the next, you have
no other thing that you can do!

And now if the wild idolatrous men did believe this, and with their fiery hearts laid hold of it to do it, in what form soever it came to them, I say it was well worthy of being believed. In one form or the other, I say it is still the one thing worthy of being believed by all men. Man does hereby become the high-priest of this Temple of a World. He is in harmony with the Decrees of the Author of this World; coöperating with them, not vainly withstanding them: I know, to this day, no better definition of Duty than that same. All that is *right* includes itself in this of coöperating with the real Tendency of the World; you succeed by this (the World's Tendency will succeed), you are good, and in the right course there. *Homoiousion, Homoousion,* vain logical jangle, then or before or at any time, may jangle itself out, and go whither and how it likes: this is the *thing* it all struggles to mean, if it would mean anything. If it do not succeed in meaning this, it means nothing. Not that Abstractions, logical Propositions, be correctly worded or incorrectly; but that living concrete Sons of Adam do lay this to heart: that is the important point. Islam devoured all these vain jangling Sects; and I think had right to do so. It was a Reality, direct from the great Heart of Nature once more. Arab idolatries, Syrian formulas, whatsoever was not equally real, had to go up in flame,—mere dead *fuel*, in various senses, for this which was *fire*.

It was during these wild warfarings and strugglings, especially after the Flight to Mecca, that Mahomet dictated at intervals his Sacred Book, which they name *Koran*, or *Reading*, 'Thing to be read.' This is the Work he and his disciples made so much of, asking all the world, Is not that a miracle? The Mahometans regard their Koran with a reverence which few Christians pay even to their Bible. It is admitted everywhere as the standard of all law and all practice; the thing to be gone-upon in speculation and life: the message sent direct out of Heaven, which this Earth has to conform to, and walk by; the thing to be read. Their Judges decide by it; all Moslem are bound to study it, seek in it for the light of their life. They have

mosques where it is all read daily; thirty relays of
priests take it up in succession, get through the whole
each day. There, for twelve-hundred years, has the
voice of this Book, at all moments, kept sounding
through the ears and the hearts of so many men. We
hear of Mahometan Doctors that had read it seventy-
thousand times !

Very curious : if one sought for ' discrepancies of
national taste,' here surely were the most eminent instance of that ! We also can read the Koran; our
Translation of it, by Sale, is known to be a very fair
one. I must say, it is as toilsome reading as I ever
undertook. A wearisome confused jumble, crude, incondite; endless iterations, long-windedness, entanglement; most crude, incondite;—insupportable stupidity,
in short ! Nothing but a sense of duty could carry any
European through the Koran. We read in it, as we
might in the State-Paper Office, unreadable masses of
lumber, that perhaps we may get some glimpses of a
remarkable man. It is true we have it under disadvantages : the Arabs see more method in it than we.
Mahomet's followers found the Koran lying all in
fractions, as it had been written-down at first promulgation; much of it, they say, on shoulder-blades of
mutton, flung pellmell into a chest : and they published
it, without any discoverable order as to time or otherwise;—merely trying, as would seem, and this not very
strictly, to put the longest chapters first. The real
beginning of it, in that way, lies almost at the end :
for the earliest portions were the shortest. Read in
its historical sequence it perhaps would not be so bad.
Much of it, too, they say, is rhythmic; a kind of wild
chanting song, in the original. This may be a great
point; much perhaps has been lost in the Translation
here. Yet with every allowance, one feels it difficult
to see how any mortal ever could consider this Koran
as a Book written in Heaven, too good for the Earth;
as a well-written book, or indeed as a *book* at all; and
not a bewildered rhapsody; *written,* so far as writing
goes, as badly as almost any book ever was. So much
for national discrepancies, and the standard of taste.

Yet I should say, it was not unintelligible how the

Arabs might so love it. When once you get this confused
coil of a Koran fairly off your hands, and have it behind you at a distance, the essential type of it begins
to disclose itself; and in this there is a merit quite
other than the literary one. If a book come from the
heart, it will contrive to reach other hearts; all art and
authorcraft are of small amount to that. One would
say the primary character of the Koran is that of its
genuineness, of its being a *bonâ-fide* book. Prideaux,
I know, and others have represented it as a mere bundle
of juggleries; chapter after chapter got-up to excuse
and varnish the author's successive sins, forward his
ambitions and quackeries: but really it is time to dismiss all that. I do not assert Mahomet's continual
sincerity: who is continually sincere? But I confess
I can make nothing of the critic, in these times, who
would accuse him of deceit *prepense;* of conscious deceit
generally, or perhaps at all;—still more, of living in
a mere element of conscious deceit, and writing this
Koran as a forger and juggler would have done! Every
candid eye, I think, will read the Koran far otherwise
than so. It is the confused ferment of a great rude
human soul; rude, untutored, that cannot even read;
but fervent, earnest, struggling vehemently to utter
itself in words. With a kind of breathless intensity he
strives to utter himself; the thoughts crowd on him
pellmell: for very multitude of things to say, he can
get nothing said. The meaning that is in him shapes
itself into no form of composition, is stated in no
sequence, method, or coherence;—they are not *shaped*
at all, these thoughts of his; flung-out unshaped, as
they struggle and tumble there, in their chaotic inarticulate state. We said ' stupid:' yet natural stupidity is
by no means the character of Mahomet's Book; it is
natural uncultivation rather. The man has not studied
speaking; in the haste and pressure of continual fighting, has not time to mature himself into fit speech.
The panting breathless haste and vehemence of a man
struggling in the thick of battle for life and salvation;
this is the mood he is in! A headlong haste; for very
magnitude of meaning, he cannot get himself articulated
into words. The successive utterances of a soul in

that mood, coloured by the various vicissitudes of three-and-twenty years; now well uttered, now worse: this is the Koran.

For we are to consider Mahomet, through these three-and-twenty years, as the centre of a world wholly in conflict. Battles with the Koreish and Heathen, quarrels among his own people, backslidings of his own wild heart; all this kept him in a perpetual whirl, his soul knowing rest no more. In wakeful nights, as one may fancy, the wild soul of the man, tossing amid these vortices, would hail any light of a decision for them as a veritable light from Heaven; *any* making-up of his mind, so blessed, indispensable for him there, would seem the inspiration of a Gabriel. Forger and juggler? No, no! This great fiery heart, seething, simmering like a great furnace of thoughts, was not a juggler's. His life was a Fact to him; this God's Universe an awful Fact and Reality. He has faults enough. The man was an uncultured semi-barbarous Son of Nature, much of the Bedouin still clinging to him: we must take him for that. But for a wretched Simulacrum, a hungry Impostor without eyes or heart, practising for a mess of pottage such blasphemous swindlery, forgery of celestial documents, continual high-treason against his Maker and Self, we will not and cannot take him.

Sincerity, in all senses, seems to me the merit of the Koran; what had rendered it precious to the wild Arab men. It is, after all, the first and last merit in a book; gives rise to merits of all kinds,—nay, at bottom, it alone can give rise to merit of any kind. Curiously, through these incondite masses of tradition, vituperation, complaint, ejaculation in the Koran, a vein of true direct insight, of what we might almost call poetry, is found straggling. The body of the Book is made-up of mere tradition, and as it were vehement enthusiastic extempore preaching. He returns forever to the old stories of the Prophets as they went current in the Arab memory: how Prophet after Prophet, the Prophet Abraham, the Prophet Hud, the Prophet Moses, Christian and other real and fabulous Prophets, had come to this Tribe and to that, warning men of their sin; and been received by them even as he Mahomet was,—which is a great solace to him. These things he repeats ten, perhaps twenty times; again and ever again with wearisome iteration; has never done repeating them. A brave Samuel Johnson, in his forlorn garret, might con-over the Biographies of Authors in that way! This is the great staple of the Koran. But curiously, through all this, comes ever and anon some glance as of the real thinker and seer. He has actually an eye for the world, this Mahomet: with a certain directness and rugged vigour, he brings home still, to our heart, the thing his own heart has been opened to. I make but little of his praises of Allah, which many praise; they are borrowed I suppose mainly from the Hebrew, at least they are far surpassed there. But the eye that flashes direct into the heart of things, and *sees* the truth of them; this is to me a highly interesting object. Great Nature's own gift; which she bestows on all; but which only one in the thousand does not cast sorrowfully away: it is what I call sincerity of vision; the test of a sincere heart.

Mahomet can work no miracles; he often answers impatiently: I can work no miracles. I? 'I am a Public Preacher;' appointed to preach this doctrine to all creatures. Yet the world, as we can see, had really from of old been all one great miracle to him. Look over the world, says he; is it not wonderful, the work of Allah; wholly 'a sign to you,' if your eyes were open! This Earth, God made it for you: 'appointed paths in it;' you can live in it, go to and fro on it.— The clouds in the dry country of Arabia, to Mahomet they are very wonderful: Great clouds, he says, born in the deep bosom of the Upper Immensity, where do they come from! They hang there, the great black monsters; pour-down their rain deluges 'to revive a dead earth,' and grass springs, and tall leafy palm-trees with their date-clusters hanging round. Is not that a sign?' Your cattle too,—Allah made them; serviceable dumb creatures; they change the grass into milk; you have your clothing from them, very strange creatures; they come ranking home at evening-time, ' and,' adds he, ' and are a credit to you!' Ships also,

—he talks often about ships : Huge moving mountains, they spread-out their cloth wings, go bounding through the water there, Heaven's wind driving them ; anon they lie motionless, God has withdrawn the wind, they lie dead, and cannot stir ! Miracles? cries he ; what miracle would you have? Are not you yourselves there? God made *you*, ' shaped you out of a little clay.' Ye were small once ; a few years ago ye were not at all. Ye have beauty, strength, thoughts, ' ye have compassion on one another.' Old age comes-on you, and gray hairs ; your strength fades into feebleness ; ye sink down, and again are not. ' Ye have compassion on one another :' this struck me much : Allah might have made you having no compassion on one another,—how had it been then ! This is a great direct thought, a glance at first-hand into the very fact of things. Rude vestiges of poetic genius, of whatsoever is best and truest, are visible in this man. A strong untutored intellect : eyesight, heart ; a strong wild man,—might have shaped himself into Poet, King, Priest, any kind of Hero.

To his eyes it is forever clear that this world wholly is miraculous. He sees what, as we said once before, all great thinkers, the rude Scandinavians themselves, in one way or other, have contrived to see : That this so solid-looking material world is, at bottom, in very deed, Nothing ; is a visual and tactual Manifestation of God's power and presence,—a shadow hung-out by Him on the bosom of the void Infinite ; nothing more. The Mountains, he says, these great rock-mountains, they shall dissipate themselves ' like clouds ;' melt into the Blue as clouds do, and not be ! He figures the Earth, in the Arab fashion, Sale tells us, as an immense Plain or flat Plate of ground, the mountains are set on that to *steady* it. At the Last Day they shall disappear ' like clouds ;' the whole Earth shall go spinning, whirl itself off into wreck, and as dust and vapour vanish in the Inane. Allah withdraws his hand from it, and it ceases to be. The universal empire of Allah, presence everywhere of an unspeakable Power, a Splendour, and a Terror not to be named, as the true force, essence and reality, in all things whatsoever, was continually clear to this man. What a modern talks-of by the name, Forces of Nature, Laws of Nature; and does not figure as a divine thing; not even as one thing at all, but as a set of things, undivine enough,—saleable, curious, good for propelling steamships! With our Sciences and Cyclopædias, we are apt to forget the *divineness*, in these laboratories of ours. We ought not to forget it! That once well forgotten, I know not what else were worth remembering. Most sciences, I think, were then a very dead thing; withered, contentious, empty;—a thistle in late autumn. The best science, without this, is but as the dead *timber;* it is not the growing tree and forest,—which gives ever-new timber, among other things! Man cannot *know* either, unless he can *worship* in some way. His knowledge is a pedantry, and dead thistle, otherwise.

Much has been said and written about the sensuality of Mahomet's Religion; more than was just. The indulgences, criminal to us, which he permitted, were not of his appointment; he found them practised, unquestioned from immemorial time in Arabia; what he did was to curtail them, restrict them, not on one but on many sides. His Religion is not an easy one : with rigorous fasts, lavations, strict complex formulas, prayers five times a day, and abstinence from wine, it did not 'succeed by being an easy religion.' As if indeed any religion, or cause holding of religion, could succeed by that! It is a calumny on men to say that they are roused to heroic action by ease, hope of pleasure, recompense,—sugar-plums of any kind, in this world or the next! In the meanest mortal there lies something nobler. The poor swearing soldier, hired to be shot, has his ' honour of a soldier,' different from drill-regulations and the shilling a day. It is not to taste sweet things, but to do noble and true things, and vindicate himself under God's Heaven as a god-made Man, that the poorest son of Adam dimly longs. Show him the way of doing that, the dullest daydrudge kindles into a hero. They wrong man greatly who say he is to be seduced by ease. Difficulty, abnegation, martyrdom, death are the *allurements* that act on the heart of

man. Kindle the inner genial life of him, you have a
flame that burns-up all lower considerations. Not
happiness, but something higher : one sees this even in
the frivolous classes, with their ' point of honour ' and
the like. Not by flattering our appetites; no, by
awakening the Heroic that slumbers in every heart, can
any Religion gain followers.

Mahomet himself, after all that can be said about him,
was not a sensual man. We shall err widely if we
consider this man as a common voluptuary, intent
mainly on base enjoyments,—nay on enjoyments of any
kind. His household was of the frugalest; his common
diet barley-bread and water : sometimes for months
there was not a fire once lighted on his hearth. They
record with just pride that he would mend his own
shoes, patch his own cloak. A poor, hard-toiling, ill-
provided man; careless of what vulgar men toil for.
Not a bad man, I should say; something better in him
than *hunger* of any sort,—or these wild Arab men,
fighting and jostling three-and-twenty years at his hand,
in close contact with him always, would not have
reverenced him so ! They were wild men, bursting
ever and anon into quarrel, into all kinds of fierce
sincerity; without right worth and manhood, no man
could have commanded them. They called him
Prophet, you say? Why, he stood there face to face
with them; bare, not enshrined in any mystery; visibly
clouting his own cloak, cobbling his own shoes; fighting, counselling, ordering in the midst of them : they
must have seen what kind of a man he *was*, let him
be *called* what you like ! No emperor with his tiaras
was obeyed as this man in a cloak of his own clouting.
During three-and-twenty years of rough actual trial.
I find something of a veritable Hero necessary for that,
of itself.

His last words are a prayer; broken ejaculations of a
heart struggling-up, in trembling hope, towards its
Maker. We cannot say that his religion made him
worse; it made him better; good, not bad. Generous
things are recorded of him : when he lost his Daughter,
the thing he answers is, in his own dialect, everyway
sincere, and yet equivalent to that of Christians, ' The

Lord giveth, and the Lord taketh away; blessed be the name of the Lord.' He answered in like manner of Seid, his emancipated well-beloved Slave, the second of the believers. Seid had fallen in the War of Tabûc, the first of Mahomet's fightings with the Greeks. Mahomet said, It was well; Seid had done his Master's work, Seid had now gone to his Master: it was all well with Seid. Yet Seid's daughter found him weeping over the body;—the old gray-haired man melting in tears! "What do I see?" said she.—"You see a friend weeping over his friend."—He went out for the last time into the mosque, two days before his death; asked, If he had injured any man? Let his own back bear the stripes. If he owed any man? A voice answered, "Yes, me three drachms," borrowed on such an occasion. Mahomet ordered them to be paid: "Better be in shame now," said he, "than at the Day of Judgment."—You remember Kadijah, and the "No, by Allah!" Traits of that kind show us the genuine man, the brother of us all, brought visible through twelve centuries,—the veritable Son of our common Mother.

Withal I like Mahomet for his total freedom from cant. He is a rough self-helping son of the wilderness; does not pretend to be what he is not. There is no ostentatious pride in him; but neither does he go much upon humility: he is there as he can be, in cloak and shoes of his own clouting; speaks plainly to all manner of Persian Kings, Greek Emperors, what it is they are bound to do; knows well enough, about himself, 'the respect due unto thee.' In a life-and-death war with Bedouins, cruel things could not fail; but neither are acts of mercy, of noble natural pity and generosity wanting. Mahomet makes no apology for the one, no boast of the other. They were each the free dictate of his heart; each called-for, there and then. Not a mealy-mouthed man! A candid ferocity, if the case call for it, is in him; he does not mince matters! The War of Tabûc is a thing he often speaks of: his men refused, many of them, to march on that occasion: pleaded the heat of the weather, the harvest, and so forth; he can never forget that. Your harvest? It

lasts for a day. What will become of your harvest
through all Eternity? Hot weather? Yes, it was hot;
' but Hell will be hotter !' Sometimes a rough sarcasm
turns-up : He says to the unbelievers, Ye shall have the
just measure of your deeds at that Great Day. They
will be weighed-out to you; ye shall not have short
weight !—Everywhere he fixes the matter in his eye;
he *sees* it : his heart, now and then, is as if struck
dumb by the greatness of it. ' Assuredly,' he says :
that word, in the Koran, is written-down sometimes as
a sentence by itself : ' Assuredly.'

No *Dilettantism* in this Mahomet; it is a business
of Reprobation and Salvation with him, of Time and
Eternity : he is in deadly earnest about it ! Dilettantism, hypothesis, speculation, a kind of amateur-search
for Truth, toying and coquetting with Truth : this is
the sorest sin. The root of all other imaginable sins.
It consists in the heart and soul of the man never having
been *open* to Truth ;—' living in a vain show.' Such
a man not only utters and produces falsehoods, but *is*
himself a falsehood. The rational moral principle,
spark of the Divinity, is sunk deep in him, in quiet
paralysis of life-death. The very falsehoods of
Mahomet are truer than the truths of such a man.
He is the insincere man : smooth-polished, respectable
in some times and places : inoffensive, says nothing
harsh to anybody; most *cleanly*.—iust as carbonic acid
is, which is death and poison.

We will not praise Mahomet's moral preceps as
always of the superfinest sort; yet it can be said that
there is always a tendency to good in them; that they
are the true dictates of a heart aiming towards what
is just and true. The sublime forgiveness of Christianity, turning of the other cheek when the one has been
smitten, is not here : you *are* to revenge yourself, but
it is to be in measure, not overmuch, or beyond justice.
On the other hand, Islam, like any great Faith, and
insight into the essence of man, is a perfect equaliser
of men : the soul of one believer outweighs all earthly
kingships; all men, according to Islam too, are equal.
Mahomet insists not on the propriety of giving alms,
but on the necessity of it; he marks-down by law how

much you are to give, and it is at your peril if you neglect. The tenth part of a man's annual income, whatever that may be, is the *property* of the poor, of those that are afflicted and need help. Good all this: the natural voice of humanity, of pity and equity dwelling in the heart of this wild Son of Nature speaks *so*.

Mahomet's Paradise is sensual, his Hell sensual: true; in the one and the other there is enough that shocks all spiritual feeling in us. But we are to recollect that the Arabs already had it so; that Mahomet, in whatever he changed of it, softened and diminished all this. The worst sensualities, too, are the work of doctors, followers of his, not his work. In the Koran there is really very little said about the joys of Paradise; they are intimated rather than insisted on. Nor is it forgotten that the highest joys even there shall be spiritual; the pure Presence of the Highest, this shall infinitely transcend all other joys. He says, ' Your salutation shall be, Peace.' *Salam*, Have Peace !—the thing that all rational souls long for, and seek, vainly here below, as the one blessing. ' Ye shall sit on seats, ' facing one another: all grudges shall be taken away out of your hearts.' All grudges ! Ye shall love one another freely; for each of you, in the eyes of his brothers, there will be Heaven enough !

In reference to this of the sensual Paradise and Mahomet's sensuality, the sorest chapter of all for us, there were many things to be said; which it is not convenient to enter upon here. Two remarks only I shall make, and therewith leave it to your candour. The first is furnished me by Goethe; it is a casual hint of his which seems well worth taking note of. In one of his Delineations, in *Meister's Travels* it is, the hero comes upon a Society of men with very strange ways, one of which was this: " We require," says the Master, " that each of our people shall restrict himself in one direction," shall go right against his desire in one matter, and *make* himself do the thing he does not wish, " should we allow him the greater latitude on all other sides." There seems to me a great justness in this. Enjoying things which are pleasant; that is not the evil: it is the reducing of our moral self to

slavery by them that is. Let a man assert withal that
he is king over his habitudes; that he could and would
shake them off, on cause shown : this is an excellent
law. The Month Ramadhan for the Moslem, much in
Mahomet's Religion, much in his own Life, bears in
that direction; if not by forethought, or clear purpose
of moral improvement on his part, then by a certain
healthy manful instinct, which is as good.

But there is another thing to be said about the
Mahometan Heaven and Hell. This namely, that,
however gross and material they may be, they are an
emblem of an everlasting truth, not always so well
remembered elsewhere. That gross sensual Paradise
of his; that horrible flaming Hell; the great enormous
Day of Judgment he perpetually insists on : what is all
this but a rude shadow, in the rude Bedouin imagination, of that grand spiritual Fact, and Beginning of
Facts, which it is ill for us too if we do not all know
and feel : the Infinite Nature of Duty? That man's
actions here are of *infinite* moment to him, and never
die or end at all; that man, with his little life, reaches
upwards high as Heaven, downwards low as Hell, and
in his threescore years of Time holds an Eternity fearfully and wonderfully hidden : all this had burnt itself,
as in flame-characters, into the wild Arab soul. As
in flame and lightning, it stands written there; awful,
unspeakable, ever present to him. With bursting
earnestness, with a fierce savage sincerity, halt, articulating, not able to articulate, he strives to speak it,
bodies it forth in that Heaven and that Hell. Bodied
forth in what way you will, it is the first of all truths.
It is venerable under all embodiments. What is the
chief end of man here below? Mahomet has answered
this question, in a way that might put some of *us* to
shame ! He does not, like a Bentham, a Paley, take
Right and Wrong, and calculate the profit and loss,
ultimate pleasure of the one and of the other; and
summing all up by addition and subtraction into a net
result, ask you, Whether on the whole the Right does
not preponderate considerably? No, it is not *better*
to do the one than the other; the one is to the other as
life is to death,—as Heaven is to Hell. The one must

in nowise be done, the other in nowise left undone. You shall not measure them; they are incommensurable : the one is death eternal to a man, the other is life eternal. Benthamee Utility, virtue by Profit and Loss; reducing this God's-world to a dead brute Steam-engine, the infinite celestial Soul of Man to a kind of Hay-balance for weighing hay and thistles on, pleasures and pains on :—If you ask me which gives, Mahomet or they, the beggarlier and falser view of Man and his Destinies in this Universe, I will answer, It is not Mahomet !——

On the whole, we will repeat that this Religion of Mahomet's is a kind of Christianity; has a genuine element of what is spiritually highest looking through it, not to be hidden by all its imperfections. The Scandinavian God *Wish*, the god of all rude men,—this has been enlarged into a Heaven by Mahomet; but a Heaven symbolical of sacred Duty, and to be earned by faith and welldoing, by valiant action, and a divine patience which is still more valiant. It is Scandinavian Paganism, and a truly celestial element superadded to that. Call it not false; look not at the falsehood of it, look at the truth of it. For these twelve centuries, it has been the religion and life-guidance of the fifth part of the whole kindred of Mankind. Above all things, it has been a religion heartily *believed*. These Arabs believe their religion, and try to live by it ! No Christians, since the early ages, or only perhaps the English Puritans in modern times, have ever stood by their Faith as the Moslem do by theirs,—believing it wholly, fronting Time with it, and Eternity with it. This night the watchman on the streets of Cairo when he cries " Who goes?" will hear from the passenger, along with his answer, " There is no God but God." *Allah akbar, Islam,* sounds through the souls, and whole daily existence, of these dusky millions. Zealous missionaries preach it abroad among Malays, black Papuans, brutal Idolaters;—displacing what is worse, nothing that is better or good.

To the Arab Nation it was as a birth from darkness into light; Arabia first became alive by means of it. A poor shepherd people, roaming unnoticed in its deserts since the creation of the world : a Hero-Prophet was sent down to them with a word they could believe : see, the unnoticed becomes world-notable, the small has grown world-great; within one century afterwards, Arabia is at Grenada on this hand, at Delhi on that;— glancing in valour and splendour and the light of genius, Arabia shines through long ages over a great section of the world. Belief is great, life-giving. The history of a Nation becomes fruitful, soul-elevating, great, so soon as it believes. These Arabs, the man Mahomet, and that one century,—is it not as if a spark had fallen, one spark, on a world of what seemed black unnoticeable sand; but lo, the sand proves explosive powder, blazes heaven-high from Delhi to Grenada ! I said, the Great Man was always as lightning out of Heaven; the rest of men waited for him like fuel, and then they too would flame.

LECTURE III

THE HERO AS POET.   DANTE; SHAKSPEARE.

[*Tuesday, 12th May* 1840]

THE Hero as Divinity, the Hero as Prophet, are productions of old ages; not to be repeated in the new. They presuppose a certain rudeness of conception, which the progress of mere scientific knowledge puts an end to. There needs to be, as it were, a world vacant, or almost vacant of scientific forms, if men in their loving wonder are to fancy their fellow-man either a god or one speaking with the voice of a god. Divinity and Prophet are past. We are now to see our Hero in the less ambitious, but also less questionable, character of Poet; a character which does not pass. The Poet is a heroic figure belonging to all ages; whom all ages possess, when once he is produced, whom the newest age as the oldest may produce;—and will produce, always when Nature pleases. Let Nature send a Hero-soul; in no age is it other than possible that he may be shaped into a Poet.

Hero, Prophet, Poet,—many different names, in different times and places, do we give to Great Men; according to varieties we note in them, according to the sphere in which they have displayed themselves! We might give many more names, on this same principle. I will remark again, however, as a fact not unimportant to be understood, that the different *sphere* constitutes the grand origin of such distinction; that the Hero can be Poet, Prophet, King, Priest or what you will, according to the kind of world he finds himself born into. I confess, I have no notion of a truly great man that could not be *all* sorts of men. The Poet who could merely sit on a chair, and compose stanzas, would never make a stanza worth much. He could not sing the Heroic warrior, unless he himself were at least a Heroic warrior too. I fancy there is in him the Politician, the Thinker, Legislator, Philosopher;—in one or the other degree, he could have been, he is all these. So too I cannot understand how a Mirabeau, with that great glowing heart, with the fire that was in it, with the bursting tears that were in it, could not have written verses, tragedies, poems, touched all hearts in that way, had his course of life and education led him thitherward. The grand fundamental character is that of Great Man; that the man be great. Napoleon has words in him which are like Austerlitz Battles. Louis Fourteenth's Marshals are a kind of poetical men withal; the things Turenne says are full of sagacity and geniality, like sayings of Samuel Johnson. The great heart, the clear deep-seeing eye: there it lies; no man whatever, in what province soever, can prosper at all without these. Petrarch and Boccaccio did diplomatic messages, it seems, quite well: one can easily believe it; they had done things a little harder than these! Burns, a gifted song-writer, might have made a still better Mirabeau. Shakspeare,—one knows not what *he* could not have made, in the supreme degree.

True, there are aptitudes of Nature too. Nature does not make all great men, more than all other men, in the self-same mould. Varieties of aptitude doubtless;

but infinitely more of circumstance; and far oftenest it is the *latter* only that are looked to. But it is as with common men in the learning of trades. You take any man, as yet a vague capability of a man, who could be any kind of craftsman; and make him into a smith, a carpenter, a mason : he is then and thenceforth that and nothing else. And if, as Addison complains, you sometimes see a street-porter staggering under his load on spindle-shanks, and near at hand a tailor with the frame of a Samson handling a bit of cloth and small Whitechapel needle,—it cannot be considered that aptitude of Nature alone has been consulted here either ! —The Great Man also, to what shall he be bound apprentice? Given your Hero, is he to become Conqueror, King, Philosopher, Poet? It is an inexplicably complex controversial-calculation between the world and him ! He will read the world and its laws; the world with its laws will be there to be read. What the world, on *this* matter, shall permit and bid is, as we said, the most important fact about the world.—

Poet and Prophet differ greatly in our loose modern notions of them. In some old languages, again, the titles are synonymous; *Vates* means both Prophet and Poet : and indeed at all times, Prophet and Poet, well understood, have much kindred of meaning. Fundamentally indeed they are still the same; in this most important respect especially, That they have penetrated both of them into the sacred mystery of the Universe; what Goethe calls 'the open secret.' "Which is the great secret?" asks one.—"The *open* secret,"—open to all, seen by almost none ! That divine mystery, which lies everywhere in all Beings, 'the Divine Idea of the World, that which lies at the bottom of Appearance,' as Fichte styles it; of which all Appearance, from the starry sky to the grass of the field, but especially the Appearance of Man and his work, is but the *vesture*, the embodiment that renders it visible. This divine mystery *is* in all times and in all places; veritably is. In most times and places it is greatly overlooked; and the Universe, definable always in one or the other dialect, as the realised Thought of God,

is considered a trivial, inert, commonplace matter,—
as if, says the Satirist, it were a dead thing, which some
upholsterer had put together! It could do no good,
at present, to *speak* much about this; but it is a pity
for every one of us if we do not know it, live ever in
the knowledge of it. Really a most mournful pity;—
a failure to live at all, if we live otherwise!

But now, I say, whoever may forget this divine
mystery, the *Vates*, whether Prophet or Poet, has penetrated into it; is a man sent hither to make it more
impressively known to us. That always is his message;
he is to reveal that to us,—that sacred mystery which
he more than others lives ever present with. While
others forget it, he knows it;—I might say, he has
been driven to know it; without consent asked of *him*,
he finds himself living in it, bound to live in it. Once
more, here is no Hearsay, but a direct Insight and
Belief; this man too could not help being a sincere
man! Whosoever may live in the shows of things, it
is for him a necessity of nature to live in the very fact
of things. A man once more, in earnest with the
Universe, though all others were but toying with it.
He is a *Vates*, first of all, in virtue of being sincere.
So far Poet and Prophet, participators in the 'open
secret,' are one.

With respect to their distinction again: The *Vates*
Prophet, we might say, has seized that sacred mystery
rather on the moral side, as Good and Evil, Duty and
Prohibition; the *Vates* Poet on what the Germans call
the æsthetic side, as Beautiful, and the like. The one
we may call a revealer of what we are to do, the other
of what we are to love. But indeed these two provinces
run into one another, and cannot be disjoined. The
Prophet too has his eye on what we are to love: how
else shall he know what it is we are to do? The highest
Voice ever heard on this earth said withal, "Consider
the lilies of the field; they toil not, neither do they spin:
yet Solomon in all his glory was not arrayed like one
of these." A glance, that, into the deepest deep of
Beauty. 'The lilies of the field,'—dressed finer than
earthly princes, springing-up there in the humble
furrow-field; a beautiful *eye* looking-out on you, from

the great inner Sea of Beauty! How could the rude Earth make these, if her Essence, rugged as she looks and is, were not inwardly Beauty? In this point of view, too, a saying of Goethe's, which has staggered several, may have meaning: 'The Beautiful,' he intimates, ' is higher than the Good: the Beautiful includes in it the Good.' The *true* Beautiful; which however, I have said somewhere, ' differs from the *false* as Heaven does from Vauxhall!' So much for the distinction and identity of Poet and Prophet.—

In ancient and also in modern periods we find a few Poets who are accounted perfect; whom it were a kind of treason to find fault with. This is noteworthy; this is right: yet in strictness it is only an illusion. At bottom, clearly enough, there is no perfect Poet! A vein of Poetry exists in the hearts of all men; no man is made altogether of Poetry. We are all poets when we *read* a poem well. The ' imagination that shudders at the Hell of Dante,' is not that the same faculty, weaker in degree, as Dante's own? No one but Shakspeare can embody, out of *Saxo Grammaticus*, the story of *Hamlet* as Shakspeare did: but every one models some kind of story out of it; every one embodies it better or worse. We need not spend time in defining. Where there is no specific difference, as between round and square, all definition must be more or less arbitrary. A man that has *so* much more of the poetic element developed in him as to have become noticeable, will be called Poet by his neighbours. World-Poets too, those whom we are to take for perfect Poets, are settled by critics in the same way. One who rises *so* far above the general level of Poets will, to such and such critics, seem a Universal Poet; as he ought to do. And yet it is, and must be, an arbitrary distinction. All Poets, all men, have some touches of the Universal; no man is wholly made of that. Most Poets are very soon forgotten: but not the noblest Shakspeare or Homer of them can be remembered *forever*;—a day comes when he too is not!

Nevertheless, you will say, there must be a difference between true Poetry and true Speech not poetical: what is the difference? On this point many things have been written, especially by late German Critics, some of which are not very intelligible at first. They say, for example, that the Poet has an *infinitude* in him; communicates an *Unendlichkeit*, a certain character of 'infinitude,' to whatsoever he delineates. This, though not very precise, yet on so vague a matter is worth remembering : if well meditated, some meaning will gradually be found in it. For my own part, I find considerable meaning in the old vulgar distinction of Poetry being *metrical*, having music in it, being a Song. Truly, if pressed to give a definition, one might say this as soon as anything else : If your delineation be authentically *musical*, musical, not in word only, but in heart and substance, in all the thoughts and utterances of it, in the whole conception of it, then it will be poetical; if not, not.—Musical : how much lies in that ! A *musical* thought is one spoken by a mind that has penetrated into the inmost heart of the thing; detected the inmost mystery of it, namely the *melody* that lies hidden in it; the inward harmony of coherence which is its soul, whereby it exists, and has a right to be, here in this world. All inmost things, we may say, are melodious; naturally utter themselves in Song. The meaning of Song goes deep. Who is there that, in logical words, can express the effect music has on us? A kind of inarticulate unfathomable speech, which leads us to the edge of the Infinite, and lets us for moments gaze into that !

Nay all speech, even the commonest speech, has something of song in it : not a parish in the world but has its parish-accent;—the rhythm or *tune* to which the people there *sing* what they have to say ! Accent is a kind of chanting; all men have accent of their own,— though they only *notice* that of others. Observe too how all passionate language does of itself become musical,—with a finer music than the mere accent; the speech of a man even in zealous anger becomes a chant, a song. All deep things are Song. It seems somehow the very central essence of us, Song; as if all the rest were but wrappages and hulls ! The primal element of us; of us, and of all things. The Greeks fabled of Sphere-Harmonies; it was the feeling they had of the inner structure of Nature; that the soul of all her voices and utterances was perfect music. Poetry, therefore, we will call *musical Thought*. The Poet is he who *thinks* in that manner. At bottom, it turns still on power of intellect; it is a man's sincerity and depth of vision that makes him a Poet. See deep enough, and you see musically; the heart of Nature *being* everywhere music, if you can only reach it.

The *Vates* Poet, with his melodious Apocalypse of Nature, seems to hold a poor rank among us, in comparison with the *Vates* Prophet; his function, and our esteem of him for his function, alike slight. The Hero taken as Divinity; the Hero taken as Prophet; then next the Hero taken only as Poet: does it not look as if our estimate of the Great Man, epoch after epoch, were continually diminishing? We take him first for a god, then for one god-inspired; and now in the next stage of it, his most miraculous word gains from us only the recognition that he is a Poet, beautiful verse-maker, man of genius, or suchlike!—It looks so; but I persuade myself that intrinsically it is not so. If we consider well, it will perhaps appear that in man still there is the *same* altogether peculiar admiration for the Heroic Gift, by what name soever called, that there at any time was.

I should say, if we do not now reckon a Great Man literally divine, it is that our notions of God, of the supreme unattainable Fountain of Splendour, Wisdom and Heroism, are ever rising *higher;* not altogether that our reverence for these qualities, as manifested in our like, is getting lower. This is worth taking thought of. Sceptical Dilettantism, the curse of these ages, a curse which will not last forever, does indeed in this the highest province of human things, as in all provinces, make sad work; and our reverence for great men, all crippled, blinded, paralytic as it is, comes out in poor plight, hardly recognisable. Men worship the shows of great men; the most disbelieve that there is any reality of great men to worship. The dreariest, fatalest faith; believing which, one would literally despair of human things. Nevertheless look, for example, at Napoleon! A Corsican lieutenant of artillery; that is the show of *him:* yet is he not obeyed, *worshipped* after his sort, as all the Tiaraed and Diademed of the world put together could not be? High Duchesses, and ostlers of inns, gather round the Scottish rustic, Burns;—a strange feeling dwelling in each that they had never heard a man like this; that, on the whole, this is the man! In the secret heart of these people it still dimly reveals itself, though there is no accredited way of uttering it at present, that this rustic, with his black brows and flashing sun-eyes, and strange words moving laughter and tears, is of a dignity far beyond all others, incommensurable with all others. Do not we feel it so? But now, were Dilettantism, Scepticism, Triviality, and all that sorrowful brood, cast-out of us,—as, by God's blessing, they shall one day be; were faith in the shows of things entirely swept-out, replaced by clear faith in the *things*, so that a man acted on the impulse of that only, and counted the other non-extant; what a new livelier feeling towards this Burns were it!

Nay here in these pages, such as they are, have we not two mere Poets, if not deified, yet we may say beatified? Shakspeare and Dante are Saints of Poetry; really, if we will think of it, *canonised*, so that it is impiety to meddle with them. The unguided instinct of the world, working across all these perverse impediments, has arrived at such result. Dante and Shakspeare are a peculiar Two. They dwell apart, in a kind of royal solitude; none equal, none second to them: in the general feeling of the world, a certain transcendentalism, a glory as of complete perfection, invests these two. They *are* canonised, though no Pope or Cardinals took hand in doing it! Such, in spite of every perverting influence, in the most unheroic times, is still our indestructible reverence for heroism.—We will look a little at these Two, the Poet Dante and the Poet Shakspeare: what little it is permitted us to say here of the Hero as Poet will most fitly arrange itself in that fashion.

Many volumes have been written by way of commentary on Dante and his Book; yet, on the whole, with no great result. His Biography is, as it were, irrecoverably lost for us. An unimportant, wandering, sorrowstricken man, not much note was taken of him while he lived; and the most of that has vanished, in the long space that now intervenes. It is five centuries since he ceased writing and living here. After all commentaries, the Book itself is mainly what we know of him. The Book;—and one might add that Portrait commonly attributed to Giotto, which, looking on it, you cannot help inclining to think genuine, whoever did it. To me it is a most touching face; perhaps of all faces that I know, the most so. Lonely there, painted as on vacancy, with the simple laurel wound round it; the deathless sorrow and pain, the known victory which is also deathless;—significant of the whole history of Dante! I think it is the mournfulest face that ever was painted from reality; an altogether tragic, heart-affecting face. There is in it, as foundation of it, the softness, tenderness, gentle affection as of a child; but all this is as if congealed into sharp contradiction, into abnegation, isolation, proud hopeless pain. A soft ethereal soul looking-out so stern, implacable, grim-trenchant, as from imprisonment of thick-ribbed ice! Withal it is a silent pain too, a silent scornful one : the lip is curled in a kind of godlike disdain of the thing that is eating-out his heart,—as if it were withal a mean insignificant thing, as if he whom it had power to torture and strangle were greater than it. The face of one wholly in protest, and life-long unsurrendering battle, against the world. Affection all converted into indignation : an implacable indignation; slow, equable, silent, like that of a god! The eye too, it looks-out as in a kind of *surprise*, a kind of inquiry, Why the world was of such a sort? This is Dante : so he looks, this 'voice of ten silent centuries,' and sings us 'his mystic unfathomable song.'

The little that we know of Dante's Life corresponds well enough with this Portrait and this Book. He was born at Florence, in the upper class of society, in the year 1265. His education was the best then going; much school-divinity, Aristotelean logic, some Latin classics,—no inconsiderable insight into certain provinces of things : and Dante, with his earnest intelligent nature, we need not doubt, learned better than most all that was learnable. He has a clear cultivated understanding, and of great subtlety; the best fruit of education he had contrived to realise from these scholastics. He knows accurately and well what lies close to him; but, in such a time, without printed books or free intercourse, he could not know well what was distant: the small clear light, most luminous for what is near, breaks itself into singular *chiaroscuro* striking on what is far off. This was Dante's learning from the schools. In life, he had gone through the usual destinies; been twice out campaigning as a soldier for the Florentine State, been on embassy; had in his thirty-fifth year, by natural gradation of talent and service, become one of the Chief Magistrates of Florence. He had met in boyhood a certain Beatrice Portinari, a beautiful little girl of his own age and rank, and grown-up thenceforth in partial sight of her, in some distant intercourse with her. All readers know his graceful affecting account of this; and then of their being parted; of her being wedded to another, and of her death soon after. She makes a great figure in Dante's Poem; seems to have made a great figure in his life. Of all beings it might seem as if she, held apart from him, far apart at last in the dim Eternity, were the only one he had ever with his whole strength of affection loved. She died: Dante himself was wedded; but it seems not happily, far from happily. I fancy, the rigorous earnest man, with his keen excitabilities, was not altogether easy to make happy.

We will not complain of Dante's miseries: had all gone right with him as he wished it, he might have been Prior, Podestà, or whatsoever they call it, of Florence, well accepted among neighbours,—and the world had wanted one of the most notable words ever spoken or sung. Florence would have had another properous Lord Mayor; and the ten dumb centuries continued voiceless, and the ten other listening centuries (for there will be ten of them and more) had no *Divina Commedia* to hear! We will complain of nothing. A nobler destiny was appointed for this Dante; and he, struggling like a man led towards death and crucifixion, could not help fulfilling it. Give *him* the choice of his happiness! He knew not, more than we do, what was really happy, what was really miserable.

In Dante's Priorship, the Guelf-Ghibelline, Bianchi-Neri, or some other confused disturbance rose to such a height, that Dante, whose party had seemed the stronger, was with his friends cast unexpectedly forth into banishment; doomed thenceforth to a life of woe and wandering. His property was all confiscated and more; he had the fiercest feeling that it was entirely unjust, nefarious in the sight of God and man. He tried what was in him to get reinstated; tried even by warlike surprisal, with arms in his hand: but it would not do; bad only had become worse. There is a record, I believe, still extant in the Florence Archives, dooming this Dante, wheresoever caught, to be burnt alive. Burnt alive; so it stands, they say: a very curious civic document. Another curious document, some considerable number of years later, is a Letter of Dante's to the Florentine Magistrates, written in answer to a milder proposal of theirs, that he should return on condition of apologising and paying a fine. He answers, with fixed stern pride: "If I cannot return without calling myself guilty, I will never return, *nunquam revertar.*"

For Dante there was now no home in this world. He wandered from patron to patron, from place to place; proving in his own bitter words, 'How hard is the path, *Come è duro calle.*' The wretched are not cheerful company. Dante, poor and banished, with his proud earnest nature, with his moody humours, was not a man to conciliate men. Petrarch reports of him that being at Can della Scala's court, and blamed one day for his gloom and taciturnity, he answered in no courtier-like way. Della Scala stood among his courtiers, with mimes and buffoons (*nebulones ac histriones*) making him heartily merry; when turning to Dante, he said: "Is it not strange, now, that this poor fool should make himself so entertaining; while you, a wise man, sit there day after day, and have nothing to amuse us with at all?" Dante answered bitterly: "No, not strange; your Highness is to recollect the Proverb, *Like to Like;*"—given the amuser, the amusee

must also be given! Such a man, with his proud silent
ways, with his sarcasms and sorrows, was not made to
succeed at court. By degrees, it came to be evident
to him that he had no longer any resting-place, or hope
of benefit, in this earth. The earthly world had cast
him forth, to wander, wander; no living heart to love
him now; for his sore miseries there was no solace
here.

The deeper naturally would the Eternal World impress itself on him; that awful reality over which, after
all, this Time-world, with its Florences and banish-
ments, only flutters as an unreal shadow. Florence
thou shalt never see: but Hell and Purgatory and
Heaven thou shalt surely see! What is Florence, Can
della Scala, and the World and Life altogether?
ETERNITY: thither, of a truth, not elsewhither, art thou
and all things bound! The great soul of Dante, homeless on earth, made its home more and more in that
awful other world. Naturally his thoughts brooded on
that, as on the one fact important for him. Bodied
or bodiless, it is the one fact important for all men:—
but to Dante, in that age, it was bodied in fixed certainty
of scientific shape; he no more doubted of that *Male-
bolge* Pool, that it all lay there with its gloomy circles,
with its *alti guai*, and that he himself should see it,
than we doubt that we should see Constantinople if
we went thither. Dante's heart, long filled with this,
brooding over it in speechless thought and awe, bursts
forth at length into ' mystic unfathomable song;' and
this his *Divine Comedy*, the most remarkable of all
modern Books, is the result.

It must have been a great solacement to Dante, and
was, as we can see, a proud thought for him at times,
That he, here in exile, could do this work; that no
Florence, nor no man or men, could hinder him from
doing it, or even much help him in doing it. He knew
too, partly, that it was great; the greatest a man
could do. ' If thou follow thy star, *Se tu segui tua
stella*,'—so could the Hero, in his forsakenness, in his
extreme need, still say to himself: " Follow thou thy
star, thou shalt not fail of a glorious haven !" The
labour of writing, we find, and indeed could know

otherwise, was great and painful for him; he says,
This Book, ' which has made me lean for many years.'
Ah yes, it was won, all of it, with pain and sore toil,—
not in sport, but in grim earnest. His Book, as indeed
most good Books are, has been written, in many senses,
with his heart's blood. It is his whole history, this
Book. He died after finishing it; not yet very old,
at the age of fifty-six;—broken-hearted rather, as is
said. He lies buried in his death-city Ravenna : *Hic
claudor Dantes patriis extorris ab oris.* The Floren-
tines begged back his body, in a century after; the
Ravenna people would not give it.   " Here am I Dante
laid, shut-out from my native shores."

I said, Dante's Poem was a Song : it is Tieck who
calls it ' a mystic unfathomable Song;' and such is
literally the character of it. Coleridge remarks very
pertinently somewhere, that wherever you find a
sentence musically worded, of true rhythm and melody
in the words, there is something deep and good in the
meaning too. For body and soul, word and idea, go
strangely together here as everywhere. Song : we said
before, it was the Heroic of Speech ! All *old* Poems,
Homer's and the rest, are authentically Songs. I
would say, in strictness, that all right Poems are; that
whatsoever is not *sung* is properly no Poem, but a piece
of Prose cramped into jingling lines,—to the great
injury of the grammar, to the great grief of the reader,
for most part ! What we want to get at is the *thought*
the man had, if he had any : why should he twist it into
jingle, if he *could* speak it out plainly? It is only when
the heart of him is rapt into true passion of melody,
and the very tones of him, according to Coleridge's
remark, become musical by the greatness, depth and
music of his thoughts, that we can give him right to
rhyme and sing; that we call him a Poet, and listen
to him as the Heroic of Speakers,—whose speech *is*
Song. Pretenders to this are many; and to an earnest
reader, I doubt, it is for most part a very melancholy,
not to say an insupportable business, that of reading
rhyme ! Rhyme that had no inward necessity to be
rhymed;—it ought to have told us plainly, without any
jingle, what it was aiming at. I would advise all men

who *can* speak their thought, not to sing it; to understand that, in a serious time, among serious men, there
is no vocation in them for singing it.   Precisely as we
love the true song, and are charmed by it as by something divine, so shall we hate the false song, and
account it a mere wooden noise, a thing hollow, superfluous, altogether an insincere and offensive thing.

I give Dante my highest praise when I say of his
Divine Comedy that it is, in all senses, genuinely a
Song.   In the very sound of it there is a *canto fermo;*
it proceeds as by a chant.   The language, his simple
terza rima, doubtless helped him in this.   One reads
along naturally with a sort of *lilt*.   But I add, that it
could not be otherwise; for the essence and material
of the work are themselves rhythmic.   Its depth, and
rapt passion and sincerity, makes its musical;—go *deep*
enough, there is music everywhere.   A true inward
symmetry, what one calls an architectural harmony,
reigns in it, proportionates it all : architectural; which
also partakes of the character of music.   The three
kingdoms, *Inferno, Purgatorio, Paradiso*, look-out on
one another like compartments of a great edifice; a
great supernatural world-cathedral, piled-up there,
stern, solemn, awful; Dante's World of Souls !   It is,
at bottom, the *sincerest* of all Poems; sincerity, here
too, we find to be the measure of worth.   It came deep
out of the author's heart of hearts; and it goes deep,
and through long generations, into ours.   The people
of Verona, when they saw him on the streets, used to
say, " *Eccovi l' uom ch' è stato all' Inferno*, See, there
is the man that was in Hell !"   Ah, yes, he had been in
Hell;—in Hell enough, in long severe sorrow and
struggle; as the like of him is pretty sure to have been.
Commedias that come-out *divine* are not accomplished
otherwise.   Thought, true labour of any kind, highest
virtue itself, is it not the daughter of Pain?   Born as
out of the black whirlwind;—true *effort,* in fact, as of
a captive struggling to free himself : that is Thought.
In all ways we are ' to become perfect through *suffering.*'—But, as I say, no work known to me is so elabor-
ated as this of Dante's.   It has all been as if molten, in
the hottest furnace of his soul.   It had made him ' lean '

for many years. Not the general whole only; every compartment of it is worked-out, with intense earnestness, into truth, into clear visuality. Each answers to the other; each fits in its place, like a marble stone accurately hewn and polished. It is the soul of Dante, and in this the soul of the middle ages, rendered forever rhythmically visible there. No light task; a right intense one : but a task which is *done*.

Perhaps one would say, *intensity*, with the much that depends on it, is the prevailing character of Dante's genius. Dante does not come before us as a large catholic mind; rather as a narrow and even sectarian mind : it is partly the fruit of his age and position, but partly too of his own nature. His greatness has, in all senses, concentered itself into fiery emphasis and depth. He is world-great not because he is world-wide, but because he is world-deep. Through all objects he pierces as it were down into the heart of Being. I know nothing so intense as Dante. Consider, for example, to begin with the outermost development of his intensity, consider how he paints. He has a great power of vision; seizes the very type of a thing; presents that and nothing more. You remember that first view he gets of the Hall of Dite : *red* pinnacle, redhot cone of iron glowing through the dim immensity of gloom ;—so vivid, so distinct, visible at once and forever ! It is as an emblem of the whole genius of Dante. There is a brevity, an abrupt precision in him : Tacitus is not briefer, more condensed; and then in Dante it seems a natural condensation, spontaneous to the man. One smiting word; and then there is silence, nothing more said. His silence is more eloquent than words. It is strange with what a sharp decisive grace he snatches the true likeness of a matter : cuts into the matter as with a pen of fire. Plutus, the blustering giant, collapses at Virgil's rebuke; it is ' as the sails sink, the mast being suddenly broken.' Or that poor Brunetto Latini, with the *cotto aspetto*, ' face *baked*,' parched brown and lean; and the ' fiery snow,' that falls on them there, a ' fiery snow without wind,' slow, deliberate, never-ending ! Or the lids of those Tombs; square sarcophaguses, in that silent dim-burning Hall, each with its Soul in torment; the lids laid open there; they are to be shut at the Day of Judgment, through Eternity. And how Farinata rises; and how Caval-cante falls—at hearing of his Son, and the past tense '*fue*'! The very movements in Dante have something brief; swift, decisive, almost military. It is of the inmost essence of his genius this sort of painting. The fiery, swift Italian nature of the man, so silent, passion-ate, with its quick abrupt movements, its silent 'pale rages,' speaks itself in these things.

For though this of painting is one of the outermost developments of a man, it comes like all else from the essential faculty of him; it is physiognomical of the whole man. Find a man whose words paint you a like-ness, you have found a man worth something; mark his manner of doing it, as very characteristic of him. In the first place, he could not have discerned the object at all, or seen the vital type of it, unless he had, what we may call, *sympathised* with it,—had sympathy in him to bestow on objects. He must have been *sincere* about it too; sincere and sympathetic : a man without worth cannot give you the likeness of any object; he dwells in vague outwardness, fallacy and trivial hearsay, about all objects. And indeed may we not say that intellect altogether expresses itself in this power of discerning what an object is? Whatsoever of faculty a man's mind may have will come out here. Is it even of business, a matter to be done? The gifted man is he who *sees* the essential point, and leaves all the rest aside as sur-plusage : it is his faculty too, the man of business's faculty, that he discern the true *likeness*, not the false superficial one, of the thing he has got to work in. And how much of *morality* is in the kind of insight we get of anything; ' the eye seeing in all things what it brought with it the faculty of seeing '! To the mean eye all things are trivial, as certainly as to the jaundiced they are yellow. Raphael, the Painters tell us, is the best of all Portrait-painters withal. No most gifted eye can exhaust the significance of any object. In the com-monest human face there lies more than Raphael will take-away with him.

Dante's painting is not graphic only, brief, true, and

of a vividness as of fire in dark night; taken on the wider scale, it is everyway noble, and the outcome of a great soul. Francesca and her Lover, what qualities in that! A thing woven as out of rainbows, on a ground of eternal black. A small flute-voice of infinite wail speaks there, into our very heart of hearts. A touch of womanhood in it too; *della bella persona, che mi fu tolta;* and how, even in the Pit of woe, it is a solace that *he* will never part from her! Saddest tragedy in these *alti guai.* And the racking winds, in that *aer bruno,* whirl them away again, to wail forever!— Strange to think: Dante was the friend of this poor Francesca's father; Francesca herself may have sat upon the Poet's knee, as a bright innocent little child. Infinite pity, yet also infinite rigour of law: it is so Nature is made; it is so Dante discerned that she was made. What a paltry notion is that of his *Divine Comedy's* being a poor splenetic impotent terrestrial libel; putting those into Hell whom he could not be avenged-upon on earth! I suppose if ever pity, tender as a mother's, was in the heart of any man, it was in Dante's. But a man who does not know rigour cannot pity either. His very pity will be cowardly, egoistic,— sentimentality, or little better. I know not in the world an affection equal to that of Dante. It is a tenderness, a trembling, longing, pitying love: like the wail of Æolean harps, soft, soft; like a child's young heart;— and then that stern, sore-saddened heart! These long- ings of his towards his Beatrice; their meeting together in the *Paradiso;* his gazing in her pure transfigured eyes, her that had been purified by death so long, separated from him so far:—one likens it to the song of angels; it is among the purest utterances of affec- tion, perhaps the very purest, that ever came out of a human soul.

For the *intense* Dante is intense in all things; he has got into the essence of all. His intellectual insight as painter, on occasion too as reasoner, is but the result of all other sorts of intensity. Morally great, above all, we must call him; it is the beginning of all. His scorn, his grief are as transcendent as his love;—as indeed, what are they but the *inverse* or *converse* of his love?

*M 2⁷⁸

' *A Dio spiacenti ed a' nemici sui*, Hateful to God and to the enemies of God :' lofty scorn, unappeasable silent reprobation and aversion ; ' *Non ragionam di lor*, We will not speak of *them*, look only and pass.' Or think of this ; ' They have not the *hope* to die, *Non han speranza di morte.*' One day, it had risen sternly benign on the scathed heart of Dante, that he, wretched, never-resting, worn as he was, would full surely *die ;* ' that Destiny itself could not doom him not to die.' Such words are in this man. For rigour, earnestness and depth, he is not to be paralleled in the modern world ; to seek his parallel we must go into the Hebrew Bible, and live with the antique Prophets there.

I do not agree with much modern criticism, in greatly preferring the *Inferno* to the two other parts of the Divine *Commedia.* Such preference belongs, I imagine, to our general Byronism of taste, and is like to be a transient feeling. The *Purgatorio* and *Paradiso*, especially the former, one would almost say, is even more excellent than it. It is a noble thing that *Purgatorio*, ' Mountain of Purification '; an emblem of the noblest conception of that age. If Sin is so fatal, and Hell is and must be so rigorous, awful, yet in Repentance too is man purified ; Repentance is the grand Christian act. It is beautiful how Dante works it out. The *tremolar dell' onde* that ' trembling ' of the ocean-waves, under the first pure gleam of morning, dawning afar on the wandering Two, is as the type of an altered mood. Hope has now dawned ; never-dying Hope, if in company still with heavy sorrow. The obscure sojourn of dæmons and reprobate is underfoot ; a soft breathing of penitence mounts higher and higher, to the Throne of Mercy itself. " Pray for me," the denizens of that Mount of Pain all say to him. " Tell my Giovanna to pray for me," my daughter Giovanna ; " I think her mother loves me no more !" They toil painfully up by that winding steep, ' bent-down like corbels of a building,' some of them,—crushed-together so ' for the sin of pride '; yet nevertheless in years, in ages and æons, they shall have reached the top, which is Heaven's gate, and by Mercy shall have been admitted in. The joy too of all, when one has prevailed ; the whole Mountain shakes with joy, and a psalm of praise rises, when one soul has perfected repentance and got its sin and misery left behind! I call all this a noble embodiment of a true noble thought.

But indeed the Three compartments mutually support one another, are indispensable to one another. The *Paradiso,* a kind of inarticulate music to me, is the redeeming side of the *Inferno;* the *Inferno* without it were untrue. All three make-up the true Unseen World, as figured in the Christianity of the Middle Ages; a thing forever memorable, forever true in the essence of it, to all men. It was perhaps delineated in no human soul with such depth of veracity as in this of Dante's; a man *sent* to sing it, to keep it long memorable. Very notable with what brief simplicity he passes out of the every-day reality, into the Invisible one; and in the second or third stanza, we find ourselves in the World of Spirits; and dwell there, as among things palpable, indubitable! To Dante they *were* so; the real world, as it is called, and its facts, was but the threshold to an infinitely higher Fact of a World. At bottom, the one was as *preter*-natural as the other. Has not each man a soul? He will not only be a spirit, but is one. To the earnest Dante it is all one visible Fact; he believes it, sees it; is the Poet of it in virtue of that. Sincerity, I say again, is the saving merit, now as always.

Dante's Hell, Purgatory, Paradise, are a symbol withal, an emblematic representation of his Belief about this Universe:—some Critic in a future age, like those Scandinavian ones the other day, who has ceased altogether to think as Dante did, may find this too all an 'Allegory,' perhaps an idle Allegory! It is a sublime embodiment, or sublimest, of the soul of Christianity. It expresses, as in huge worldwide architectural emblems, how the Christian Dante felt Good and Evil to be the two polar elements of this Creation, on which it all turns; that these two differ not by *preferability* of one to the other, but by incompatibility absolute and infinite; that the one is excellent and high as light and Heaven, the other hideous, black as Gehenna and the Pit of Hell! Everlasting Justice, yet with Penitence,

with everlasting Pity,—all Christianism, as Dante and
the Middle Ages had it, is emblemed here. Emblemed:
and yet, as I urged the other day, with what entire
truth of purpose; how unconscious of any embleming!
Hell, Purgatory, Paradise: these things were not
fashioned as emblems; was there, in our Modern
European Mind, any thought at all of their being
emblems? Were they not indubitable awful facts; the
whole heart of man taking them for practically true,
all Nature everywhere confirming them? So is it
always in these things. Men do not believe an Allegory.
The future Critic, whatever his new thought may be,
who considers this of Dante to have been all got-up as
an Allegory, will commit one sore mistake!—Paganism
we recognised as a veracious expression of the earnest
awe-struck feeling of man towards the Universe; veracious, true once, and still not without worth for us. But
mark here the difference of Paganism and Christianism;
one great difference. Paganism emblemed chiefly the
Operations of Nature; the destinies, efforts, combinations, vicissitudes of things and men in this world;
Christianism emblemed the Law of Human Duty, the
Moral Law of Man. One was for the sensuous nature:
a rude helpless utterance of the *first* Thought of men,
—the chief recognised virtue, Courage, Superiority to
Fear. The other was not for the sensuous nature, but
for the moral. What a progress is here, if in that
one respect only!—

And so in this Dante, as we said, had ten silent
centuries, in a very strange way, found a voice. The
Divina Commedia is of Dante's writing; yet in truth
it belongs to ten Christian centuries, only the finishing
of it is Dante's. So always. The craftsman there, the
smith with that metal of his, with these tools, with
these cunning methods,—how little of all he does is
properly *his* work! All past inventive men work there
with him;—as indeed with all of us, in all things.
Dante is the spokesman of the Middle Ages; the
Thought they lived by stands here in everlasting music.
These sublime ideas of his, terrible and beautiful, are
the fruit of the Christian Meditation of all the good men

who had gone before him. Precious they; but also is not he precious? Much, had not he spoken, would have been dumb; not dead, yet living voiceless.

On the whole, is it not an utterance, this Mystic Song, at once of one of the greatest human souls, and of the highest thing that Europe had hitherto realised for itself? Christianism, as Dante sings it, is another than Paganism in the rude Norse mind; another than ' Bastard Christianity ' half-articulately spoken in the Arab Desert seven-hundred years before!—The noblest *idea* made *real* hitherto among men, is sung, and emblemed-forth abidingly, by one of the noblest men. In the one sense and in the other, are we not right glad to possess it? As I calculate, it may last yet for long thousands of years. For the thing that is uttered from the inmost parts of a man's soul, differs altogether from what is uttered by the outer part. The outer is of the day, under the empire of mode; the outer passes away, in swift endless changes; the inmost is the same yesterday, today and forever. True souls, in all generations of the world, who look on this Dante, will find a brotherhood in him; the deep sincerity of his thoughts, his woes and hopes, will speak likewise to their sincerity; they will feel that this Dante too was a brother. Napoleon in Saint-Helena is charmed with the genial veracity of old Homer. The oldest Hebrew Prophet, under a vesture the most diverse from ours, does yet, because he speaks from the heart of man, speak to all men's hearts. It is the one sole secret of continuing long memorable. Dante, for depth of sincerity, is like an antique Prophet too; his words, like theirs, come from his very heart. One need not wonder if it were predicted that his Poem might be the most enduring thing our Europe has yet made; for nothing so endures as a truly spoken word. All cathedrals, pontificalities, brass and stone, and outer arrangement never so lasting, are brief in comparison to an unfathomable heart-song like this: one feels as if it might survive, still of importance to men, when these had all sunk into new irrecognisable combinations, and had ceased individually to be. Europe has made much; great cities, great empires, encyclopædias,

creeds, bodies of opinion and practice : but it has made
little of the class of Dante's Thought. Homer yet *is*,
veritably present face to face with every open soul of
us ; and Greece, where is *it?* Desolate for thousands
of years ; away, vanished ; a bewildered heap of stones
and rubbish, the life and existence of it all gone.
Like a dream ; like the dust of King Agamemnon !
Greece was ; Greece, except in the *words* it spoke,
is not.

The uses of this Dante? We will not say much
about his ' uses.' A human soul who has once got
into that primal element of *Song*, and sung-forth fitly
somewhat therefrom, has worked in the *depths* of our
existence ; feeding through long times the life-*roots* of
all excellent human things whatsoever,—in a way that
' utilities ' will not succeed well in calculating ! We
will not estimate the Sun by the quantity of gas-light
it saves us ; Dante shall be invaluable, or of no value.
One remark I may make : the contrast in this respect
between the Hero-Poet and the Hero-Prophet. In a
hundred years, Mahomet, as we saw, had his Arabians
at Grenada and at Delhi ; Dante's Italians seem to be
yet very much where they were. Shall we say, then,
Dante's effect on the world was small in comparison?
Not so : his arena is far more restricted : but also it
is far nobler, clearer ;—perhaps not less but more important. Mahomet speaks to great masses of men, in
the coarse dialect adapted to such ; a dialect filled with
inconsistencies, crudities, follies : on the great masses
alone can he act, and there with good and with evil
strangely blended. Dante speaks to the noble, the
pure and great, in all times and places. Neither does
he grow obsolete, as the other does. Dante burns as
a pure star, fixed there in the firmament, at which the
great and the high of all ages kindle themselves : he
is the possession of all the chosen of the world for un-
counted time. Dante, one calculates, may long survive
Mahomet. In this way the balance may be made
straight again.

But, at any rate, it is not by what is called their
effect on the world by what *we* can judge of their effect
there, that a man and his work are measured. Effect?

Influence? Utility? Let a man *do* his work; the fruit of it is the care of Another than he. It will grow its own fruit; and whether embodied in Caliph Thrones and Arabian Conquests, so that it 'fills all Morning and Evening Newspapers,' and all Histories, which are a kind of distilled Newspapers; or not embodied so at all;—what matters that? That is not the real fruit of it! The Arabian Caliph, in so far only as he did something, was something. If the great Cause of Man, and Man's work in God's Earth, got no furtherance from the Arabian Caliph, then no matter how many scimetars he drew, how many gold piasters pocketed, and what uproar and blaring he made in this world— *he* was but a loud-sounding inanity and futility; at bottom, he *was* not at all. Let us honour the great empire of *Silence*, once more! The boundless treasury which we do *not* jingle in our pockets, or count up and present before men! It is perhaps, of all things, the usefulest for each of us to do, in these loud times.——

As Dante, the Italian man, was sent into our world to embody musically the Religion of the Middle Ages, the Religion of our Modern Europe, its Inner Life; so Shakspeare, we may say, embodies for us the Outer Life of our Europe as developed then, its chivalries, courtesies, humours, ambitions, what practical way of thinking, acting, looking at the world, men then had. As in Homer we may still construe Old Greece; so in Shakspeare and Dante, after thousands of years, what our modern Europe was, in Faith and in Practice, will still be legible. Dante has given us the Faith or soul; Shakspeare, in a not less noble way, has given us the Practice or body. This latter also we were to have: a man was sent for it, the man Shakspeare. Just when that chivalry way of life had reached its last finish, and was on the point of breaking down into slow or swift dissolution, as we now see it everywhere, this other sovereign Poet, with his seeing eye, with his perennial singing voice, was sent to take note of it, to give long-enduring record of it. Two fit men: Dante, deep, fierce as the central fire of the world; Shakspeare, wide, placid, far-seeing, as the Sun, the upper light of the

world.   Italy produced the one world-voice; we English
had the honour of producing the other.

Curious enough how, as it were by mere accident, this
man came to us.   I think always, so great, quiet,
complete and self-sufficing is this Shakspeare, had the
Warwickshire Squire not prosecuted him for deer-
stealing, we had perhaps never heard of him as a Poet !
The woods and skies, the rustic Life of Man in Stratford
there, had been enough for this man !   But indeed that
strange outbudding of our whole English Existence,
which we call the Elizabethan Era, did not it too come
as of its own accord?   The ' Tree Igdrasil ' buds and
withers by its own laws,—too deep for our scanning.
Yet it does bud and wither, and every bough and leaf
of it is there, by fixed eternal laws; not a Sir Thomas
Lucy but comes at the hour fit for him.   Curious, I
say, and not sufficiently considered: how everything
does coöperate with all; not a leaf rotting on the highway but is indissoluble portion of solar and stellar
systems; no thought, word or act of man but has
sprung withal out of all men, and works sooner or
later, recognisably or irrecognisably, on all men !   It is
all a Tree : circulation of sap and influences, mutual
communication of every minutest leaf with the lowest
talon of a root, with every other greatest and minutest
portion of the whole.   The Tree Igdrasil, that has its
roots down in the Kingdoms of Hela and Death, and
whose boughs overspread the highest Heaven !—

In some sense it may be said that this glorious Elizabethan Era with its Shakspeare, as the outcome and
flowerage of all which had preceded it, is itself attribut-
able to the Catholicism of the Middle Ages.   The
Christian Faith, which was the theme of Dante's Song,
had produced this Practical Life which Shakspeare was
to sing.   For Religion then, as it now and always is,
was the soul of Practice; the primary vital fact in men's
life.   And remark here, as rather curious, that Middle-
Age Catholicism was abolished, so far as Acts of Parliament could abolish it, before Shakspeare, the noblest
product of it, made his appearance.   He did make his
appearance nevertheless.   Nature at her own time, with
Catholicism or what else might be necessary, sent him

forth; taking small thought of Acts of Parliament. King-Henrys, Queen-Elizabeths go their way; and Nature too goes hers. Acts of Parliament, on the whole, are small, notwithstanding the noise they make. What Act of Parliament, debate at St. Stephen's, on the hustings or elsewhere, was it that brought this Shakspeare into being? No dining at Freemasons' Tavern, opening subscription-lists, selling of shares, and infinite other jangling and true or false endeavouring! This Elizabethan Era, and all its nobleness and blessedness, came without proclamation, preparation of ours. Priceless Shakspeare was the free gift of Nature; given altogether silently;—received altogether silently, as if it had been a thing of little account. And yet, very literally, it is a priceless thing. One should look at that side of matters too.

Of this Shakspeare of ours, perhaps the opinion one sometimes hears a little idolatrously expressed is, in fact, the right one; I think the best judgment not of this country only, but of Europe at large, is slowly pointing to the conclusion, That Shakspeare is the chief of all Poets hitherto; the greatest intellect who, in our recorded world, has left record of himself in the way of Literature. On the whole, I know not such a power of vision, such a faculty of thought, if we take all the characters of it, in any other man. Such a calmness of depth; placid joyous strength; all things imaged in that great soul of his so true and clear, as in a tranquil unfathomable sea! It has been said, that in the constructing of Shakspeare's Dramas there is, apart from all other ' faculties ' as they are called, an understanding manifested, equal to that in Bacon's *Novum Organum*. That is true; and it is not a truth that strikes every one. It would become more apparent if we tried, any of us for himself, how, out of Shakspeare's dramatic materials, *we* could fashion such a result! The built house seems all so fit,—everyway as it should be, as if it came there by its own law and the nature of things,—we forget the rude disorderly quarry it was shaped from. The very perfection of the house, as if Nature herself had made it, hides the builder's merit. Perfect, more perfect than any other man, we may call Shakspeare in this : he discerns, knows as by instinct, what condition he works under, what his materials are, what his own force and its relation to them is. It is not a transitory glance of insight that will suffice ; it is deliberate illumination of the whole matter; it is a calmly *seeing* eye; a great intellect, in short. How a man, of some wide thing that he has witnessed, will construct a narrative, what kind of picture and delineation he will give of it,—is the best measure you could get of what intellect is in the man. Which circumstance is vital and shall stand prominent; which unessential, fit to be suppressed; where is the true *beginning*, the true sequence and ending? To find out this, you task the whole force of insight that is in the man. He must *understand* the thing; according to the depth of his understanding, will the fitness of his answer be. You will try him so. Does like join itself to like; does the spirit of method stir in that confusion, so that its embroilment becomes order? Can the man say, *Fiat lux*, Let there be light; and out of chaos make a world? Precisely as there is *light* in himself, will he accomplish this.

Or indeed we may say again, it is in what I called Portrait-painting, delineating of men and things, especially of men, that Shakspeare is great. All the greatness of the man comes out decisively here. It is unexampled, I think, that calm creative perspicacity of Shakspeare. The thing he looks at reveals not this or that face of it, but its inmost heart, and generic secret : it dissolves itself as in light before him, so that he discerns the perfect structure of it. Creative, we said : poetic creation, what is this too but *seeing* the thing sufficiently? The *word* that will describe the thing, follows of itself from such clear intense sight of the thing. And is not Shakspeare's *morality*, his valour, candour, tolerance, truthfulness; his whole victorious strength and greatness, which can triumph over such obstructions, visible there too? Great as the world ! No *twisted*, poor convex-concave mirror, reflecting all objects with its own convexities and concavities ; a perfectly *level* mirror ;—that is to say withal, if we will

understand it, a man justly related to all things and
men, a good man. It is truly a lordly spectacle how
this great soul takes-in all kinds of men and objects,
a Falstaff, an Othello, a Juliet, a Coriolanus; sets them
all forth to us in their round completeness; loving,
just, the equal brother of all. *Novum Organum*, and
all the intellect you will find in Bacon, is of a quite
secondary order; earthly, material, poor in comparison
with this. Among modern men, one finds, in strictness, almost nothing of the same rank. Goethe alone,
since the days of Shakspeare, reminds me of it. Of
him too you say that he *saw* the object; you may say
what he himself says of Shakspeare : ' His characters
are like watches with dial-plates of transparent crystal;
they show you the hour like others, and the inward
mechanism also is all visible.'

The seeing eye ! It is this that discloses the inner
harmony of things; what Nature meant, what musical
idea Nature has wrapped-up in these often rough
embodiments. Something she did mean. To the seeing
eye that something were discernible. Are they base,
miserable things? You can laugh over them, you can
weep over them; you can in some way or other genially
relate yourself to them;—you can, at lowest, hold your
peace about them, turn away your own and others' face
from them, till the hour come for practically extermin-
ating and extinguishing them ! At bottom, it is the
Poet's first gift, as it is all men's, that he have intellect
enough. He will be a Poet if he have : a Poet in word;
or failing that, perhaps still better, a Poet in act.
Whether he write at all; and if so, whether in prose or
in verse, will depend on accidents : who knows on what
extremely trivial accidents,—perhaps on his having had
a singing-master, on his being taught to sing in his
boyhood ! But the faculty which enables him to discern
the inner heart of things, and the harmony that dwells
there (for whatsoever exists has a harmony in the heart
of it, or it would not hold together and exist), is not
the result of habits or accidents, but the gift of Nature
herself; the primary outfit for a Heroic Man in what
sort soever. To the Poet, as to every other, we say

first of all, *See*. If you cannot do that, it is of no use to keep stringing rhymes together, jingling sensibilities against each other, and *name* yourself a Poet; there is no hope for you. If you can, there is, in prose or verse, in action or speculation, all manner of hope. The crabbed old Schoolmaster used to ask, when they brought him a new pupil, " But are ye sure he's *not a dunce?*" Why, really one might ask the same thing, in regard to every man proposed for whatsoever function; and consider it as the one inquiry needful : Are ye sure he's not a dunce? There is, in this world, no other entirely fatal person.

For, in fact, I say the degree of vision that dwells in a man is a correct measure of the man. If called to define Shakspeare's faculty, I should say superiority of Intellect, and think I had included all under that. What indeed are faculties? We talk of faculties as if they were distinct, things separable; as if a man had intellect, imagination, fancy, &c., as he has hands, feet and arms. That is a capital error. Then again, we hear of a man's ' intellectual nature,' and of his ' moral nature,' as if these again were divisible, and existed apart. Necessities of language do perhaps prescribe such forms of utterance; we must speak, I am aware, in that way, if we are to speak at all. But words ought not to harden into things for us. It seems to me, our apprehension of this matter is, for the most part, radically falsified thereby. We ought to know withal, and to keep for ever in mind, that these divisions are at bottom but *names;* that man's spiritual nature, the vital Force which dwells in him, is essentially one and indivisible; that what we call imagination, fancy, understanding, and so forth, are but different figures of the same Power of Insight, all indissolubly connected with each other, physiognomically related; that if we knew one of them, we might know all of them. Morality itself, what we call the moral quality of a man, what is this but another *side* of the one vital Force whereby he is and works? All that a man does is physiognomical of him. You may see how a man would fight, by the way in which he sings; his courage, or want of courage, is visible in the word he utters, in the opinion he has formed, no less than in the stroke he strikes. He is *one;* and preaches the same Self abroad in all these ways.

Without hands a man might have feet, and could still walk : but, consider it,—without morality, intellect were impossible for him; a thoroughly immoral *man* could not know anything at all ! To know a thing, what we can call knowing, a man must first *love* the thing, sympathise with it : that is, be *virtuously* related to it. If he have not the justice to put down his own selfishness at every turn, the courage to stand by the dangerous-true at every turn, how shall he know? His virtues, all of them, will lie recorded in his knowledge. Nature, with her truth, remains to the bad, to the selfish and the pusillanimous forever a sealed book : what such can know of Nature is mean, superficial, small; for the uses of the day merely.—But does not the very Fox know something of Nature? Exactly so : it knows where the geese lodge ! The human Reynard, very frequent everywhere in the world, what more does he know but this and the like of this? Nay, it should be considered, too, that if the Fox had not a certain vulpine *morality*, he could not even know where the geese were, or get at the geese ! If he spent his time in splenetic atrabiliar reflections on his own misery, his ill usage by Nature, Fortune and other Foxes, and so forth; and had not courage, promptitude, practicality, and other suitable vulpine gifts and graces, he would catch no geese. We may say of the Fox too, that his morality and insight are of the same dimensions; different faces of the same internal unity of vulpine life !—These things are worth stating; for the contrary of them acts with manifold very baleful perversion, in this time : what limitations, modifications they require, your own candour will supply.

If I say, therefore, that Shakspeare is the greatest of Intellects, I have said all concerning him. But there is more in Shakspeare's intellect than we have yet seen. It is what I call an unconscious intellect; there is more virtue in it than he himself is aware of. Novalis beautifully remarks of him, that those Dramas of his are Products of Nature too, deep as Nature herself. I find a great truth in this saying. Shakspeare's Art is not Artifice; the noblest worth of it is not there by plan or precontrivance. It grows-up from the deeps of Nature, through this noble sincere soul, who is a voice of Nature. The latest generations of men will find new meanings in Shakspeare, new elucidations of their own human being; ' new harmonies with the infinite structure of the Universe; concurrences with later ideas, affinities with the higher powers and senses of man.' This well deserves meditating. It is Nature's highest reward to a true simple great soul, that he get thus to be *a part of herself.* Such a man's works, whatsoever he with utmost conscious exertion and forethought shall accomplish, grow up withal *un*consciously, from the unknown deeps in him;—as the oak-tree grows from the Earth's bosom, as the mountains and waters shape themselves; with a symmetry grounded on Nature's own laws, conformable to all Truth whatsoever. How much in Shakspeare lies hid; his sorrows, his silent struggles known to himself; much that was not known at all, not speakable at all; like *roots,* like sap and forces working underground! Speech is great; but Silence is greater.

Withal the joyful tranquillity of this man is notable. I will not blame Dante for his misery: it is as battle without victory; but true battle,—the first, indispensable thing. Yet I call Shakspeare greater than Dante, in that he fought truly, and did conquer. Doubt it not, he had his own sorrows: those *Sonnets* of his will even testify expressly in what deep waters he had waded, and swum struggling for his life;—as what man like him ever failed to have to do? It seems to me a heedless notion, our common one, that he sat like a bird on the bough; and sang forth, free and offhand, never knowing the troubles of other men. Not so; with no man is it so. How could a man travel forward from rustic deer-poaching to such tragedy-writing, and not fall-in with sorrows by the way? Or, still better, how could a man delineate a Hamlet, a Coriolanus, a Macbeth, so many suffering heroic hearts, if his own heroic heart had never suffered?—And now, in contrast with all this, observe his mirthfulness, his genuine overflowing love

of laughter! You would say, in no point does he
exaggerate but only in laughter. Fiery objurgations,
words that pierce and burn, are to be found in Shakspeare; yet he is always in measure here; never what
Johnson would remark as a specially ' good hater.'
But his laughter seems to pour from him in floods; he
heaps all manner of ridiculous nicknames on the butt
he is bantering, tumbles and tosses him in all sorts of
horse-play; you would say, with his whole heart laughs.
And then, if not always the finest, it is always a genial
laughter. Not at mere weakness, at misery or poverty;
never. No man who *can* laugh, what we call laughing,
will laugh at these things. It is some poor character
only *desiring* to laugh, and have the credit of wit, that
does so. Laughter means sympathy; good laughter is
not ' the crackling of thorns under the pot.' Even at
stupidity and pretension this Shakspeare does not laugh
otherwise than genially. Dogberry and Verges tickle
our very hearts; and we dismiss them covered with explosions of laughter : but we like the poor fellows only
the better for our laughing; and hope they will get on
well there, and continue Presidents of the City-watch.
Such laughter, like sunshine on the deep sea, is very
beautiful to me.

We have no room to speak of Shakspeare's individual
works; though perhaps there is much still waiting to
be said on that head. Had we, for instance, all his
plays reviewed as *Hamlet*, in *Wilhelm Meister*, is ! A
thing which might, one day, be done. August Wilhelm
Schlegel has a remark on his Historical Plays, *Henry
Fifth* and the others, which is worth remembering. He
calls them a kind of National Epic. Marlborough, you
recollect, said, he knew no English History but what
he had learned from Shakspeare. There are really, if
we look to it, few as memorable Histories. The great
salient points are admirably seized; all rounds itself off,
into a kind of rhythmic coherence; it is, as Schlegel says,
epic;—as indeed all delineation by a great thinker will
be. There are right beautiful things in those Pieces,
which indeed together form one beautiful thing. That
battle of Agincourt strikes me as one of the most per-

fect things, in its sort, we anywhere have of Shakspeare's. The description of the two hosts: the worn-
out, jaded English; the dread hour, big with destiny,
when the battle shall begin; and then that deathless
valour: "Ye good yeomen, whose limbs were made in
England!" There is a noble Patriotism in it,—far
other than the 'indifference' you sometimes hear as-
cribed to Shakspeare. A true English heart breathes,
calm and strong, through the whole business; not
boisterous, protrusive; all the better for that. There
is a sound in it like the ring of steel. This man too had
a right stroke in him, had it come to that!

But I will say, of Shakspeare's works generally, that
we have no full impress of him there; even as full as
we have of many men. His works are so many windows,
through which we see a glimpse of the world that was
in him. All his works seem, comparatively speaking,
cursory, imperfect, written under cramping circumstances; giving only here and there a note of the full
utterance of the man. Passages there are that come
upon you like splendour out of Heaven; bursts of
radiance, illuminating the very heart of the thing: you
say, "That is *true*, spoken once and forever; wheresoever and whensoever there is an open human soul,
that will be recognised as true!" Such bursts, however, make us feel that the surrounding matter is not
radiant; that it is, in part, temporary, conventional.
Alas, Shakspeare had to write for the Globe Play-house:
his great soul had to crush itself, as it could, into that
and no other mould. It was with him, then, as it is
with us all. No man works save under conditions. The
sculptor cannot set his own free Thought before us; but
his Thought as he could translate it into the stone that
was given, with the tools that were given. *Disjecta
membra* are all that we find of any Poet, or of any man.

Whoever looks intelligently at this Shakspeare may
recognise that he too was a *Prophet*, in his way; of an
insight analogous to the Prophetic, though he took it
up in another strain. Nature seemed to this man also
divine; *un*speakable, deep as Tophet, high as Heaven:
'We are such stuff as Dreams are made of!' That

scroll in Westminster Abbey, which few read with understanding, is of the depth of any seer. But the man sang; did not preach, except musically. We called Dante the melodious Priest of Middle-Age Catholicism. May we not call Shakspeare the still more melodious Priest of a *true* Catholicism, the ' Universal Church ' of the Future and of all times ? No narrow super-stition, harsh asceticism, intolerance, fanatical fierce-ness or perversion : a Revelation, so far as it goes, that such a thousandfold hidden beauty and divineness dwells in all Nature; which let all men worship as they can ! We may say without offence, that there rises a kind of universal Psalm out of this Shakspeare too; not unfit to make itself heard among the still more sacred Psalms. Not in disharmony with these, if we under-stood them, but in harmony !—I cannot call this Shak-speare a ' Sceptic,' as some do; his indifference to the creeds and theological quarrels of his time misleading them. No : neither unpatriotic, though he says little about his Patriotism; nor sceptic, though he says little about his Faith. Such ' indifference ' was the fruit of his greatness withal : his whole heart was in his own grand sphere of worship (we may call it such) : these other controversies, vitally important to other men, were not vital to him.

But call it worship, call it what you will, is it not a right glorious thing, and set of things, this that Shak-speare has brought us? For myself, I feel that there is actually a kind of sacredness in the fact of such a man being sent into this Earth. Is he not an eye to us all; a blessed heaven-sent Bringer of Light?—And, at bottom, was it not perhaps far better that this Shak-speare, everyway an unconscious man, was *conscious* of no Heavenly message? He did not feel, like Maho-met, because he saw into those internal Splendours, that he specially was the ' Prophet of God :' and was he not greater than Mahomet in that? Greater; and also, if we compute strictly, as we did in Dante's case, more successful. It was intrinsically an error that notion of Mahomet's, of his supreme Prophethood : and has come down to us inextricably involved in error to this day; dragging along with it such a coil of fables, impurities, intolerances, as makes it a questionable step for me here and now to say, as I have done, that Mahomet was a true Speaker at all, and not rather an ambitious charlatan, perversity and simulacrum; no Speaker, but a Babbler! Even in Arabia, as I compute, Mahomet will have exhausted himself and become obsolete, while this Shakspeare, this Dante may still be young;—while this Shakspeare may still pretend to be a Priest of Mankind, of Arabia as of other places, for unlimited periods to come!

Compared with any speaker or singer one knows, even with Æschylus or Homer, why should he not, for veracity and universality, last like them? He is *sincere* as they; reaches deep down like them, to the universal and perennial. But as for Mahomet, I think it had been better for him *not* to be so conscious! Alas, poor Mahomet; all that he was *conscious* of was a mere error; a futility and triviality,—as indeed such ever is. The truly great in him too was the unconscious: that he was a wild Arab lion of the desert, and did speak-out with that great thunder-voice of his, not by words which he *thought* to be great, but by actions, by feelings, by a history which *were* great! His Koran has become a stupid piece of prolix absurdity; we do not believe, like him, that God wrote that! The Great Man here too, as always, is a Force of Nature: whatsoever is truly great in him springs-up from the *in*articulate deeps.

Well: this is our poor Warwickshire Peasant, who rose to be Manager of a Playhouse, so that he could live without begging; whom the Earl of Southampton cast some kind glances on; whom Sir Thomas Lucy, many thanks to him, was for sending to the Treadmill! We did not account him a god, like Odin, while he dwelt with us;—on which point there were much to be said. But I will say rather, or repeat: In spite of the sad state Hero-worship now lies in, consider what this Shakspeare has actually become among us. Which Englishman we ever made, in this land of ours, which million of Englishmen, would we not give-up rather than the Stratford Peasant? There is no regiment of highest Dignitaries that **we** would sell him for. He is the grand-

est thing we have yet done. For our honour among
foreign nations, as an ornament to our English Household, what item is there that we would not surrender
rather than him? Consider now, if they asked us, Will
you give-up your Indian Empire or your Shakspeare,
you English; never have had any Indian Empire, or
never have had any Shakspeare? Really it were a grave
question. Official persons would answer doubtless in
official language; but we, for our part too, should not
we be forced to answer: Indian Empire, or no Indian
Empire; we cannot do without Shakspeare! Indian
Empire will go, at any rate, some day; but this Shakspeare does not go, he lasts forever with us; we cannot
give-up our Shakspeare!

Nay, apart from spiritualities; and considering him
merely as a real, marketable, tangibly-useful possession.
England, before long, this Island of ours, will hold but
a small fraction of the English: in America, in New
Holland, east and west to the very Antipodes, there will
be a Saxondom covering great spaces of the Globe.
And now, what is it that can keep all these together into
virtually one Nation, so that they do not fall-out and
fight, but live at peace, in brotherlike intercourse, helping one another? This is justly regarded as the greatest
practical problem, the thing all manner of sovereignties
and governments are here to accomplish: what is it
that will accomplish this? Acts of Parliament, adminis-
trative prime-ministers cannot. America is parted from
us, so far as Parliament could part it. Call it not
fantastic, for there is much reality in it: Here, I say,
is an English King, whom no time or chance, Parliament or combination of Parliaments, can dethrone!
This King Shakspeare, does not he shine, in crowned
sovereignty, over us all, as the noblest, gentlest, yet
strongest of rallying-signs; *in*destructible; really more
valuable in that point of view than any other means or
appliance whatsoever? We can fancy him as radiant
aloft over all the Nations of Englishmen, a thousand
years hence. From Paramatta, from New York, wheresoever, under what sort of Parish-Constable soever,
English men and women are, they will say to one
another: " Yes, this Shakspeare is ours; we produced

him, we speak and think by him; we are of one blood
and kind with him." The most common-sense politician,
too, if he pleases, may think of that.

Yes, truly, it is a great thing for a Nation that it get
an articulate voice; that it produce a man who will
speak-forth melodiously what the heart of it means!
Italy, for example, poor Italy lies dismembered,
scattered asunder, not appearing in any protocol or
treaty as a unity at all; yet the noble Italy is actually
one: Italy produced its Dante; Italy can speak! The
Czar of all the Russias, he is strong, with so many
bayonets, Cossacks and cannons; and does a great feat
in keeping such a tract of Earth politically together;
but he cannot yet speak. Something great in him, but
it is a dumb greatness. He has had no voice of genius,
to be heard of all men and times. He must learn to
speak. He is a great dumb monster hitherto. His
cannons and Cossacks will all have rusted into nonentity,
while that Dante's voice is still audible. The Nation
that has a Dante is bound together as no dumb Russia
can be.—We must here end what we had to say of the
Hero-Poet.

LECTURE IV

THE HERO AS PRIEST.   LUTHER; REFORMATION: KNOX; PURITANISM.

[*Friday, 15th May* 1840]

OUR present discourse is to be of the Great Man as
Priest. We have repeatedly endeavoured to explain
that all sorts of Heroes are intrinsically of the same
material; that given a great soul, open to the Divine
Significance of Life, then there is given a man fit to
speak of this, to sing of this, to fight and work for
this, in a great, victorious, enduring manner; there
is given a Hero,—the outward shape of whom will
depend on the time and the environment he finds himself
in. The priest too, as I understand it, is a kind of

Prophet; in him too there is required to be a light of inspiration, as we must name it. He presides over the worship of the people; is the Uniter of them with the Unseen Holy. He is the spiritual Captain of the people; as the Prophet is their spiritual King with many captains : he guides them heavenward, by wise guidance through this Earth and its work. The ideal of him is, that he too be what we can call a voice from the unseen Heaven; interpreting, even as the Prophet did, and in a more familiar manner unfolding the same to men. The unseen Heaven,—the ' open secret of the Universe,' —which so few have an eye for ! He is the Prophet shorn of his more awful splendour; burning with mild equable radiance, as the enlightener of daily life. This, I say, is the ideal of a Priest. So in old times; so in these, and in all times. One knows very well that, in reducing ideals to practice, great latitude of tolerance is needful; very great. But a Priest who is not this at all, who does not any longer aim or try to be this, is a character—of whom we had rather not speak in this place.

Luther and Knox were by express vocation Priests, and did faithfully perform that function in its common sense. Yet it will suit us better here to consider them chiefly in their historical character, rather as Reformers than Priests. There have been other Priests perhaps equally notable, in calmer times, for doing faithfully the office of a Leader of Worship; bringing down, by faithful heroism in that kind, a light from Heaven into the daily life of their people; leading them forward, as under God's guidance, in the way wherein they were to go. But when this same *way* was a rough one, of battle, confusion and danger, the spiritual Captain, who led through that, becomes, especially to us who live under the fruit of his leading, more notable than any other. He is the warfaring and battling Priest; who led his people, not to quiet faithful labour as in smooth times, but to faithful valorous conflict, in times all violent, dismembered : a more perilous service, and a more memorable one, be it higher or not. These two men we will account our best Priests, inasmuch as they were our best Reformers. Nay I may ask, Is not every

true Reformer, by the nature of him, a *Priest* first of all?
He appeals to Heaven's invisible justice against Earth's
visible force; knows that it, the invisible, is strong and
alone strong.   He is a believer in the divine truth of
things; a *seer,* seeing through the shows of things; a
worshipper, in one way or the other, of the divine truth
of things; a Priest, that is.   If he be not first a Priest,
he will never be good for much as a Reformer.

Thus, then, as we have seen Great Men, in various
situations, building up Religions, heroic Forms of
human Existence in this world, Theories of Life worthy
to be sung by a Dante, Practices of Life by a Shakspeare,—we are now to see the reverse process; which
also is necessary, which also may be carried on in the
Heroic manner.   Curious how this should be necessary:
yet necessary it is.   The mild shining of the Poet's light
has to give place to the fierce lightning of the Reformer:
unfortunately the Reformer too is a personage that cannot fail in History!   The Poet indeed, with his mild-
ness, what is he but the product and ultimate adjustment
of Reform, or Prophecy with its fierceness?   No wild
Saint Dominics and Thebaïd Eremites, there had been
no melodious Dante; rough Practical Endeavour, Scandinavian and other, from Odin to Walter Raleigh, from
Ulfila to Cranmer, enabled Shakspeare to speak.   Nay
the finished Poet, I remark sometimes, is a symptom
that his epoch itself has reached perfection and is
finished; that before long there will be a new epoch,
new Reformers needed.

Doubtless it were finer, could we go along always in
the way of *music;* be tamed and taught by our Poets,
as the rude creatures were by their Orpheus of old.   Or
failing this rhythmic *musical* way, how good were it
could we get so much as into the *equable* way; I mean,
if *peaceable* Priests, reforming from day to day, would
always suffice us!   But it is not so; even this latter
has not yet been realised.   Alas, the battling Reformer
too is, from time to time, a needful and inevitable phenomenon.   Obstructions are never wanting: the very
things that were once indispensable furtherances become
obstructions; and need to be shaken off, and left behind
us,—a business often of enormous difficulty.   It is

notable enough, surely, how a Theorem or spiritual Representation, so we may call it, which once took in the whole Universe, and was completely satisfactory in all parts of it to the highly-discursive acute intellect of Dante, one of the greatest in the world,—had in the course of another century become dubitable to common intellects; become deniable; and is now, to every one of us, flatly incredible, obsolete as Odin's Theorem! To Dante, human Existence, and God's ways with men, were all well represented by those *Malebolges, Purgatorios;* to Luther not well. How was this? Why could not Dante's Catholicism continue; but Luther's Protestantism must needs follow? Alas, nothing will *continue.*

I do not make much of ' Progress of the Species,' as handled in these times of ours; nor do I think you would care to hear much about it. The talk on that subject is too often of the most extravagant, confused sort. Yet I may say, the fact itself seems certain enough; nay we can trace out the inevitable necessity of it in the nature of things. Every man, as I have stated somewhere, is not only a learner but a doer: he learns with the mind given him what has been; but with the same mind he discovers farther, he invents and devises somewhat of his own. Absolutely without originality there is no man. No man whatever believes, or can believe, exactly what his grandfather believed: he enlarges somewhat, by fresh discovery, his view of the Universe, and consequently his Theorem of the Universe,—which is an *infinite* Universe, and can never be embraced wholly or finally by any view or Theorem, in any conceivable enlargement: he enlarges somewhat, I say; finds somewhat that was credible to his grandfather incredible to him, false to him, inconsistent with some new thing he has discovered or observed. It is the history of every man; and in the history of Mankind we see it summed-up into great historical amounts,—revolutions, new epochs. Dante's Mountain of Purgatory does *not* stand ' in the ocean of the other Hemisphere,' when Columbus has once sailed thither! Men find no such thing extant in the other Hemisphere. It is not there. It must cease to be believed to be there. So with all beliefs whatsoever in this world,—all Systems of Belief, and Systems of Practice that spring from these.

If we add now the melancholy fact, that when Belief waxes uncertain, Practice too becomes unsound, and errors, injustices and miseries everywhere more and more prevail, we shall see material enough for revolution. At all turns, a man who will *do* faithfully, needs to believe firmly. If he have to ask at every turn the world's suffrage; if he cannot dispense with the world's suffrage, and make his own suffrage serve, he is a poor eye-servant; the work committed to him will be *misdone*. Every such man is a daily contributor to the inevitable downfall. Whatsoever work he does, dishonestly, with an eye to the outward look of it, is a new offence, parent of new misery to somebody or other. Offences accumulate till they become insupportable; and are then violently burst through, cleared off as by explosion. Dante's sublime Catholicism, incredible now in theory, and defaced still worse by faithless, doubting and dishonest practice, has to be torn asunder by a Luther; Shakspeare's noble feudalism, as beautiful as it once looked and was, has to end in a French Revolution. The accumulation of offences is, as we say, too literally *exploded*, blasted asunder volcanically; and there are long troublous periods before matters come to a settlement again.

Surely it were mournful enough to look only at this face of the matter, and find in all human opinions and arrangements merely the fact that they were uncertain, temporary, subject to the law of death! At bottom, it is not so: all death, here too we find, is but of the body, not of the essence or soul; all destruction, by violent revolution or howsoever it be, is but new creation on a wider scale. Odinism was *Valour;* Christianism was *Humility*, a nobler kind of Valour. No thought that ever dwelt honestly as true in the heart of man but *was* an honest insight into God's truth on man's part, and *has* an essential truth in it which endures through all changes, an everlasting possession for us all. And, on the other hand, what a melancholy notion is that, which has to represent all men, in all countries and times except our own, as having spent their life in blind condemnable error, mere lost Pagans, Scandinavians, Mahometans, only that we might have the true ultimate knowledge! All generations of men were lost and wrong, only that this present little section of a generation might be saved and right. They all marched forward there, all generations since the beginning of the world, like the Russian soldiers into the ditch of Schweidnitz Fort, only to fill-up the ditch with their dead bodies, that we might march-over and take the place! It is an incredible hypothesis.

Such incredible hypothesis we have seen maintained with fierce emphasis; and this or the other poor individual man, with his sect of individual men, marching as over the dead bodies of all men, towards sure victory : but when he too, with his hypothesis and ultimate infallible credo, sank into the ditch, and became a dead body, what was to be said?—Withal, it is an important fact in the nature of man, that he tends to reckon his own insight as final, and goes upon it as such. He will always do it, I suppose, in one or the other way; but it must be in some wider, wiser way than this. Are not all true men that live, or that ever lived, soldiers of the same army, enlisted, under Heaven's captaincy, to do battle against the same enemy, the Empire of Darkness and Wrong? Why should we misknow one another, fight not against the enemy but against ourselves, from mere difference of uniform? All uniforms shall be good, so they hold in them true valiant men. All fashions of arms, the Arab turban and swift scimetar, Thor's strong hammer smiting down *Jötuns,* shall be welcome. Luther's battle-voice, Dante's march-melody, all genuine things are with us, not against us. We are all under one Captain, soldiers of the same host.—Let us now look a little at this Luther's fighting; what kind of battle it was, and how he comported himself in it. Luther too was of our spiritual Heroes; a Prophet to his country and time.

As introductory to the whole, a remark about Idolatry will perhaps be in place here. One of Mahomet's characteristics, which indeed belongs to all Prophets, is unlimited implacable zeal against Idolatry. It is the *divine* beauty and significance in stars and all natural objects whatsoever. Why should the Prophet so mercilessly condemn him? The poorest mortal worshipping his Fetish, while his heart is full of it, may be an object of pity, of contempt and avoidance, if you will; but cannot surely be an object of hatred. Let his heart *be* honestly full of it, the whole space of his dark narrow mind illuminated thereby; in one word, let him entirely *believe* in his Fetish,—it will then be, I should say, if not well with him, yet as well as it can readily be made to be, and you will leave him alone, unmolested there.

But here enters the fatal circumstance of Idolatry, that, in the era of the Prophets, no man's mind *is* any longer honestly filled with his Idol or Symbol. Before the Prophet can arise who, seeing through it, knows it to be mere wood, many men must have begun dimly to doubt that it was little more. Condemnable Idolatry is *insincere* Idolatry. Doubt has eaten-out the heart of it: a human soul is seen clinging spasmodically to an Ark of the Covenant, which it half-feels now to have become a Phantasm. This is one of the balefulest sights. Souls are no longer *filled* with their Fetish; but only pretend to be filled, and would fain make themselves feel that they are filled. "You do not believe," said Coleridge; "you only believe that you believe." It is the final scene in all kinds of Worship and Symbolism; the sure symptom that death is now nigh. It is equivalent to what we call Formulism, and Worship of Formulas, in these days of ours. No more immoral act can be done by a human creature; for it is the beginning of all immorality, or rather it is the impossibility henceforth of any morality whatsoever: the innermost moral soul is paralysed thereby, cast into fatal magnetic sleep! Men are no longer *sincere* men. I do not wonder that the earnest man denounces this, brands it, prosecutes it with unextinguishable aversion. He and it, all good and it, are at death-feud. Blamable Idolatry is *Cant*, and even what one may call Sincere-Cant. Sincere-Cant: that is worth thinking of! Every sort of Worship ends with this phasis.

I find Luther to have been a Breaker of Idols, no less than any other Prophet. The wooden gods of the

Koreish, made of timber and bees-wax, were not more hateful to Mahomet than Tetzel's Pardons of Sin, made of sheepskin and ink, were to Luther. It is the property of every Hero, in every time, in every place and situation, that he come back to reality; that he stand upon things, and not shows of things. According as he loves, and venerates, articulately or with deep speechless thought, the awful realities of things, so will the hollow shows of things, however regular, decorous, accredited by Koreishes or Conclaves, be intolerable and detestable to him. Protestantism too is the work of a Prophet: the prophet-work of that sixteenth century. The first stroke of honest demolition to an ancient thing grown false and idolatrous; preparatory afar off to a new thing, which shall be true, and authentically divine!—

At first view it might seem as if Protestantism were entirely destructive to this that we call Hero-worship, and represent as the basis of all possible good, religious or social, for mankind. One often hears it said that Protestantism introduced a new era, radically different from any the world had eve seen before: the era of 'private judgment,' as they call it. By this revolt against the Pope, every man became his own Pope; and learnt, among other things, that he must never trust any Pope, or spiritual Hero-captain, any more! Whereby, is not spiritual union, all hierarchy and subordination among men, henceforth an impossibility? So we hear it said.—Now I need not deny that Protestantism was a revolt against spiritual sovereignties, Popes and much else. Nay I will grant that English Puritanism, revolt against earthly sovereignties, was the second act of it; that the enormous French Revolution itself was the third act, whereby all sovereignties earthly and spiritual were, as might seem, abolished or made sure of abolition. Protestantism is the grand root from which our whole subsequent European History branches out. For the spiritual will always body itself forth in the temporal history of men; the spiritual is the beginning of the temporal. And now, sure enough, the cry is everywhere for Liberty and Equality, Independence and so forth: instead of *Kings*, Ballot-boxes and

Electoral suffrages; it seems made out that any Hero-sovereign, or loyal obedience of men to a man, in things temporal or things spiritual, has passed away forever from the world. I should despair of the world altogether, if so. One of my deepest convictions is, that it is not so. Without sovereigns, true sovereigns, temporal and spiritual, I see nothing possible but an anarchy : the hatefulest of things. But I find Protestantism, whatever anarchic democracy it have produced, to be the beginning of new genuine sovereignty and order. I find it to be a revolt against *false* sovereigns; the painful but indispensable first preparative for *true* sovereigns getting place among us! This is worth explaining a little.

Let us remark, therefore, in the first place, that this of ' private judgment ' is, at bottom, not a new thing in the world, but only new at that epoch of the world. There is nothing generically new or peculiar in the Reformation; it was a return to Truth and Reality in opposition to Falsehood and Semblance, as all kinds of Improvement and genuine Teaching are and have been. Liberty of private judgment, if we will consider it, must at all times have existed in the world. Dante had not put-out his eyes, or tied shackles on himself; he was at home in that Catholicism of his, a free-seeing soul in it, if many a poor Hogstraten, Tetzel and Dr. Eck had now become slaves in it. Liberty of judgment? No iron chain, or outward force of any kind, could ever compel the soul of a man to believe or to disbelieve : it is his own indefeasible light, that judgment of his; he will reign, and believe there, by the grace of God alone! The sorriest sophistical Bellarmine, preaching sightless faith and passive obedience, must first, by some kind of *conviction*, have abdicated his right to be convinced. His ' private judgment ' indicated that, as the advisablest step *he* could take. The right of private judgment will subsist, in full force, wherever true men subsist. A true man *believes* with his whole judgment, with all the illumination and discernment that is in him, and has always so believed. A false man, only struggling to ' believe that he believes,' will naturally manage it in some other way. Protest-

antism said to this latter, Woe! and to the former,
Well done! At bottom, it was no new saying; it was
a return to all old sayings that ever had been said.
Be genuine, be sincere: that was, once more, the
meaning of it. Mahomet believed with his whole mind;
Odin with his whole mind,—he, and all *true* Followers
of Odinism. They, by their private judgment, had
' judged '—*so*.

And now, I venture to assert, that the exercise of
private judgment, faithfully gone about, does by no
means necessarily end in selfish independence, isolation;
but rather ends necessarily in the opposite of that. It
is not honest inquiry that makes anarchy; but it is
error, insincerity, half-belief and untruth that make it.
A man protesting against error is on the way towards
uniting himself with all men that believe in truth.
There is no communion possible among men who believe
only in hearsays. The heart of each is lying dead; has
no power of sympathy even with *things*,—or he would
believe *them* and not hearsays. No sympathy even with
things; how much less with his fellow-men! He cannot unite with men; he is an anarchic man. Only in
a world of sincere men is unity possible;—and there, in
the longrun, it is as good as *certain*.

For observe one thing, a thing too often left out of
view, or rather altogether lost sight of, in this controversy: That it *is* not necessary a man should himself
have *discovered* the truth he is to believe in, and never
so *sincerely* to believe in. A Great Man, we said, was
always sincere, as the first condition of him. But a
man need not be great in order to be sincere; that is
not the necessity of Nature and all Time, but only of
certain corrupt unfortunate epochs of Time. A man
can believe, and make his own, in the most genuine
way, what he has received from another;—and with
boundless gratitude to that other! The merit of *originality* is not novelty; it is sincerity. The believing
man is the original man; whatsoever he believes, he
believes it for himself, not for another. Every son of
Adam can become a sincere man, an original man, in
this sense; no mortal is doomed to be an insincere
man. Whole ages, what we call ages of Faith, are

original; all men in them, or the most of men in them, sincere. These are the great and fruitful ages : every worker, in all spheres, is a worker not on semblance but on substance; every work issues in a result : the general sum of such work is great; for all of it, as genuine, tends towards one goal; all of it is *additive*, none of it subtractive. There is true union, true kingship, loyalty, all true and blessed things, so far as the poor Earth can produce blessedness for men.

Hero-worship? Ah me, that a man be self-subsistent, original, true, or what we call it, is surely the farthest in the world from indisposing him to reverence and believe other men's truth ! It only disposes, necessitates and invincibly compels him to *dis*believe other men's dead formulas, hearsays and untruths. A man embraces truth with his eyes open, and because his eyes are open : does he need to shut them before he can love his Teacher of truth? He alone can love, with a right gratitude and genuine loyalty of soul, the Hero-Teacher who has delivered him out of darkness into light. Is not such a one a true Hero and Serpent-queller ; worthy of all reverence ! The black monster, Falsehood, our one enemy in this world, lies prostrate by his valour; it was he that conquered the world for us !—See, accordingly, was not Luther himself reverenced as a true Pope, or Spiritual Father, *being* verily such? Napoleon, from amid boundless revolt of Sansculottism, became a King. Hero-worship never dies, nor can die. Loyalty and Sovereignty are everlasting in the world : —and there is this in them, that they are grounded not on garnitures and semblances, but on realities and sincerities. Not by shutting your eyes, your ' private judgment;' no, but by opening them, and by having something to see ! Luther's message was deposition and abolition to all false Popes and Potentates, but life and strength, though afar off, to new genuine ones.

All this of Liberty and Equality, Electoral suffrages, Independence and so forth, we will take, therefore, to be a temporary phenomenon, by no means a final one. Though likely to last a long time, with sad enough embroilments for us all, we must welcome it, as the penalty of sins that are past, the pledge of inestimable benefits

that are coming. In all ways, it behoved men to quit
simulacra and return to fact; cost what it might, that
did behove to be done. With spurious Popes, and Believers having no private judgment,—quacks pretending
to command over dupes,—what can you do? Misery
and mischief only. You cannot make an association
out of insincere men; you cannot build an edifice except
by plummet and level,—at *right*-angles to one another!
In all this wild revolutionary work, from Protestantism
downwards, I see the blessedest result preparing itself:
not abolition of Hero-worship, but rather what I would
call a whole World of Heroes. If Hero mean *sincere
man*, why may not every one of us be a Hero? A world
all sincere, a believing world: the like has been; the
like will again be,—cannot help being. That were the
right sort of Worshippers for Heroes: never could
the truly Better be so reverenced as where all were True
and Good!—But we must hasten to Luther and his
Life.

Luther's birthplace was Eisleben in Saxony; he came
into the world there on the 10th of November 1483.
It was an accident that gave this honour to Eisleben.
His parents, poor mine-labourers in a village of that
region, named Mohra, had gone to the Eisleben Winter-
Fair: in the tumult of this scene the Frau Luther was
taken with travail, found refuge in some poor house
there, and the boy she bore was named MARTIN LUTHER.
Strange enough to reflect upon it. This poor Frau
Luther, she had gone with her husband to make her
small merchandisings; perhaps to sell the lock of yarn
she had been spinning, to buy the small winter-neces-
saries for her narrow hut or household; in the whole
world, that day, there was not a more entirely unim-
portant-looking pair of people than this Miner and his
Wife. And yet what were all Emperors, Popes and
Potentates, in comparison? There was born here, once
more, a Mighty Man; whose light was to flame as the
beacon over long centuries and epochs of the world; the
whole world and its history was waiting for this man.
It is strange, it is great. It leads us back to another
Birth-hour, in a still meaner environment, Eighteen

Hundred years ago,—of which it is fit that we *say* nothing, that we think only in silence; for what words are there! The Age of Miracles past? The Age of Miracles is forever here ' —

I find it altogether suitable to Luther's function in this Earth, and doubtless wisely ordered to that end by the Providence presiding over him and us and all things, that he was born poor, and brought-up poor, one of the poorest of men. He had to beg, as the school-children in those times did; singing for alms and bread, from door to door. Hardship, rigorous Necessity was the poor boy's companion; no man nor no thing would put-on a false face to flatter Martin Luther. Among things, not among the shows of things, had he to grow. A boy of rude figure, yet with weak health, with his large greedy soul, full of all faculty and sensibility, he suffered greatly. But it was his task to get acquainted with *realities*, and keep acquainted with them, at whatever cost : his task was to bring the whole world back to reality, for it had dwelt too long with semblance ! A youth nursed-up in wintry whirlwinds, in desolate darkness and difficulty, that he may step-forth at last from his stormy Scandinavia, strong as a true man, as a god : a Christian Odin,—a right Thor once more, with his thunder-hammer, to smite asunder ugly enough *Jötuns* and Giant-monsters !

Perhaps the turning incident of his life, we may fancy, was that death of his friend Alexis, by lightning, at the gate of Erfurt. Luther had struggled-up through boyhood, better and worse; displaying, in spite of all hindrances, the largest intellect, eager to learn : his father judging doubtless that he might promote himself in the world, set him upon the study of Law. This was the path to rise; Luther, with little will in it either way, had consented : he was now nineteen years of age. Alexis and he had been to see the old Luther people at Mansfeldt; were got back again near Erfurt, when a thunderstorm came on; the bolt struck Alexis, he fell dead at Luther's feet. What is this Life of ours?— gone in a moment, burnt-up like a scroll, into the blank Eternity ! What are all earthly preferments, Chancellorships, Kingships? They lie shrunk together—

there! The Earth has opened on them; in a moment
they are not, and Eternity is. Luther, struck to the
heart, determined to devote himself to God and God's
service alone. In spite of all dissuasions from his
father and others, he became a Monk in the Augustine
Convent at Erfurt.

This was probably the first light-point in the history
of Luther, his purer will now first decisively uttering
itself; but, for the present, it was still as one light-
point in an element all of darkness. He says he was a
pious monk, *ich bin ein frommer Mönch gewesen;* faithfully, painfully struggling to work-out the truth of this
high act of his; but it was to little purpose. His misery
had not lessened; had rather, as it were, increased into
infinitude. The drudgeries he had to do, as novice
in his Convent, all sorts of slave-work, were not his
grievance : the deep earnest soul of the man had fallen
into all manner of black scruples, dubitations; he believed himself likely to die soon, and far worse than
die. One hears with a new interest for poor Luther
that, at this time, he lived in terror of the unspeakable
misery; fancied that he was doomed to eternal reprobation. Was it not the humble sincere nature of the
man? What was he, that he should be raised to
Heaven! He that had known only misery, and mean
slavery: the news was too blessed to be credible. It
could not become clear to him how, by fasts, vigils,
formalities and mass-work, a man's soul could be
saved. He fell into the blackest wretchedness; had
to wander staggering as on the verge of bottomless
Despair.

It must have been a most blessed discovery, that of
an old Latin Bible which he found in the Erfurt Library
about this time. He had never seen the Book before.
It taught him another lesson than that of fasts and
vigils. A brother monk too, of pious experience, was
helpful. Luther learned now that a man was saved
not by singing masses, but by the infinite grace of God :
a more credible hypothesis. He gradually got himself
founded, as on the rock. No wonder he should venerate
the Bible, which had brought this blessed help to him.
He prized it as the Word of the Highest must be prized

by such a man. He determined to hold by that; as
through life and to death he firmly did.

This, then, is his deliverance from darkness, his final
triumph over darkness, what we call his conversion;
for himself the most important of all epochs. That he
should now grow daily in peace and clearness; that,
unfolding now the great talents and virtues implanted
in him, he should rise to importance in his Convent, in
his country, and be found more and more useful in all
honest business of life, is a natural result. He was
sent on missions by his Augustine Order, as a man of
talent and fidelity fit to do their business well: the
Elector of Saxony, Friedrich, named the Wise, a truly
wise and just prince, had cast his eye on him as a valuable person; made him Professor in his new University
of Wittenberg, Preacher too at Wittenberg; in both
which capacities, as in all duties he did, this Luther, in
the peaceable sphere of common life, was gaining more
and more esteem with all good men.

It was in his twenty-seventh year that he first saw
Rome; being sent thither, as I said, on mission from
his Convent. Pope Julius the Second, and what was
going-on at Rome, must have filled the mind of Luther
with amazement. He had come as to the Sacred City,
throne of God's Highpriest on Earth; and he found
it—what we know! Many thoughts it must have given
the man; many which we have no record of, which
perhaps he did not himself know how to utter. This
Rome, this scene of false priests, clothed not in the
beauty of holiness, but in far other vesture, is *false*:
but what is it to Luther? A mean man he, how shall
he reform a world? That was far from his thoughts.
A humble, solitary man, why should he at all meddle
with the world? It was the task of quite higher men
than he. His business was to guide his own footsteps
wisely through the world. Let him do his own obscure
duty in it well; the rest, horrible and dismal as it looks,
is in God's hand, not in his.

It is curious to reflect what might have been the issue,
had Roman Popery happened to pass this Luther by;
to go on in its great wasteful orbit, and not come
athwart his little path, and force him to assault it!

Conceivable enough that, in this case, he might have held his peace about the abuses of Rome; left Providence, and God on high, to deal with them! A modest quiet man; not prompt he to attack irreverently persons in authority. His clear task, as I say, was to do his own duty; to walk wisely in this world of confused wickedness, and save his own soul alive. But the Roman Highpriesthood did come athwart him: afar off at Wittenberg he, Luther, could not get lived in honesty for it; he remonstrated, resisted, came to extremity; was struck-at, struck again, and so it came to wager of battle between them! This is worth attending to in Luther's history. Perhaps no man of so humble, peaceable a disposition ever filled the world with contention. We cannot but see that he would have loved privacy, quiet diligence in the shade; that it was against his will he ever became a notoriety. Notoriety: what would that do for him? The goal of his march through this world was the Infinite Heaven; an indubitable goal for him: in a few years, he should either have attained that, or lost it forever! We will say nothing at all, I think, of that sorrowfulest of theories, of its being some mean shopkeeper grudge, of the Augustine Monk against the Dominican, that first kindled the wrath of Luther, and produced the Protestant Reformation. We will say to the people who maintain it, if indeed any such exist now: Get first into the sphere of thought by which it is so much as possible to judge of Luther, or of any man like Luther, otherwise than distractedly; we may then begin arguing with you.

The Monk Tetzel, sent out carelessly in the way of trade, by Leo Tenth,—who merely wanted to raise a little money, and for the rest seems to have been a Pagan rather than a Christian, so far as he was anything,—arrived at Wittenberg, and drove his scandalous trade there. Luther's flock bought Indulgences: in the confessional of his Church, people pleaded to him that they had already got their sins pardoned. Luther, if he would not be found wanting at his own post, a false sluggard and coward at the very centre of the little space of ground that was his own and no other man's, had to step-forth against Indulgences, and declare aloud that *they* were a futility and sorrowful mockery, that no man's sins could be pardoned by *them*. It was the beginning of the whole Reformation. We know how it went; forward from this first public challenge of Tetzel, on the last day of October 1517, through remonstrance and argument;—spreading ever wider, rising ever higher; till it became unquenchable, and enveloped all the world. Luther's heart's-desire was to have this grief and other griefs amended; his thought was still far other than that of introducing separation in the Church, or revolting against the Pope, Father of Christendom.—The elegant Pagan Pope cared little about this Monk and his doctrines; wished, however, to have done with the noise of him : in a space of some three years, having tried various softer methods, he thought good to end it by *fire*. He dooms the Monk's writings to be burnt by the hangman, and his body to be sent bound to Rome,—probably for a similar purpose. It was the way they had ended with Huss, with Jerome, the century before. A short argument, fire. Poor Huss : he came to that Constance Council, with all imaginable promises and safe-conducts; an earnest, not rebellious kind of man : they laid him instantly in a stone dungeon ' three-feet wide, six-feet high, seven-feet long;' *burnt* the true voice of him out of this world; choked it in smoke and fire. That was *not* well done !

I, for one, pardon Luther for now altogether revolting against the Pope. The elegant Pagan, by this fire-decree of his, had kindled into noble just wrath the bravest heart then living in this world. The bravest, if also one of the humblest, peaceablest; it was now kindled. These words of mine, words of truth and soberness, aiming faithfully, as human inability would allow, to promote God's truth on Earth, and save men's souls, you, God's vicegerent on earth, answer them by the hangman and fire? You will burn me and them, for answer to the God's-message they strove to bring you? *You* are not God's vicegerent; you are another's than his, I think I take your Bull, as an emparchmented Lie, and burn *it*. You will do what you see good next : this is what I do.—It was on the 10th of

December 1520, three years after the beginning of the business, that Luther, 'with a great concourse of people,' took this indignant step of burning the Pope's fire-decree ' at the Elster-Gate of Wittenberg.' Wittenberg looked on ' with shoutings;' the whole world was looking on. The Pope should not have provoked that 'shout'! It was the shout of the awakening of nations. The quiet German heart, modest, patient of much, had at length got more than it could bear. Formulism, Pagan Popeism, and other Falsehood and corrupt Semblance had ruled long enough : and here once more was a man found who durst tell all men that God's-world stood not on semblances but on realities; that Life was a truth, and not a lie !

At bottom, as was said above, we are to consider Luther as a Prophet Idol-breaker; a bringer-back of men to reality. It is the function of great men and teachers. Mahomet said, These idols of yours are wood; you put wax and oil on them, the flies stick on them : they are not God, I tell you, they are black wood ! Luther said to the Pope, This thing of yours that you call a Pardon of Sins, it is a bit of rag-paper with ink. It *is* nothing else; it, and so much like it, is nothing else. God alone can pardon sins. Popeship, spiritual Fatherhood of God's Church, is that a vain semblance, of cloth and parchment? It is an awful fact. God's Church is not a semblance, Heaven and Hell are not semblances. I stand on this, since you drive me to it. Standing on this, I a poor German monk am stronger than you all. I stand solitary, friendless, but on God's Truth; you with your tiaras, triple-hats, with your treasuries and armories, thunders spiritual and temporal, stand on the Devil's Lie, and are not so strong !—

The Diet of Worms, Luther's appearance there on the 17th of April 1521, may be considered as the greatest scene in Modern European History; the point, indeed, from which the whole subsequent history of civilisation takes its rise. After multiplied negotiations, disputations, it had come to this. The young Emperor Charles Fifth, with all the Princes of Germany, Papal nuncios, dignitaries spiritual and temporal, are assembled there : Luther is to appear and answer for himself, whether he will recant or not. The world's pomp and power sits there on this hand : on that, stands-up for God's Truth, one man, the poor miner Hans Luther's Son. Friends had reminded him of Huss, advised him not to go; he would not be advised. A large company of friends rode-out to meet him, with still more earnest warnings; he answered, " Were there as many Devils in Worms as there are roof-tiles, I would on." The people, on the morrow, as he went to the Hall of the Diet, crowded the windows and housetops, some of them calling out to him, in solemn words, not to recant : " Whosoever denieth me before men !" they cried to him,—as in a kind of solemn petition and adjuration. Was it not in reality our petition too, the petition of the whole world, lying in dark bondage of soul, paralysed under a black spectral Nightmare and triple-hatted Chimera, calling itself Father in God, and what not : " Free us; it rests with thee; desert us not !"

Luther did not desert us. His speech, of two hours, distinguished itself by its respectful, wise and honest tone; submissive to whatsoever could lawfully claim submission, not submissive to any more than that. His writings, he said, were partly his own, partly derived from the Word of God. As to what was his own, human infirmity entered into it; unguarded anger, blindness, many things doubtless which it were a bless-ing for him could he abolish altogether. But as to what stood on sound truth and the Word of God, he could not recant it. How could he? " Confute me," he concluded, " by proofs of Scripture, or else by plain just arguments : I cannot recant otherwise. For it is neither safe nor prudent to do ought against conscience. Here stand I; I can do no other : God assist me !"— It is, as we say, the greatest moment in the Modern History of Men. English Puritanism, England and its Parliaments, Americas, and vast work these two cen-turies ; French Revolution, Europe and its work every-where at present : the germ of it all lay there : had Luther in that moment done other, it had all been other-wise ! The European World was asking him : Am I to sink ever lower into falsehood, stagnant putrescence, loathsome accursed death ; or, with whatever paroxysm, to cast the falsehoods out of me, and be cured and live?—

Great wars, contentions and disunion followed out of this Reformation; which last down to our day, and are yet far from ended. Great talk and crimination has been made about these. They are lamentable, undeniable; but after all what has Luther or his cause to do with them? It seems strange reasoning to charge the Reformation with all this. When Hercules turned the purifying river into King Augeas's stables, I have no doubt the confusion that resulted was considerable all around : but I think it was not Hercules's blame; it was some other's blame! The Reformation might bring what results it liked when it came, but the Reformation simply could not help coming. To all Popes and Popes' advocates, expostulating, lamenting and accusing, the answer of the world is : Once for all, your Popehood has become untrue. No matter how good it was, how good you say it is, we cannot believe it; the light of our whole mind, given us to walk-by from Heaven above, finds it henceforth a thing unbelievable. We will not believe it, we will not try to believe it,—we dare not! The thing is *untrue;* we were traitors against the Giver of all Truth, if we durst pretend to think it true. Away with it; let whatsoever likes come in the place of it : with *it* we can have no farther trade !—Luther and his Protestantism is not responsible for wars; the false Simulacra that forced him to protest, they are responsible. Luther did what every man that God has made has not only the right, but lies under the sacred duty, to do : answered a Falsehood when it questioned him, Dost thou believe me?—No !—At what cost soever, without counting of costs, this thing behoved to be done. Union, organisation spiritual and material, a far nobler than any Popedom or Feudalism in their truest days, I never doubt, is coming for the world; sure to come. But on Fact alone, not on Semblance and Simulacrum, will it be able either to come, or to stand when come. With union grounded on falsehood, and ordering us to speak and act lies, we will not have anything to do. Peace?

A brutal lethargy is peaceable, the noisome grave is peaceable. We hope for a living peace, not a dead one!

And yet, in prizing justly the indispensable blessings of the New, let us not be unjust to the Old. The Old *was* true, if it no longer is. In Dante's days it needed no sophistry, self-blinding, or other dishonesty, to get itself reckoned true. It was good then; nay there is in the soul of it a deathless good. The cry of ' No Popery ' is foolish enough in these days. The speculation that Popery is on the increase, building new chapels and so forth, may pass for one of the idlest ever started. Very curious : to count-up a few Popish chapels, listen to a few Protestant logic-choppings,— to much dull-droning, drowsy inanity that still calls itself Protestant, and say : See, Protestantism is *dead;* Popeism is more alive than it, will be alive after it !— Drowsy inanities, not a few, that call themselves Protestant are dead; but *Protestantism* has not died yet, that I hear of ! Protestantism, if we will look, has in these days produced its Goethe, its Napoleon; German Literature and the French Revolution; rather considerable signs of life ! Nay, at bottom, what else is alive *but* Protestantism? The life of most else that one meets is a galvanic one merely,—not a pleasant, not a lasting sort of life !

Popery can build new chapels; welcome to do so, to all lengths. Popery cannot come back, any more than Paganism can,—*which* also still lingers in some countries. But, indeed, it is with these things, as with the ebbing of the sea : you look at the waves oscillating hither, thither on the beach; for *minutes* you cannot tell how it is going; look in half an hour where it is,—look in half a century where your Popehood is ! Alas, would there were no greater danger to our Europe than the poor old Pope's revival ! Thor may as soon try to revive.—And withal this oscillation has a meaning. The poor old Popehood will not die away entirely, as Thor has done, for some time yet; nor ought it. We may say, the Old never dies till this happen, Till all the soul of good that was in it have got itself transfused into the practical New. While a good work remains capable of being done by the Romish form;

or, what is inclusive of all, while a *pious life* remains capable of being led by it, just so long, if we consider, will this or the other human soul adopt it, go about as a living witness of it. So long it will obtrude itself on the eye of us who reject it, till we in our practice too have appropriated whatsoever of truth was in it. Then, but also not till then, it will have no charm more for any man. It lasts here for a purpose. Let it last as long as it can.—

Of Luther I will add now, in reference to all these wars and bloodshed, the noticeable fact that none of them began so long as he continued living. The controversy did not get to fighting so long as he was there. To me it is proof of his greatness in all senses, this fact. How seldom do we find a man that has stirred-up some vast commotion, who does not himself perish, swept-away in it! Such is the usual course of revolutionists. Luther continued, in a good degree, sovereign of this greatest revolution; all Protestants, of what rank or function soever, looking much to him for guidance: and he held it peaceable, continued firm at the centre of it. A man to do this must have a kingly faculty: he must have the gift to discern at all turns where the true heart of the matter lies, and to plant himself courageously on that, as a strong true man, that other true men may rally round him there. He will not continue leader of men otherwise. Luther's clear deep force of judgment, his force of all sorts, of *silence*, of tolerance and moderation, among others, are very notable in these circumstances.

Tolerance, I say; a very genuine kind of tolerance: he distinguishes what is essential, and what is not; the unessential may go very much as it will. A complaint comes to him that such and such a Reformed Preacher, 'will not preach without a cassock.' Well, answers Luther, what harm will a cassock do the man? ' Let him have a cassock to preach in; let him have three cassocks if he find benefit in them!' His conduct in the matter of Karlstadt's wild image-breaking; of the Anabaptists; of the Peasants' War, shows a noble strength, very different from spasmodic violence. With sure prompt insight he discriminates what is what : a strong just man, he speaks-forth what is the wise course, and all men follow him in that. Luther's Written Works give similar testimony of him. The dialect of these speculations is now grown obsolete for us ; but one still reads them with a singular attraction. And indeed the mere grammatical diction is still legible enough ; Luther's merit in literary history is of the greatest ; his dialect became the language of all writing. They are not well written, these Four-and-twenty Quartos of his ; written hastily, with quite other than literary objects. But in no Books have I found a more robust, genuine, I will say noble faculty of a man than in these. A rugged honesty, homeliness, simplicity ; a rugged sterling sense and strength. He flashes-out illumination from him ; his smiting idiomatic phrases seem to cleave into the very secret of the matter. Good humour too, nay tender affection, nobleness, and depth : this man could have been a Poet too ! He had to *work* an Epic Poem, not write one. I call him a great Thinker ; as indeed his greatness of heart already betokens that.

Richter says of Luther's words, ' his words are half-battles.' They may be called so. The essential quality of him was, that he could fight and conquer ; that he was a right piece of human Valour. No more valiant man, no mortal heart to be called *braver*, that one has record of, ever lived in that Teutonic Kindred, whose character is valour. His defiance of the ' Devils ' in Worms was not a mere boast, as the like might be if now spoken. It was a faith of Luther's that there were Devils, spiritual denizens of the Pit, continually besetting men. Many times, in his writings, this turns-up ; and a most small sneer has been grounded on it by some. In the room of the Wartburg where he sat translating the Bible, they still show you a black spot on the wall ; the strange memorial of one of these conflicts. Luther sat translating one of the Psalms ; he was worn-down with long labour, with sickness, abstinence from food : there rose before him some hideous indefinable Image, which he took for the Evil One, to forbid his work : Luther started-up, with fiend-defiance ;

flung his inkstand at the spectre, and it disappeared!
The spot still remains there; a curious monument of
several things. Any apothecary's apprentice can now
tell us what we are to think of this apparition, in a
scientific sense: but the man's heart that dare rise
defiant, face to face, against Hell itself, can give no
higher proof of fearlessness. The thing he will quail
before exists not on this Earth or under it.—Fearless
enough! 'The Devil is aware,' writes he on one occasion, 'that this does not proceed out of fear in me. I
have seen and defied innumerable Devils. Duke
George,' of Leipzig, a great enemy of his, 'Duke
George is not equal to one Devil,'—far short of a
Devil! 'If I had business at Leipzig, I would ride
into Leipzig, though it rained Duke-Georges for nine
days running.' What a reservoir of Dukes to ride
into!—

At the same time, they err greatly who imagine that
this man's courage was ferocity, mere coarse disobed-
ient obstinacy and savagery, as many do. Far from
that. There may be an absence of fear which arises
from the absence of thought or affection, from the presence of hatred and stupid fury. We do not value the
courage of the tiger highly! With Luther it was far
otherwise; no accusation could be more unjust than
this of mere ferocious violence brought against him.
A most gentle heart withal, full of pity and love, as
indeed the truly valiant heart ever is. The tiger before
a *stronger* foe—flies: the tiger is not what we call
valiant, only fierce and cruel. I know few things more
touching than those soft breathings of affection, soft
as a child's or a mother's, in this great wild heart of
Luther. So honest, unadulterated with any cant;
homely, rude in their utterance; pure as water welling
from the rock. What, in fact, was all that downpressed
mood of despair and reprobation, which we saw in his
youth, but the outcome of pre-eminent thoughtful gentle-
ness, affections too keen and fine? It is the course
such men as the poor Poet Cowper fall into. Luther
to a slight observer might have seemed a timid, weak
man; modesty, affectionate shrinking tenderness the
chief distinction of him. It is a noble valour which is

roused in a heart like this, once stirred-up into defiance, all kindled into a heavenly blaze.

In Luther's *Table-Talk*, a posthumous Book of anecdotes and sayings collected by his friends, the most interesting now of all the Books proceeding from him, we have many beautiful unconscious displays of the man, and what sort of nature he had. His behaviour at the deathbed of his little Daughter, so still, so great and loving, is among the most affecting things. He is resigned that his little Magdalene should die, yet longs inexpressibly that she might live; —follows, in awe-struck thought, the flight of her little soul through those unknown realms. Awe-struck; most heartfelt, we can see; and sincere,—for after all dogmatic creeds and articles, he feels what nothing it is that we know, or can know : His little Magdalene shall be with God, as God wills; for Luther too that is all; *Islam* is all.

Once, he looks-out from his solitary Patmos, the Castle of Coburg, in the middle of the night : The great vault of Immensity, long flights of clouds sailing through it,—dumb, gaunt, huge :—who supports all that? " None ever saw the pillars of it; yet it is supported." God supports it. We must know that God is great, that God is good; and trust, where we cannot see.—Returning home from Leipzig once, he is struck by the beauty of the harvest-fields : How it stands, that golden yellow corn, on its fair taper stem, its golden head bent, all rich and waving there,—the meek Earth, at God's kind bidding, has produced it once again ; the bread of man !—In the garden at Wittenburg one evening at sunset, a little bird was perched for the night : That little bird, says Luther, above it are the stars and deep Heaven of worlds ; yet it has folded its little wings ; gone trustfully to rest there as in its home : the Maker of it has given it too a home !——Neither are mirthful turns wanting : there is a great free human heart in this man. The common speech of him has a rugged nobleness, idiomatic, expressive, genuine ; gleams here and there with beautiful poetic tints. One feels him to be a great brother man. His love of Music, indeed, is not this, as it were, the summary of all these affections in him? Many a wild unutterability he spoke-

forth from him in the tones of his flute. The Devils
fled from his flute, he says. Death-defiance on the one
hand, and such love of music on the other; I could
call these the two opposite poles of a great soul; between
these two all great things had room.

Luther's face is to me expressive of him; in Kranach's
best portraits I find the true Luther. A rude plebeian
face; with its huge crag-like brows and bones, the
emblem of rugged energy; at first, almost a repulsive
face. Yet in the eyes especially there is a wild silent
sorrow; an unnamable melancholy, the element of all
gentle and fine affections; giving to the rest the true
stamp of nobleness. Laughter was in this Luther, as
we said; but tears also were there. Tears also were
appointed him; tears and hard toil. The basis of his
life was Sadness, Earnestness. In his latter days, after
all triumphs and victories, he expresses himself heartily
weary of living; he considers that God alone can and
will regulate the course things are taking, and that
perhaps the Day of Judgment is not far. As for him,
he longs for one thing: that God would release him
from his labour, and let him depart and be at rest.
They understand little of the man who cite this in *dis*-
credit of him!—I will call this Luther a true Great Man;
great in intellect, in courage, affection and integrity;
one of our most lovable and precious men. Great, not
as a hewn obelisk; but as an Alpine mountain,—so
simple, honest, spontaneous, not setting-up to be great
at all; there for quite another purpose than being great!
Ah yes, unsubduable granite, piercing far and wide
into the Heavens; yet in the clefts of it fountains, green
beautiful valleys with flowers! A right Spiritual Hero
and Prophet; once more, a true Son of Nature and
Fact, for whom these centuries, and many that are to
come yet, will be thankful to Heaven.

The most interesting phasis which the Reformation
anywhere assumes, especially for us English, is that of
Puritanism. In Luther's own country Protestantism
soon dwindled into a rather barren affair: not a religion
or faith, but rather now a theological jangling of argument, the proper seat of it not the heart; the essence
of it sceptical contention: which indeed has jangled

more and more, down to Voltaireism itself,—through
Gustavus-Adolphus contentions onward to French-Re-
volution ones! But in our Island there arose a Puritanism, which even got itself established as a Presbyterian-
ism and National Church among the Scotch; which
came forth as a real business of the heart; and has
produced in the world very notable fruit. In some
senses, one may say it is the only phasis of Protestantism
that ever got to the rank of being a Faith, a true heart-
communication with Heaven, and of exhibiting itself in
History as such. We must spare a few words for Knox;
himself a brave and remarkable man; but still more important as Chief Priest and Founder, which one may
consider him to be, of the Faith that became Scotland's,
New England's, Oliver Cromwell's. History will have
something to say about this, for some time to come!

We may censure Puritanism as we please; and no
one of us, I suppose, but would find it a very rough
defective thing. But we, and all men, may understand
that it was a genuine thing; for Nature has adopted
it, and it has grown, and grows. I say sometimes, that
all goes by wager-of-battle in this world; that *strength,*
well understood, is the measure of all worth. Give a
thing time; if it can succeed, it is a right thing. Look
now at American Saxondom; and at that little Fact of
the sailing of the Mayflower, two hundred years ago,
from Delft Haven in Holland! Were we of open sense
as the Greeks were, we had found a Poem here; one of
Nature's own Poems; such as she writes in broad facts
over great continents. For it was properly the beginning of America: there were straggling settlers in
America before, some material as of a body was there;
but the soul of it was first this. These poor men,
driven-out of their country, not able well to live in
Holland, determine on settling in the New World.
Black untamed forests are there, and wild savage
creatures; but not so cruel as Starchamber hangmen.
They thought the Earth would yield them food, if they
tilled honestly; the everlasting heaven would stretch
there too, overhead; they should be left in peace, to
prepare for Eternity by living well in this world of
Time; worshipping in what they thought the true, not

the idolatrous way. They clubbed their small means together; hired a ship, the little ship Mayflower, and made ready to set sail.

In Neal's *History of the Puritans* [1] is an account of the ceremony of their departure : solemnity, we might call it rather, for it was a real act of worship. Their minister went down with them to the beach, and their brethren whom they were to leave behind; all joined in solemn prayer, That God would have pity on His poor children, and *go* with them into that waste wilderness, for He also had made that, He was there also as well as here.—Hah ! These men, I think, had a work ! The weak thing, weaker than a child, becomes strong one day, if it be a true thing. Puritanism was only despicable, laughable then ; but nobody can manage to laugh at it now. Puritanism has got weapons and sinews ; it has fire-arms, war-navies ; it has cunning in its ten fingers, strength in its right arm ; it can steer ships, fell forests, remove mountains ;—it is one of the strongest things under the sun at present !

In the history of Scotland, too, I can find properly but one epoch : we may say it contains nothing of world-interest at all but this Reformation by Knox. A poor barren country, full of continual broils, dissensions, massacrings ; a people in the last state of rudeness and destitution, little better perhaps than Ireland at this day. Hungry fierce barons, not so much as able to form any arrangement with each other *how to divide* what they fleeced from these poor drudges ; but obliged, as the Columbian Republics are at this day, to make of every alteration a revolution ; no way of changing a ministry but by hanging the old ministers on gibbets : this is a historical spectacle of no very singular significance ! ' Bravery ' enough, I doubt not ; fierce fighting in abundance : but not braver or fiercer than that of their old Scandinavian Sea-king ancestors ; *whose* exploits we have not found worth dwelling on ! It is a country as yet without a soul : nothing developed in it but what is rude, external, semi-animal. And now at the Reformation, the internal life is kindled, as it were, under the ribs of this outward material death. A

[1] Neal (London, 1755), i. 490.

cause, the noblest of causes kindles itself, like a beacon set on high; high as Heaven, yet attainable from Earth; —whereby the meanest man becomes not a Citizen only, but a Member of Christ's visible Church; a veritable Hero, if he prove a true man!

Well; this is what I mean by a whole 'nation of heroes;' a *believing* nation. There needs not a great soul to make a hero; there needs a god-created soul which will be true to its origin; that will be a great soul! The like has been seen, we find. The like will be again seen, under wider forms than the Presbyterian: there can be no lasting good done till then.—Impossible! say some. Possible? Has it not *been*, in this world, as a practised fact? Did Hero-worship fail in Knox's case? Or are we made of other clay now? Did the Westminster Confession of Faith add some new property to the soul of man? God made the soul of man. He did not doom any soul of man to live as a Hypothesis and Hearsay, in a world filled with such, and with the fatal work and fruit of such!——

But to return: This that Knox did for his Nation, I say, we may really call a resurrection as from death. It was not a smooth business; but it was welcome surely, and cheap at that price, had it been far rougher. On the whole, cheap at any price;—as life is. The people began to *live:* they needed first of all to do that, at what cost and costs soever. Scotch Literature and Thought, Scotch Industry; James Watt, David Hume, Walter Scott, Robert Burns: I find Knox and the Reformation acting in the heart's core of every one of these persons and phenomena; I find that without the Reformation they would not have been. Or what of Scotland? The Puritanism of Scotland became that of England, of New England. A tumult in the High Church of Edinburgh spread into a universal battle and struggle over all these realms;—there came out, after fifty years' struggling, what we call the 'Glorious Revolution,' a *Habeas-Corpus* Act, Free Parliaments, and much else! —Alas, is it not too true what we said, That many men in the van do always, like Russian soldiers, march into the ditch of Schweidnitz, and fill it up with their dead bodies, that the rear may pass over them dry-shod

and gain the honour? How many earnest rugged
Cromwells, Knoxes, poor Peasant Covenants, wrestling, battling for very life, in rough miry places, have
to struggle, and suffer, and fall, greatly censured, *be-
mired*,—before a beautiful Revolution of Eighty-eight
can step-over them in official pumps and silk-stockings,
with universal three-times-three !

It seems to me hard measure that this Scottish man,
now after three-hundred years, should have to plead
like a culprit before the world; intrinsically for having
been, in such way as it was then possible to be, the
bravest of all Scotchmen ! Had he been a poor Half-
and-half, he could have crouched into the corner, like
so many others; Scotland had not been delivered; and
Knox had been without blame. He is the one Scotch-
man to whom, of all others, his country and the world
owe a debt. He has to plead that Scotland would forgive him for having been worth to it any million ' unblamable ' Scotchmen that need no forgiveness ! He
bared his breast to the battle; had to row in French
galleys, wander forlorn in exile, in clouds and storms;
was censured, shot-at through his windows; had a right
sore fighting life : if this world were his place of recompense, he had made but a bad venture of it. I cannot
apologise for Knox. To him it is very indifferent, these
two-hundred-and-fifty years or more, what men say of
him. But we, having got above all those details of his
battle, and living now in clearness on the fruits of his
victory, we, for our own sake, ought to look through
the rumours and controversies enveloping the man, into
the man himself.

For one thing, I will remark that this post of Prophet
to his Nation was not of his seeking; Knox had lived
forty years quietly obscure, before he became conspicuous. He was the son of poor parents; had got a
college education; become a Priest; adopted the Reformation, and seemed well content to guide his own
steps by the light of it, nowise unduly intruding it on
others. He had lived as Tutor in gentlemen's families;
preaching when any body of persons wished to hear his
doctrine : resolute he to walk by the truth, and speak
the truth when called to do it; not ambitious of more;

not fancying himself capable of more. In this entirely
obscure way he had reached the age of forty; was with
the small body of Reformers who were standing siege
in St Andrew's Castle,—when one day in their chapel,
the Preacher after finishing his exhortation to these
fighters in the forlorn hope, said suddenly, That there
ought to be other speakers, that all men who had a
priest's heart and gift in them ought now to speak;—
which gifts and heart one of their own number, John
Knox the name of him, had: Had he not? said the
Preacher, appealing to all the audience: what then is
his duty? The people answered affirmatively; it was
a criminal forsaking of his post, if such a man held the
word that was in him silent. Poor Knox was obliged
to stand-up; he attempted to reply; he could say no
word;—burst into a flood of tears, and ran out. It is
worth remembering, that scene. He was in grievous
trouble for some days. He felt what a small faculty
was his for this great work. He felt what a baptism he
was called to be baptised withal. He ' burst into tears.'

Our primary characteristic of a Hero, that he is sincere, applies emphatically to Knox. It is not denied
anywhere that this, whatever might be his other qualities
or faults, is among the truest of men. With a singular
instinct he holds to the truth and fact; the truth alone
is there for him, the rest a mere shadow and deceptive
nonentity. However feeble, forlorn the reality may
seem, on that and that only *can* he take his stand. In
the Galleys of the River Loire, whither Knox and the
others, after their Castle of St Andrew's was taken, had
been sent as Galley-slaves,—some officer or priest, one
day, presented them an Image of the Virgin Mother,
requiring that they, the blasphemous heretics, should
do it reverence. Mother? Mother of God? said Knox,
when the turn came to him : This is no Mother of God :
this is ' a *pented bredd*,'—a piece of wood, I tell you,
with paint on it! She is fitter for swimming, I think,
than for being worshipped, added Knox, and flung the
thing into the river. It was not very cheap jesting
there : but come of it what might, this thing to Knox
was and must continue nothing other than the real truth;
it was a *pented bredd;* worship it he would not.

He told his fellow-prisoners, in this darkest time, to be of courage; the Cause they had was the true one, and must and would prosper; the whole world could not put it down. Reality is of God's making; it is alone strong. How many *pented bredds*, pretending to be real, are fitter to swim than to be worshipped!— This Knox cannot live but by fact: he clings to reality as the shipwrecked sailor to the cliff. He is an instance to us how a man, by sincerity itself, becomes heroic: it is the grand gift he has. We find in Knox a good honest intellectual talent, no transcendent one;—a narrow, inconsiderable man, as compared with Luther: but in heartfelt instinctive adherence to truth, in *sincerity*, as we say, he has no superior; nay, one might ask, What equal he has? The heart of him is of the true Prophet cast. " He lies there," said the Earl of Morton at his grave, " who never feared the face of man." He resembles, more than any of the moderns, an Old-Hebrew Prophet. The same inflexibility, intolerance, rigid narrow-looking adherence to God's truth, stern rebuke in the name of God to all that forsake truth: an Old-Hebrew Prophet in the guise of an Edinburgh Minister of the Sixteenth Century. We are to take him for that; not require him to be other.

Knox's conduct to Queen Mary, the harsh visits he used to make in her own palace, to reprove her there, have been much commented upon. Such cruelty, such coarseness fills us with indignation. On reading the actual narrative of the business, what Knox said, and what Knox meant, I must say one's tragic feeling is rather disappointed. They are not so coarse, these speeches; they seem to me about as fine as the circumstances would permit! Knox was not there to do the courtier; he came on another errand. Whoever, reading these colloquies of his with the Queen, thinks they are vulgar insolences of a plebeian priest to a delicate high lady, mistakes the purport and essence of them altogether. It was unfortunately not possible to be polite with the Queen of Scotland, unless one proved untrue to the Nation and Cause of Scotland. A man who did not wish to see the land of his birth made a hunting-field for intriguing ambitious Guises, and the Cause of

God trampled underfoot of Falsehoods, Formulas and the Devil's Cause, had no method of making himself agreeable! " Better that women weep," said Morton, " than that bearded men be forced to weep." Knox was the constitutional opposition-party in Scotland : the Nobles of the country, called by their station to take that post, were not found in it; Knox had to go or no one. The hapless Queen;—but the still more hapless Country, if *she* were made happy! Mary herself was not without sharpness enough, among her other qualities : " Who are you," said she once, " that presume to school the nobles and sovereign of this realm?" —" Madam, a subject born within the same," answered he. Reasonably answered! If the ' subject ' have truth to speak, it is not the ' subject's ' footing that will fail him here.—

We blame Knox for his intolerance. Well, surely it is good that each of us be as tolerant as possible. Yet, at bottom, after all the talk there is and has been about it, what is tolerance? Tolerance has to tolerate the *un*essential; and to see well what that is. Tolerance has to be noble, measured, just in its very wrath, when it can tolerate no longer. But, on the whole, we are not altogether here to tolerate! We are here to resist, to control and vanquish withal. We do not ' tolerate ' Falsehoods, Thieveries, Iniquities, when they fasten on us; we say to them, Thou art false, thou art not tolerable! We are here to extinguish Falsehoods, and put an end to them, in some wise way! I will not quarrel so much with the way; the doing of the thing is our great concern. In this sense Knox was, full surely, intolerant.

A man sent to row in French Galleys, and suchlike, for teaching the Truth in his own land, cannot always be in the mildest humour! I am not prepared to say that Knox had a soft temper; nor do I know that he had what we call an ill-temper. An ill nature he decidedly had not. Kind honest affections dwell in the much-enduring, hard-worn, ever-battling man. That he *could* rebuke Queens, and had such weight among those proud turbulent Nobles, proud enough whatever else they were; and could maintain to the

end a kind of virtual Presidency and Sovereignty
in that wild realm, he who was only ' a subject born
within the same : ' this of itself will prove to us that he
was found, close at hand, to be no mean acrid man ; but
at heart a healthful, strong, sagacious man.   Such alone
can bear rule in that kind.   They blame him for pulling-
down cathedrals, and so forth, as if he were a seditious
rioting demagogue :   precisely the reverse is seen to be
the fact, in regard to cathedrals and the rest of it, if we
examine !   Knox wanted no pulling-down of stone
edifices ; he wanted leprosy and darkness to be thrown
out of the lives of men.   Tumult was not his element ;
it was the tragic feature of his life that he was forced
to dwell so much in that.   Every such man is the born
enemy of Disorder ; hates to be in it : but what then ?
Smooth Falsehood is not Order ; it is the general sum-
total of *Dis*order.   Order is *Truth*,—each thing standing on the basis that belongs to it : Order and Falsehood
cannot subsist together.

Withal, unexpectedly enough, this Knox has a vein
of drollery in him ; which I like much, in combination
with his other qualities.   He has a true eye for the
ridiculous.   His *History*, with its rough earnestness, is
curiously enlivened with this.   When the two Prelates,
entering Glasgow Cathedral, quarrel about precedence ;
march rapidly up, take to hustling one another, twitch-
ing one another's rochets, and at last flourishing their
crosiers like quarter-staves, it is a great sight for him
everyway !   Not mockery, scorn, bitterness alone ;
though there is enough of that too.   But a true, loving,
illuminating laugh mounts-up over the earnest visage ;
not a loud laugh ; you would say, a laugh in the *eyes*
most of all.   An honest-hearted, brotherly man ; brother
to the high, brother also to the low ; sincere in his sympathy with both.   He has his pipe of Bourdeaux too, we
find, in that old Edinburgh house of his ; a cheery social
man, with faces that loved him !   They go far wrong
who think this Knox was a gloomy, spasmodic, shrieking fanatic.   Not at all : he is one of the solidest of
men.   Practical, cautious-hopeful, patient ; a most
shrewd, observing, quietly discerning man.   In fact, he
has very much the type of character we assign to the

Scotch at present : a certain sardonic taciturnity is in him; insight enough; and a stouter heart than he himself knows of. He has the power of holding his peace over many things which do not vitally concern him,— "They? what are they?" But the thing which does vitally concern him, that thing he will speak of; and in a tone the whole world shall be made to hear : all the more emphatic for his long silence.

This Prophet of the Scotch is to me no hateful man ! —He had a sore fight of an existence : wrestling with Popes and Principalities; in defeat, contention, life-long struggle; rowing as a galley-slave, wandering as an exile. A sore fight : but he won it. "Have you hope?" they asked him in his last moment, when he could no longer speak. He lifted his finger, 'pointed upwards with his finger,' and so died. Honour to him ! His works have not died. The letter of his work dies, as of all men's; but the spirit of it never.

One word more as to the letter of Knox's work. The unforgivable offence in him is, that he wished to set-up Priests over the head of Kings. In other words he strove to make the Government of Scotland a *Theocracy*. This indeed is properly the sum of his offences, the essential sin; for which what pardon can there be? It is most true, he did, at bottom, consciously or unconsciously, mean a Theocracy, or Government of God. He did mean that Kings and Prime Ministers, and all manner of persons, in public or private, diplomatising or whatever else they might be doing, should walk according to the Gospel of Christ, and understand that this was their Law, supreme over all laws. He hoped once to see such a thing realised; and the Petition, *Thy Kingdom come*, no longer an empty word. He was sore grieved when he saw greedy worldly Barons clutch hold of the Church's property; when he expostulated that it was not secular property, that it was spiritual property, and should be turned to *true* churchly uses, education, schools, worship;—and the Regent Murray had to answer, with a shrug of the shoulders, "It is a devout imagination!" This was Knox's scheme of right and truth; this he zealously endeavoured after, to realise it. If we think this scheme of truth was too narrow, was not true, we may rejoice that he could not realise it; that it remained after two centuries of effort, unrealisable, and is a ' devout imagination ' still.   But how shall we blame *him* for struggling to realise it? Theocracy, Government of God, is precisely the thing to be struggled for !   All Prophets, zealous Priests, are there for that purpose.   Hildebrand wished a Theocracy; Cromwell wished it, fought for it; Mahomet attained it.   Nay, is it not what all zealous men, whether called Priests, Prophets, or whatsoever else called, do essentially wish, and must wish?   That right and truth, or God's Law, reign supreme among men, this is the Heavenly Ideal (well named in Knox's time, and namable in all times, a revealed ' Will of God ') towards which the Reformer will insist that all be more and more approximated.   All true Reformers, as I said, are by the nature of them Priests, and strive for a Theocracy.

How far such Ideals can ever be introduced into Practice, and at what point our impatience with their non-introduction ought to begin, is always a question. I think we may say safely, Let them introduce themselves as far as they can contrive to do it !   If they are the true faith of men, all men ought to be more or less impatient always where they are not found introduced. There will never be wanting Regent Murrays enough to shrug their shoulders, and say, " A devout imagination !"   We will praise the Hero-priest, rather, who does what is in *him* to bring them in ; and wears out, in toil, calumny, contradiction, a noble life, to make a God's Kingdom of this Earth.   The Earth will not become too godlike !

LECTURE V

THE HERO AS A MAN OF LETTERS.   JOHNSON, ROUSSEAU,
BURNS.

[*Tuesday, 19th May* 1840]

HERO-GODS, Prophets, Poets, Priests are forms of
Heroism that belong to the old ages, make their appearance in the remotest times; some of them have ceased to
be possible long since, and cannot any more show themselves in this world. The Hero as *Man of Letters*, again,
of which class we are to speak today, is altogether a product of these new ages; and so long as the wondrous
art of *Writing*, or of Ready-writing which we call *Printing*, subsists, he may be expected to continue, as one
of the main forms of Heroism for all future ages.   He
is, in various respects, a very singular phenomenon.

He is new, I say; he has hardly lasted above a century
in the world yet.   Never, till about a hundred years
ago, was there seen any figure of a Great Soul living
apart in that anomalous manner; endeavouring to speak-
forth the inspiration that was in him by Printed Books,
and find place and subsistence by what the world would
please to give him for doing that.   Much had been sold
and bought, and left to make its own bargain in the
marketplace; but the inspired wisdom of a Heroic Soul
never till then, in that naked manner.   He, with his
copy-rights and copy-wrongs, in his squalid garret, in
his rusty coat; ruling (for this is what he does), from
his grave, after death, whole nations and generations
who would, or would not, give him bread while living,
—is a rather curious spectacle!   Few shapes of Heroism
can be more unexpected.

Alas, the Hero from of old has had to cramp himself
into strange shapes: the world knows not well at any
time what to do with him, so foreign is his aspect in
the world!   It seemed absurd to us, that men, in their
rude admiration, should take some wise great Odin for
a god, and worship him as such; some wise great Maho-

o 278

met for one god-inspired, and religiously follow his Law
for twelve centuries : but that a wise great Johnson, a
Burns, a Rousseau, should be taken for some idle nondescript, extant in the world to amuse idleness, and
have a few coins and applauses thrown in, that he might
live thereby; *this* perhaps, as before hinted, will one
day seem a still absurder phasis of things !—Meanwhile,
since it is the spiritual always that determines the
material, this same Man-of-Letters Hero must be regarded as our most important modern person.   He,
such as he may be, is the soul of all.   What he teachers,
the whole world will do and make.   The world's manner
of dealing with him is the most significant feature of
the world's general position.   Looking well at his life,
we may get a glance, as deep as is readily possible for
us, into the life of those singular centuries which have
produced him, in which we ourselves live and work.

There are genuine Men of Letters, and not genuine;
as in every kind there is a genuine and a spurious.   If
Hero be taken to mean genuine, then I say the Hero
as Man of Letters will be found discharging a function
for us which is ever honourable, ever the highest; and
was once well known to be the highest.   He is uttering-
forth, in such a way as he has, the inspired soul of him;
all that a man, in any case, can do.   I say *inspired;*
for what we call ' originality,' ' sincerity,' ' genius,' the
heroic quality we have no good name for, signifies that.
The Hero is he who lives in the inward sphere of things,
in the True, Divine and Eternal, which exists always,
unseen to most, under the Temporary, Trivial : his being
is in that; he declares that abroad, by act or speech as
it may be, in declaring himself abroad.   His life, as
we said before, is a piece of the everlasting heart of
Nature herself : all men's life is,—but the weak many
know not the fact, and are untrue to it, in most times;
the strong few are strong, heroic, perennial, because it
cannot be hidden from them.   The Man of Letters, like
every Hero, is there to proclaim this in such sort as
he can.   Intrinsically it is the same function which the
old generations named a man Prophet, Priest, Divinity
for doing; which all manner of Heroes, by speech or
by act, are sent into the world to do.

Fichte the German Philosopher delivered, some forty years ago at Erlangen, a highly remarkable Course of Lectures on this subject : ' *Ueber das Wesen des Gelehrten*, On the Nature of the Literary Man.' Fichte, in conformity with the Transcendental Philosophy, of which he was a distinguished teacher, declares first : That all things which we see or work with in this Earth, especially we ourselves and all persons, are as a kind of vesture or sensuous Appearance : that under all there lies, as the essence of them, what he calls the ' Divine Idea of the World;' this is the Reality which ' lies at the bottom of all Appearance.' To the mass of men no such Divine Idea is recognisable in the world; they live merely, says Fichte, among the superficialities, practicalities and shows of the world, not dreaming that there is anything divine under them. But the Man of Letters is sent hither specially that he may discern for himself, and make manifest to us, this same Divine Idea : in every new generation it will manifest itself in a new dialect; and he is there for the purpose of doing that. Such is Fichte's phraseology; with which we need not quarrel. It is his way of naming what I here, by other words, am striving imperfectly to name; what there is at present no name for : The unspeakable Divine Significance, full of splendour, of wonder and terror, that lies in the being of every man, of every thing,—the Presence of the God who made every man and thing. Mahomet taught this in his dialect; Odin in his : it is the thing which all thinking hearts, in one dialect or another, are here to teach.

Fichte calls the Man of Letters, therefore, a Prophet, or as he prefers to phrase it, a Priest, continually unfolding the Godlike to men : Men of Letters are a perpetual Priesthood, from age to age, teaching all men that a God is still present in their life; that all ' Appearance,' whatsoever we see in the world, is but as a vesture for the ' Divine Idea of the World,' for ' that which lies at the bottom of Appearance.' In the true Literary Man there is thus ever, acknowledged or not by the world, a sacredness : he is the light of the world; the world's Priest :—guiding it, like a sacred Pillar of Fire, in its dark pilgrimage through the waste of Time. Fichte discriminates with sharp zeal the *true* Literary Man, what we here call the *Hero* as Man of Letters, from multitudes of false unheroic. Whoever lives not wholly in this Divine Idea, or living partially in it, struggles not, as for the one good, to live wholly in it,—he is, let him live where else he like, in what pomps and prosperities he like, no Literary Man; he is, says Fichte, a ' Bungler, *Stümper*.' Or at best, if he belong to the prosaic provinces, he may be a ' Hodman;' Fichte even calls him elsewhere a ' Nonentity,' and has in short no mercy for him, no wish that *he* should continue happy among us ! This is Fichte's notion of the Man of Letters. It means, in its own form, precisely what we here mean.

In this point of view, I consider that, for the last hundred years, by far the notablest of all Literary Men is Fichte's countryman, Goethe. To that man too, in a strange way, there was given what we may call a life in the Divine Idea of the World; vision of the inward divine mystery : and strangely, out of his Books, the world rises imaged once more as godlike, the workmanship and temple of a God. Illuminated all, not in fierce impure fire-splendour as of Mahomet, but in mild celestial radiance;—really a Prophecy in these most unprophetic times; to my mind, by far the greatest, though one of the quietest, among all the great things that have come to pass in them. Our chosen specimen of the Hero as Literary Man would be this Goethe. And it were a very pleasant plan for me here to discourse of his heroism : for I consider him to be a true Hero; heroic in what he said and did, and perhaps still more in what he did not say and did not do; to me a noble spectacle : a great heroic ancient man, speaking and keeping silence as an ancient Hero, in the guise of a most modern, high-bred, high-cultivated Man of Letters ! We have had no such spectacle; no man capable of affording such, for the last hundred-and-fifty years.

But at present, such is the general state of knowledge about Goethe, it were worse than useless to attempt speaking of him in this case. Speak as I might, Goethe, to the great majority of you, would remain problematic, vague; no impression but a false one could be realised.

Him we must leave to future times. Johnson, Burns, Rousseau, three great figures from a prior time, from a far inferior state of circumstances, will suit us better here. Three men of the Eighteenth Century; the conditions of their life far more resemble what those of ours still are in England, than what Goethe's in Germany were. Alas, these men did not conquer like him; they fought bravely, and fell. They were not heroic bringers of the light, but heroic seekers of it. They lived under galling conditions; struggling as under mountains of impediment, and could not unfold themselves into clearness, or victorious interpretation of that ' Divine Idea.' It is rather the *Tombs* of three Literary Heroes that I have to show you. There are the monumental heaps, under which three spiritual giants lie buried. Very mournful, but also great and full of interest for us. We will linger by them for a while.

Complaint is often made, in these times, of what we call the disorganised condition of society : how ill many arranged forces of society fulfil their work; how many powerful forces are seen working in a wasteful, chaotic, altogether unarranged manner. It is too just a complaint, as we all know. But perhaps if we look at this of Books and the Writers of Books, we shall find here, as it were, the summary of all other disorganisation ;— a sort of *heart,* from which, and to which, all other confusion circulates in the world ! Considering what Book-writers do in the world, and what the world does with Book-writers, I should say, It is the most anomalous thing the world at present has to show.—We should get into a sea far beyond sounding, did we attempt to give account of this : but we must glance at it for the sake of our subject. The worst element in the life of these three Literary Heroes was, that they found their business and position such a chaos. On the beaten road there is tolerable travelling; but it is sore work, and many have to perish, fashioning a path through the impassable !

Our pious Fathers, feeling well what importance lay in the speaking of man to men, founded churches, made endowments, regulations; everywhere in the civilised world there is a Pulpit, environed with all manner of complex dignified appurtenances and furtherances, that therefrom a man with the tongue may, to best advantage, address his fellow-men. They felt that this was the most important thing; that without this there was no good thing. It is a right pious work, that of theirs; beautiful to behold! But now with the art of Writing, with the art of Printing, a total change has come over that business. The Writer of a Book, is not he a Preacher preaching not to this parish or that, on this day or that, but to all men in all times and places? Surely it is of the last importance that *he* do his work right, whoever do it wrong;—that the *eye* report not falsely, for then all the other members are astray! Well; how he may do his work, whether he do it right or wrong, or do it at all, is a point which no man in the world has taken the pains to think of. To a certain shopkeeper, trying to get some money for his books, if lucky, he is of some importance; to no other man of any. Whence he came, whither he is bound, by what ways he arrived, by what he might be furthered on his course, no one asks. He is an accident in society. He wanders like a wild Ishmaelite, in a world of which he is as the spiritual light, either the guidance or the misguidance!

Certainly the art of writing is the most miraculous of all things man has devised. Odin's *Runes* were the first form of the work of a Hero; *Books*, written words, are still miraculous *Runes*, of the latest form! In Books lies the *soul* of the whole Past Time; the articulate audible voice of the Past, when the body and material substance of it has altogether vanished like a dream. Mighty fleets and armies, harbours and arsenals, vast cities, high-domed, many-engined,—they are precious, great: but what do they become? Agamemnon, the many Agamemnons, Pericleses, and their Greece; all is gone now to some ruined fragments, dumb mournful wrecks and blocks: but the Books of Greece! There Greece, to every thinker, still very literally lives; can be called-up again into life. No magic *Rune* is stranger than a Book. All that Mankind has done, thought, gained or been: it is lying as in magic preservation in the pages of Books. They are the chosen possession of men.

Do not Books still accomplish *miracles* as *Runes* were fabled to do? They persuade men. Not the wretchedest circulating-library novel, which foolish girls thumb and con in remote villages but will help to regulate the actual practical weddings and households of those foolish girls. So ' Celia ' felt, so ' Clifford ' acted : the foolish Theorem of Life, stamped into those young brains, comes out as a solid Practice one day. Consider whether any *Rune* in the wildest imagination of Mythologist ever did such wonders as, on the actual firm Earth, some Books have done ! What built St Paul's Cathedral? Look at the heart of the matter, it was that divine Hebrew Book,—the word partly of the man Moses, an outlaw tending his Midianitish herds, four thousand years ago, in the wildernesses of Sinai ! It is the strangest of things, yet nothing is truer. With the art of Writing, of which Printing is a simple, an inevitable and comparatively insignificant corollary, the true reign of miracles for mankind commenced. It related, with a wondrous new contiguity and perpetual closeness, the Past and Distant with the Present in time and place; all times and all places with this our actual Here and Now. All things were altered for men ; all modes of important work of men : teaching, preaching, governing, and all else.

To look at Teaching, for instance. Universities are a notable, respectable product of the modern ages. Their existence too is modified, to the very basis of it, by the existence of Books. Universities arose while there were yet no Books procurable ; while a man, for a single Book, had to give an estate of land. That, in those circumstances, when a man had some knowledge to communicate, he should do it by gathering the learners round him, face to face, was a necessity for him. If you wanted to know what Abelard knew, you must go and listen to Abelard. Thousands, as many as thirty-thousand, went to hear Abelard and that metaphysical theology of his. And now for any other teacher who had something of his own to teach, there was a great convenience opened : so many thousands eager to learn were already assembled yonder ; of all places the best place for him was that. For any third teacher it was better still; and grew ever the better, the more teachers there came. It only needed now that the King took notice of this new phenomenon; combined or agglomerated the various schools into one school; gave it edifices, privileges, encouragements, and named it *Universitas*, or School of all Sciences : the University of Paris, in its essential characters, was there. The model of all subsequent Universities; which down even to these days, for six centuries now, have gone on to found themselves. Such, I conceive, was the origin of Universities.

It is clear, however, that with this simple circumstance, facility of getting Books, the whole conditions of the business from top to bottom were changed. Once invent Printing, you metamorphosed all Universities, or superseded them ! The Teacher needed not now to gather men personally round him, that he might *speak* to them what he knew : print it in a Book, and all learners far and wide, for a trifle, had it each at his own fireside, much more effectually to learn it !—Doubtless there is still peculiar virtue in Speech; even writers of Books may still, in some circumstances, find it convenient to speak also,—witness our present meeting here ! There is, one would say, and must ever remain while man has a tongue, a distinct province for Speech as well as for Writing and Printing. In regard to all things this must remain; to Universities among others. But the limits of the two have nowhere yet been pointed out, ascertained; much less put in practice : the University which would completely take-in that great new fact, of the existence of Printed Books, and stand on a clear footing for the Nineteenth Century as the Paris one did for the Thirteenth, has not yet come into existence. If we think of it, all that a University, or final highest School can do for us, is still but what the first School began doing,—teach us to *read*. We learn to *read*, in various languages, in various sciences; we learn the alphabet and letters of all manner of Books. But the place where we go to get knowledge, even theoretic knowledge, is the Books themselves ! It depends on what we read, after all manner of Professors have done their best for us. The true University of these days is a Collection of Books.

But to the Church itself, as I hinted already, all is changed, in its preaching, in its working, by the introduction of Books. The Church is the working recognised Union of our Priests or Prophets, of those who by wise teaching guide the souls of men. While there was no Writing, even while there was no Easy-writing or *Printing*, the preaching of the voice was the natural sole method of performing this. But now with Books! —He that can write a true Book, to persuade England, is not he the Bishop and Archbishop, the Primate of England and of All England? I many a time say, the writers of Newspapers, Pamphlets, Poems, Books, these *are* the real working effective Church of a modern country. Nay not only our preaching, but even our worship, is not it too accomplished by means of Printed Books? The noble sentiment which a gifted soul has clothed for us in melodious words, which brings melody into our hearts,—is not this essentially, if we will understand it, of the nature of worship? There are many, in all countries, who, in this confused time, have no other method of worship. He who, in any way, shows us better than we knew before that a lily of the fields is beautiful, does he not show it us as an effluence of the Fountain of all Beauty; as the *handwriting*, made visible there, of the great Maker of the Universe? He has sung for us, made us sing with him, a little verse of a sacred Psalm. Essentially so. How much more he who sings, who says, or in any way brings home to our heart the noble doings, feelings, darings and endurances of a brother man! He has verily touched our hearts as with a live coal *from the altar*. Perhaps there is no worship more authentic.

Literature, so far as it is Literature, is an 'apocalypse of Nature,' a revealing of the 'open secret.' It may well enough be named, in Fichte's style, a 'continuous revelation' of the Godlike in the Terrestrial and Common. The Godlike does ever, in very truth, endure there; is brought out, now in this dialect, now in that, with various degrees of clearness: all true gifted Singers and Speakers are, consciously or unconsciously, doing so. The dark stormful indignation of a Byron, so wayward and perverse, may have touches of it; nay the withered mockery of a French sceptic,—his mockery of the False, a love and worship of the True. How much more the sphere-harmony of a Shakspeare, of a Goethe; the cathedral-music of a Milton! They are something too, those humble genuine lark-notes of a Burns,—skylark, starting from the humble furrow, far overhead into the blue depths, and singing to us so genuinely there! For all true singing is of the nature of worship; as indeed all true *working* may be said to be,—whereof such *singing* is but the record, and fit melodious representation, to us. Fragments of a real ' Church Liturgy' and ' Body of Homilies,' strangely disguised from the common eye, are to be found weltering in that huge froth-ocean of Printed Speech we loosely call Literature! Books are our Church too.

Or turning now to the Government of men. Witenagemote, old Parliament, was a great thing. The affairs of the nation were there deliberated and decided; what we were to *do* as a nation. But does not, though the name Parliament subsists, the parliamentary debate go on now, everywhere and at all times, in a far more comprehensive way, *out* of Parliament altogether? Burke said there were Three Estates in Parliament; but, in the Reporters' Gallery yonder, there sat a *Fourth Estate* more important far than they all. It is not a figure of speech, or a witty saying; it is a literal fact,—very momentous to us in these times. Literature is our Parliament too. Printing, which comes necessarily out of Writing, I say often, is equivalent to Democracy: invent Writing, Democracy is inevitable. Writing brings Printing; brings universal every-day extempore Printing, as we see at present. Whoever can speak, speaking now to the whole nation, becomes a power, a branch of government, with inalienable weight in lawmaking, in all acts of authority. It matters not what rank he has, what revenues or garnitures: the requisite thing is, that he have a tongue which others will listen to; this and nothing more is requisite. The nation is governed by all that has tongue in the nation: Democracy is virtually *there*. Add only, that whatsoever power exists will have itself, by and by, organised; working secretly under bandages, obscurations, obstructions, it will never rest till it get to work free, unencumbered, visible to all. Democracy virtually extant will insist on becoming palpably extant.—

On all sides, are we not driven to the conclusion that, of the things which man can do or make here below, by far the most momentous, wonderful and worthy are the things we call Books! Those poor bits of rag-paper with black ink on them;—from the Daily Newspaper to the sacred Hebrew BOOK, what have they not done, what are they not doing!—For indeed, whatever be the outward form of the thing (bits of paper, as we say, and black ink), is it not verily, at bottom, the highest act of man's faculty that produces a Book? It is the *Thought* of man; the true thaumaturgic virtue; by which man works all things whatsoever. All that he does, and brings to pass, is the vesture of a Thought. This London City, with all its houses, palaces, steam-engines, cathedrals, and huge immeasurable traffic and tumult, what is it but a Thought, but millions of Thoughts made into One;—a huge immeasurable Spirit of a THOUGHT, embodied in brick, in iron, smoke, dust, Palaces, Parliaments, Hackney Coaches, Katherine Docks, and the rest of it! Not a brick was made but some man had to *think* of the making of that brick.—The thing we called ' bits of paper with traces of black ink,' is the *purest* embodiment a Thought of man can have. No wonder it is, in all ways, the activest and noblest.

All this, of the importance and supreme importance of the Man of Letters in modern Society, and how the Press is to such a degree superseding the Pulpit, the Senate, the *Senatus Academicus* and much else, has been admitted for a good while; and recognised often enough, in late times, with a sort of sentimental triumph and wonderment. It seems to me, the Sentimental by and by will have to give place to the Practical. If Men of Letters *are* so incalculably influential, actually performing such work for us from age to age, and even from day to day, then I think we may conclude that Men of Letters will not always wander like unrecognised unregulated Ishmaelites among us! Whatsoever thing, as I said above, has virtual unnoticed power will cast-

off its wrappages, bandages, and step-forth one day
with palpably articulated, universally visible power.
That one man wear the clothes, and take the wages, of
a function which is done by quite another: there can
be no profit in this; this is not right, it is wrong.   And
yet, alas, the *making* of it right,—what a business, for
long times to come! Sure enough, this that we call
Organisation of the Literary Guild is still a great way
off, encumbered with all manner of complexities.   If
you asked me what were the best possible organisation
for the Men of Letters in modern society; the arrangement of furtherance and regulation, grounded the most
accurately on the actual facts of their position and of
the world's position,—I should beg to say that the problem far exceeded my faculty! It is not one man's
faculty; it is that of many successive men turned earnestly upon it, that will bring-out even an approximate
solution.   What the best arrangement were, none of us
could say.   But if you ask, Which is the worst? I
answer: This which we now have, that Chaos should
sit umpire in it; this is the worst.   To the best, or any
good one, there is yet a long way.

One remark I must not omit, That royal or parliamentary grants of money are by no means the chief
thing wanted! To give our Men of Letters stipends,
endowments and all furtherance of cash, will do little
towards the business.   On the whole, one is weary of
hearing about the omnipotence of money.   I will say
rather that, for a genuine man, it is no evil to be poor;
that there ought to be Literary Men poor,—to show
whether they are genuine or not! Mendicant Orders,
bodies of good men doomed to *beg*, were instituted in
the Christian Church; a most natural and even necessary development of the spirit of Christianity.   It was
itself founded on Poverty, on Sorrow, Contradiction,
Crucifixion, every species of worldly Distress and Degradation.   We may say, that he who has not known
those things, and learned from them the priceless lessons
they have to teach, has missed a good opportunity of
schooling.   To beg, and go barefoot, in coarse woollen
cloak with a rope round your loins, and be despised
of all the world, was no beautiful business;—nor an

honourable one in any eye, till the nobleness of those who did so had made it honoured of some !

Begging is not in our course at the present time : but for the rest of it, who will say that a Johnson is not perhaps the better for being poor? It is needful for him, at all rates, to know that outward profit, that success of any kind is *not* the goal he has to aim at. Pride, vanity, ill-conditioned egoism of all sorts, are bred in his heart, as in every heart; need, above all, to be cast-out of his heart,—to be, with whatever pangs, torn-out of it, cast-forth from it, as a thing worthless. Byron, born rich and noble, made-out even less than Burns, poor and plebeian. Who knows but, in that same ' best possible organisation ' as yet far off, Poverty may still enter as an important element? What if our Men of Letters, Men setting-up to be Spiritual Heroes, were still *then*, as they now are, a kind of ' involuntary monastic order;' bound still to this same ugly Poverty,—till they had tried what was in it too, till they had learned to make it too do for them ! Money, in truth, can do much, but it cannot do all. We must know the province of it, and confine it; and even spurn it back, when it wishes to get farther.

Besides, were the money-furtherances, the proper season for them, the fit assigner of them, all settled,— how is the Burns to be recognised that merits these? He must pass through the ordeal, and prove himself. *This* ordeal; this wild welter of a chaos which is called Literary Life; this too is a kind of ordeal ! There is clear truth in the idea that a struggle from the lower classes of society, towards the upper regions and rewards of society, must ever continue. Strong men are born there, who ought to stand elsewhere than there. The manifold, inextricably complex, universal struggle of these constitutes, and must constitute, what is called the progress of society. For Men of Letters, as for all other sorts of men. How to regulate that struggle? There is the whole question. To leave it as it is, at the mercy of blind Chance; a whirl of distracted atoms, one cancelling the other; one of the thousand arriving saved, nine-hundred-and-ninety-nine lost by the way; your royal Johnson languishing inactive in garrets, or harnessed to the yoke of Printer Cave; your Burns dying broken-hearted as a Gauger; your Rousseau driven into mad exasperation, kindling French Revolutions by his paradoxes : this, as we said, is clearly enough the *worst* regulation. The *best*, alas, is far from us !

And yet there can be no doubt but it is coming; advancing on us, as yet hidden in the bosom of centuries : this is a prophecy one can risk. For so soon as men get to discern the importance of a thing, they do infallibly set about arranging it, facilitating, forwarding it; and rest not till, in some approximate degree, they have accomplished that. I say, of all Priesthoods, Aristocracies, Governing Classes at present extant in the world, there is no class comparable for importance to that Priesthood of the Writers of Books. This is a fact which he who runs may read,—and draw inferences from. " Literature will take care of itself," answered Mr Pitt, when applied-to for some help for Burns. " Yes," adds Mr Southey, " it will take care of itself; *and of you too*, if you do not look to it !''

The result to individual Men of Letters is not the momentous one; they are but individuals, an infinitesimal fraction of the great body; they can struggle on, and live or else die, as they have been wont. But it deeply concerns the whole society, whether it will set its *light* on high places, to walk thereby; or trample it under foot, and scatter it in all ways of wild waste (not without conflagration), as heretofore ! Light is the one thing wanted for the world. Put wisdom in the head of the world, the world will fight its battle victoriously, and be the best world man can make it. I call this anomaly of a disorganic Literary Class the heart of all other anomalies, at once product and parent; some good arrangement for that would be as the *punctum saliens* of a new vitality and just arrangement for all. Already, in some European countries, in France, in Prussia, one traces some beginnings of an arrangement for the Literary Class; indicating the gradual possibility of such. I believe that it is possible; that it will have to be possible.

By far the most interesting fact I hear about the

Chinese is one on which we cannot arrive at clearness, but which excites endless curiosity even in the dim state : this namely, that they do attempt to make their Men of Letters their Governors ! It would be rash to say, one understood how this was done, or with what degree of success it was done. All such things must be very *un*successful; yet a small degree of success is precious; the very attempt how precious ! There does seem to be, all over China, a more or less active search everywhere to discover the men of talent that grow up in the young generation. Schools there are for every one : a foolish sort of training, yet still a sort. The youths who distinguish themselves in the lower school are promoted into favourable stations in the higher, that they may still more distinguish themselves,—forward and forward : it appears to be out of these that the Official Persons, and incipient Governors, are taken. These are they whom they *try* first, whether they can govern or not. And surely with the best hope : for they are the men that have already shown intellect. Try them : they have not governed or administered as yet; perhaps they cannot; but there is no doubt they *have* some Understanding, without which no man can ! Neither is Understanding a *tool,* as we are too apt to figure; ' it is a *hand* which can handle any tool.' Try these men : they are of all others the best worth trying.—Surely there is no kind of government, constitution, revolution, social apparatus or arrangement, that I know of in this world, so promising to one's scientific curiosity as this. The man of intellect at the top of affairs : this is the aim of all constitutions and revolutions, if they have any aim. For the man of true intellect, as I assert and believe always, is the noblehearted man withal, the true, just, humane and valiant man. Get *him* for governor, all is got; fail to get him, though you had Constitutions plentiful as blackberries, and a Parliament in every village, there is nothing yet got !—

These things look strange, truly; and are not such as we commonly speculate upon. But we are fallen into strange times; these things will require to be speculated upon; to be rendered practicable, to be in some way put in practice. These and many others. On all hands of us, there is the announcement, audible enough, that the old Empire of Routine has ended; that to say a thing has long been, is no reason for its continuing to be. The things which have been are fallen into decay, are fallen into incompetence; large masses of mankind, in every society of our Europe, are no longer capable of living at all by the things which have been. When millions of men can no longer by their utmost exertion gain food for themselves, and ' the third man for thirty-six weeks each year is short of third-rate potatoes,' the things which have been must decidedly prepare to alter themselves !—I will now quit this of the organisation of Men of Letters.

Alas, the evil that pressed heaviest on those Literary Heroes of ours was not the want of organisation for Men of Letters, but a far deeper one; out of which, indeed, this and so many other evils for the Literary Man, and for all men, had, as from their fountain, taken rise. That our Hero as Man of Letters had to travel without highway, companionless, through an inorganic chaos,—and to leave his own life and faculty lying there, as a partial contribution towards *pushing* some highway through it : this, had not his faculty itself been so perverted and paralysed, he might have put up with, might have considered to be but the common lot of Heroes. His fatal misery was the *spiritual paralysis*, so we may name it, of the Age in which his life lay; whereby his life too, do what he might, was half-paralysed ! The Eighteenth was a *Sceptical* Century; in which little word there is a whole Pandora's Box of miseries. Scepticism means not intellectual Doubt alone, but moral Doubt; all sorts of *in*fidelity, insincerity, spiritual paralysis. Perhaps, in few centuries that one could specify since the world began, was a life of Heroism more difficult for a man. That was not an age of Faith,—an age of Heroes ! The very possibility of Heroism had been, as it were, formally abnegated in the minds of all. Heroism was gone forever; Triviality, Formulism and Commonplace were come forever. The ' age of miracles ' had been, or perhaps had not been; but it was not any longer. An effete world; wherein Wonder, Greatness, Godhood could not now dwell;—in one word, a godless world!

How mean, dwarfish are their ways of thinking, in this time,—compared not with the Christian Shakspeares and Miltons, but with the old Pagan Skalds, with any species of believing men! The living TREE Igdrasil, with the melodious prophetic waving of its world-wide boughs, deep-rooted as Hela, has died-out into the clanking of a World-MACHINE. ' Tree ' and ' Machine ': contrast these two things. I, for my share, declare the world to be no machine! I say that it does not go by wheel-and-pinion ' motives,' self-interests, checks, balances; that there is something far other in it than the clank of spinning-jennies, and parliamentary majorities; and, on the whole, that it is not a machine at all!—The old Norse Heathen had a truer notion of God's-world than these poor Machine-Sceptics: the old Heathen Norse were *sincere* men. But for these poor Sceptics there was no sincerity, no truth. Half-truth and hearsay was called truth. Truth, for most men, meant plausibility; to be measured by the number of votes you could get. They had lost any notion that sincerity was possible, or of what sincerity was. How many Plausibilities asking, with unaffected surprise and the air of offended virtue, What! am not I sincere? Spiritual Paralysis, I say, nothing left but a Mechanical life, was the characteristic of that century. For the common man, unless happily he stood *below* his century and belonged to another prior one, it was impossible to be a Believer, a Hero; he lay buried, unconscious, under these baleful influences. To the strongest man, only with infinite struggle and confusion was it possible to work himself half-loose; and lead as it were, in an enchanted, most tragical way, a spiritual death-in-life, and be a Half-Hero!

Scepticism is the name we give to all this; as the chief symptom, as the chief origin of all this. Concerning which so much were to be said! It would take many Discourses, not a small fraction of one Discourse, to state what one feels about that Eighteenth Century and its ways. As indeed this, and the like of this, which we now call Scepticism, is precisely the black malady and life-foe, against which all teaching and discoursing since man's life began has directed itself : the battle of Belief against Unbelief is the never-ending battle ! Neither is it in the way of crimination that one would wish to speak. Scepticism, for that century, we must consider as the decay of old ways of believing, the preparation afar off for new better and wider ways, —an inevitable thing. We will not blame men for it ; we will lament their hard fate. We will understand that destruction of old *forms* is not destruction of everlasting *substances ;* that Scepticism, as sorrowful and hateful as we see it, is not an end but a beginning.

The other day speaking, without prior purpose that way, of Bentham's theory of man and man's life, I chanced to call it a more beggarly one than Mahomet's. I am bound to say, now when it is once uttered, that such is my deliberate opinion. Not that one would mean offence against the man Jeremy Bentham, or those who respect and believe him. Bentham himself, and even the creed of Bentham, seems to me comparatively worthy of praise. It is a determinate *being* what all the world, in a cowardly, half-and-half manner, was tending to be. Let us have the crisis ; we shall either have death or the cure. I call this gross, steam-engine Utilitarianism an approach towards new Faith. It was a laying down of cant ; a saying to oneself : " Well then, this world is a dead iron machine, the god of it Gravitation and selfish Hunger ; let us see what, by checking and balancing, and good adjustment of tooth and pinion, can be made of it !" Benthamism has something complete, manful, in such fearless committal of itself to what it finds true ; you may call it Heroic, though a Heroism with its *eyes* put out ! It is the culminating point, and fearless ultimatum, of what lay in the half-and-half state, pervading man's whole existence in that Eighteenth Century. It seems to me, all deniers of Godhood, and all lip-believers of it, are bound to be Benthamites, if they have courage and honesty. Benthamism is an *eyeless* Heroism : the Human Species, like a hapless blinded Samson grinding in the Philistine Mill, clasps convulsively the pillars of its Mill ; brings huge ruin down, but ultimately deliverance withal. Of Bentham I meant to say no harm.

But this I do say, and would wish all men to know and lay to heart, that he who discerns nothing but Mechanism in the Universe has in the fatalest way missed the secret of the Universe altogether. That all Godhood should vanish out of men's conception of this Universe seems to me precisely the most brutal error,—I will not disparage Heathenism by calling it a Heathen error,—that men could fall into. It is not true; it is false at the very heart of it. A man who thinks so will think *wrong* about all things in the world; this original sin will vitiate all other conclusions he can form. One might call it the most lamentable of delusions,—not forgetting Witchcraft itself! Witchcraft worshipped at least a living Devil: but this worships a dead iron Devil; no God, not even a Devil!—Whatsoever is noble, divine, inspired, drops thereby out of life. There remains everywhere in life a despicable *caput-mortuum;* the mechanical hull, all soul fled out of it. How can a man act heroically? The 'Doctrine of Motives' will teach him that it is, under more or less disguise, nothing but a wretched love of Pleasure, fear of Pain; that Hunger, of applause, of cash, of whatsoever victual it may be, is the ultimate fact of man's life. Atheism, in brief;—which does indeed frightfully punish itself. The man, I say, is become spiritually a paralytic man; this god-like Universe a dead mechanical steam-engine, all working by motives, checks, balances, and I know not what; wherein, as in the detestable belly of some Phalaris'-Bull of his own contriving, he the poor Phalaris sits miserably dying!

Belief I define to be the healthy act of a man's mind. It is a mysterious indescribable process, that of getting to believe;—indescribable, as all vital acts are. We have our mind given us, not that it may cavil and argue, but that it may see into something, give us clear belief and understanding about something, whereon we are then to proceed to act. Doubt, truly, is not itself a crime. Certainly we do not rush out, clutch-up the first thing we find, and straightway believe that! All manner of doubt, inquiry, σκέψις as it is named, about

all manner of objects, dwells in every reasonable mind.
It is the mystic working of the mind, on the object it is
getting to know and believe. Belief comes out of all
this, above ground, like the tree from its hidden *roots*.
But now if, even on common things, we require that
a man keep his doubts *silent*, and not babble of them
till they in some measure become affirmations or denials ;
how much more in regard to the highest things, impossible to speak of in words at all ! That a man
parade his doubt, and get to imagine that debating and
logic (which means at best only the manner of *telling*
us your thought, your belief or disbelief, about a thing)
is the triumph and true work of what intellect he has :
alas, this is as if you should *overturn* the tree, and
instead of green boughs, leaves, and fruits, show us
ugly taloned roots turned-up into the air,—and no
growth, only death and misery going on !

For the Scepticism, as I said, is not intellectual only ;
it is moral also ; a chronic atrophy and disease of the
whole soul. A man lives by believing something ; not
by debating and arguing about many things. A sad
case for him when all that he can manage to believe is
something he can button in his pocket, and with one or
the other organ eat and digest ! Lower than that he
will not get. We call those ages in which he gets so
low the mournfulest, sickest, and meanest of all ages.
The world's heart is palsied, sick : how can any limb of
it be whole ? Genuine Acting ceases in all departments
of the world's work ; dextrous Similitude of Acting
begins. The world's wages are pocketed, the world's
work is not done. Heroes have gone out ; quacks
have come in. Accordingly, what Century, since the
end of the Roman world, which also was a time of
scepticism, simulacra and universal decadence, so
abounds with Quacks as that Eighteenth ! Consider
them, with their tumid sentimental vapouring about
virtue, benevolence,—the wretched Quack-squadron,
Cagliostro at the head of them ! Few men were without
quackery ; they had got to consider it a necessary
ingredient and amalgam for truth. Chatham, our brave
Chatham himself, comes down to the House, all wrapt
and bandaged ; he ' has crawled out in great bodily

suffering,' and so on;—*forgets*, says Walpole, that he is acting the sick man; in the fire of debate, snatches his arm from the sling, and oratorically swings and brandishes it! Chatham himself lives the strangest mimetic life, half hero, half quack, all along. For indeed the world is full of dupes; and you have to gain the *world's* suffrage! How the duties of the world will be done in that case, what quantities of error, which means failure, which means sorrow and misery, to some and to many, will gradually accumulate in all provinces of the world's business, we need not compute.

It seems to me, you lay your finger here on the heart of the world's maladies, when you call it a Sceptical World. An insincere world; a godless untruth of a world! It is out of this, as I consider, that the whole tribe of social pestilences, French Revolutions, Chartisms, and what not, have derived their being, their chief necessity to be. This must alter. Till this alter, nothing can beneficially alter. My one hope of the world, my inexpugnable consolation in looking at the miseries of the world, is that this is altering. Here and there one does now find a man who knows, as of old, that this world is a Truth, and no Plausibility and Falsity; that he himself is alive, not dead or paralytic; and that the world is alive, instinct with Godhood, beautiful and awful, even as in the beginning of days! One man once knowing this, many men, all men, must by and by come to know it. It lies there clear, for whosoever will take the *spectacles* off his eyes and honestly look, to know! For such a man, the Unbelieving Century, with its unblessed Products, is already past : a new century is already come. The old unblessed Products and Performances, as solid as they look, are Phantasms, preparing speedily to vanish. To this and the other noisy, very great-looking Simulacrum with the whole world huzzahing at its heels, he can say, composedly stepping aside : Thou art not *true;* thou art not extant, only semblant; go thy way!—Yes, hollow Formulism, gross Benthamism, and other unheroic atheistic Insincerity is visibly and even rapidly declining. An unbelieving Eighteenth Century is but an exception,—such as now and then occurs. I prophesy that the world will once more become *sincere;* a believing world : with *many* Heroes in it, a heroic world ! It will then be a victorious world; never till then !

Or indeed what of the world and its victories? Men speak too much about the world. Each one of us here, let the world go how it will, and be victorious or not victorious, has he not a Life of his own to lead? One Life; a little gleam of Time between two Eternities; no second chance to us forevermore ! It were well for *us* to live not as fools and simulacra, but as wise and realities. The world's being saved will not save us; nor the world's being lost destroy us. We should look to ourselves : there is great merit here in the ' duty of staying at home ' ! And, on the whole, to say truth, I never heard of ' worlds ' being ' saved ' in any other way. That mania of saving worlds is itself a piece of the Eighteenth Century with its windy sentimentalism. Let us not follow it too far. For the saving of the *world* I will trust confidently to the Maker of the world; and look a little to my own saving, which I am more competent to !—In brief, for the world's sake, and for our own, we will rejoice greatly that Scepticism, Insincerity, Mechanical Atheism, with all their poison-dews, are going, and as good as gone.—

Now it was under such conditions, in those times of Johnson, that our Men of Letters had to live. Times in which there was properly no truth in life. Old truths had fallen nigh dumb; the new lay yet hidden, not trying to speak. That Man's Life here below was a Sincerity and Fact, and would forever continue such, no new intimation, in that dusk of the world, had yet dawned. No intimation; not even any French Revolution,—which we define to be a Truth once more, though a Truth clad in hellfire ! How different was the Luther's Pilgrimage, with its assured goal, from the Johnson's, girt with mere traditions, suppositions, grown now incredible, unintelligible ! Mahomet's Formulas were of ' wood waxed and oiled,' and could be *burnt* out of one's way : poor Johnson's were far more difficult to burn.—The strong man will ever find *work*, which means difficulty, pain, to the full measure of his strength. But to make-out a victory, in those circumstances of our poor Hero as Man of Letters, was perhaps more difficult than in any. Not obstruction, disorganisation, Bookseller Osborne and Fourpence-halfpenny a day; not this alone; but the light of his own soul was taken from him. No landmark on the Earth; and, alas, what is that to having no loadstar in the Heaven! We need not wonder that none of those Three men rose to victory. That they fought truly is the highest praise. With a mournful sympathy we will contemplate, if not three living victorious Heroes, as I said, the Tombs of three fallen Heroes! They fell for us too; making a way for us. There are the mountains which they hurled abroad in their confused War of the Giants; under which, their strength and life spent, they now lie buried.

I have already written of these three Literary Heroes, expressly or incidentally; what I suppose is known to most of you; what need not be spoken or written a second time. They concern us here as the singular *Prophets* of that singular age; for such they virtually were; and the aspect they and their world exhibit, under this point of view, might lead us into reflections enough! I call them, all three, Genuine Men more or less; faithfully, for most part unconsciously, struggling to be genuine, and plant themselves on the everlasting truth of things. This to a degree that eminently distinguishes them from the poor artificial mass of their contemporaries; and renders them worthy to be considered as Speakers, in some measure, of the everlasting truth, as Prophets in that age of theirs. By Nature herself, a noble necessity was laid on them to be so. They were men of such magnitude that they could not live on unrealities,— clouds, froth and all inanity gave-way under them: there was no footing for them but on firm earth; no rest or regular motion for them, if they got not footing there. To a certain extent, they were Sons of Nature once more in an age of Artifice; once more, Original Men.

As for Johnson, I have always considered him to be, by nature, one of our great English souls. A strong and noble man; so much left undeveloped in him to the last: in a kindlier element what might he not have been,

—Poet, Priest, sovereign Ruler! On the whole, a man must not complain of his 'element,' of his 'time,' or the like; it is thriftless work doing so. His time is bad: well then, he is there to make it better!—Johnson's youth was poor, isolated, hopeless, very miserable. Indeed, it does not seem possible that, in any the favourablest outward circumstances, Johnson's life could have been other than a painful one. The world might have had more of profitable *work* out of him, or less; but his *effort* against the world's work could never have been a light one. Nature, in return for his nobleness, had said to him, Live in an element of diseased sorrow. Nay, perhaps the sorrow and the nobleness were intimately and even inseparably connected with each other. At all events, poor Johnson had to go about girt with continual hypochondria, physical and spiritual pain. Like a Hercules with the burning Nessus'-shirt on him, which shoots-in on him dull incurable misery: the Nessus'-shirt not to be stript-off, which is his own natural skin! In this manner *he* had to live. Figure him there, with his scrofulous diseases, with his great greedy heart, and unspeakable chaos of thoughts; stalking mournful as a stranger in this Earth; eagerly devouring what spiritual thing he could come at: school-languages and other merely grammatical stuff, if there were nothing better! The largest soul that was in all England; and provision made for it of 'fourpence-halfpenny a day.' Yet a giant invincible soul; a true man's. One remembers always that story of the shoes at Oxford: the rough, seamy-faced, rawboned College Servitor stalking about, in winter-season, with his shoes worn-out; how the charitable Gentleman Commoner secretly places a new pair at his door; and the rawboned Servitor, lifting them, looking at them near, with his dim eyes, with what thoughts,—pitches them out of window! Wet feet, mud, frost, hunger or what you will; but not beggary: we cannot stand beggary! Rude stubborn self-help here; a whole world of squalor, rudeness, confused misery and want, yet of nobleness and manfulness withal. It is a type of the man's life, this pitching-away of the shoes. An original man;— not a secondhand, borrowing or begging man. Let us

stand on our own basis, at any rate! On such shoes
as we ourselves can get. On frost and mud, if you
will, but honestly on that;—on the reality and substance
which Nature gives *us*, not on the semblance, on the
thing she has given another than us!—

And yet with all this rugged pride of manhood and
self-help was there ever soul more tenderly affectionate,
loyally submissive to what was really higher than he?
Great souls are always loyally submissive, reverent to
what is over them; only small mean souls are otherwise.
I could not find a better proof of what I said the other
day, That the sincere man was by nature the obedient
man; that only in a World of Heroes was there loyal
Obedience to the Heroic. The essence of *originality*
is not that it be *new*: Johnson believed altogether in
the old; he found the old opinions credible for him, fit
for him; and in a right heroic manner lived under them.
He is well worth study in regard to that. For we are
to say that Johnson was far other than a mere man of
words and formulas; he was a man of truths and facts.
He stood by the old formulas; the happier was it for
him that he could so stand: but in all formulas that
he could stand by, there needed to be a most genuine
substance. Very curious how, in that poor Paper-age,
so barren, artificial, thick-quilted with Pedantries, Hearsays, the great Fact of this Universe glared in, forever
wonderful, indubitable, unspeakable, divine-infernal,
upon this man too! How he harmonised his Formulas
with it, how he managed at all under such circumstances: that is a thing worth seeing. A thing ' to be
looked at with reverence, with pity, with awe.' That
Church of St. Clement Danes, where Johnson still *worshipped* in the era of Voltaire, is to me a venerable
place.

It was in virtue of his *sincerity*, of his speaking still
in some sort from the heart of Nature, though in the
current artificial dialect, that Johnson was a Prophet.
Are not all dialects ' artificial '? Artificial things are not
all false;—nay every true Product of Nature will infallibly *shape* itself; we may say all artificial things are,
at the starting of them, *true*. What we call ' Formulas '
are not in their origin bad; they are indispensably good.

Formula is *method*, habitude; found wherever man is found. Formulas fashion themselves as Paths do, as beaten Highways, leading towards some sacred or high object, whither many men are bent. Consider it. One man, full of heartfelt earnest impulse, finds-out a way of doing somewhat,—were it of uttering his soul's reverence for the Highest, were it but of fitly saluting his fellow-man. An inventor was needed to do that, a *poet;* he has articulated the dim-struggling thought that dwelt in his own and many hearts. This is his way of doing that; these are his footsteps, the beginning of a ' Path.' And now see : the second man travels naturally in the footsteps of his foregoer, it is the *easiest* method. In the footsteps of his foregoer; yet with improvements, with changes where such seem good; at all events with enlargements, the Path ever *widening* itself as more travel it;—till at last there is a broad Highway whereon the whole world may travel and drive. While there remains a City or Shrine, or any Reality to drive to, at the farther end, the Highway shall be right welcome ! When the City is gone, we will forsake the Highway. In this manner all Institutions, Practices, Regulated Things in the world have come into existence, and gone out of existence. Formulas all begin by being *full* of substance; you may call them the *skin,* the articulation into shape, into limbs and skin, of a substance that is already there : *they* had not been there otherwise. Idols, as we said, are not idolatrous till they become doubtful, empty for the worshipper's heart. Much as we talk against Formulas, I hope no one of us is ignorant withal of the high significance of *true* Formulas; that they were, and will ever be, the indispensablest furniture of our habitation in this world.——

Mark, too, how little Johnson boasts of his ' sincerity.' He has no suspicion of his being particularly sincere,— of his being particularly anything ! A hard-struggling, weary-hearted man, or ' scholar ' as he calls himself, trying hard to get some honest livelihood in the world, not to starve, but to live—without stealing ! A noble unconsciousness is in him. He does not ' engrave *Truth* on his watch-seal;' no, but he stands by truth, speaks

by it, works and lives by it. Thus it ever is. Think
of it once more. The man whom Nature has appointed
to do great things is, first of all, furnished with that
openness to Nature which renders him incapable of being
*in*sincere ! To his large, open, deep-feeling heart Nature
is a Fact: all hearsay is hearsay; the unspeakable
greatness of this Mystery of Life, let him acknowledge
it or not, nay even though he seem to forget it or deny
it, is ever present to *him*,—fearful and wonderful, on
this hand and on that. He has a basis of sincerity;
unrecognised, because never questioned or capable of
question. Mirabeau, Mahomet, Cromwell, Napoleon:
all the Great Men I ever heard-of have this as the
primary material of them. Innumerable commonplace
men are debating, are talking everywhere their commonplace doctrines, which they have learned by logic, by
rote, at secondhand: to that kind of man all this is
still nothing. He must have truth; truth which *he*
feels to be true. How shall he stand otherwise? His
whole soul, at all moments, in all ways, tells him
that there is no standing. He is under the noble
necessity of being true. Johnson's way of thinking
about this world is not mine, any more than Mahomet's
was: but I recognise the everlasting element of heart-
sincerity in both; and see with pleasure how neither of
them remains ineffectual. Neither of them is as *chaff*
sown; in both of them is something which the seed-field
will *grow*.

Johnson was a Prophet to his people; preached a
Gospel to them,—as all like him always do. The highest
Gospel he preached we may describe as a kind of Moral
Prudence: ' in a world where much is to be done, and
little is to be known,' see how you will *do* it ! A thing
well worth preaching. ' A world where much is to be
done, and little is to be known :' do not sink yourselves
in boundless bottomless abysses of Doubt, of wretched
god-forgetting Unbelief;—you were miserable then,
powerless, mad : how could you *do* or work at all?
Such Gospel Johnson preached and taught;—coupled,
theoretically and practically, with this other great
Gospel, ' Clear your mind of Cant !' Have no trade
with Cant: stand on the cold mud in the frosty

weather, but let it be in your own *real* torn shoes :
' that will be better for you,' as Mahomet says ! I call
this, I call these two things *joined together*, a great
Gospel, the greatest perhaps that was possible at that
time.

Johnson's Writings, which once had such currency
and celebrity, are now, as it were, disowned by the
young generation. It is not wonderful; Johnson's
opinions are fast becoming obsolete : but his style of
thinking and of living, we may hope, will never become
obsolete. I find in Johnson's Books the indisputablest
traces of a great intellect and great heart :—ever welcome, under what obstructions and perversions soever.
They are *sincere* words, those of his ; he means things
by them. A wondrous buckram style,—the best he
could get to then ; a measured grandiloquence, stepping
or rather stalking along in a very solemn way, grown
obsolete now ; sometimes a tumid *size* of phraseology
not in proportion to the contents of it : all this you will
put-up with. For the phraseology, tumid or not, has
always *something within it.* So many beautiful styles
and books, with *nothing* in them ;—a man is a *male-
factor* to the world who writes such ! *They* are the
avoidable kind !—Had Johnson left nothing but his
Dictionary, one might have traced there a great intellect, a genuine man. Looking to its clearness of definition, its general solidity, honesty, insight, and successful method, it may be called the best of all Dictionaries.
There is in it a kind of architectural nobleness ; it stands
there like a great solid square-built edifice, finished,
symmetrically complete : you judge that a true Builder
did it.

One word, in spite of our haste, must be granted to
poor Bozzy. He passes for a mean, inflated, gluttonous
creature ; and was so in many senses. Yet the fact of
his reverence for Johnson will ever remain noteworthy.
The foolish conceited Scotch Laird, the most conceited
man of his time, approaching in such awestruck attitude
the great dusty irascible Pedagogue in his mean garret
there : it is a genuine reverence for Excellence ; a *worship* for Heroes, at a time when neither Heroes nor
worship were surmised to exist. Heroes, it would seem,

exist always, and a certain worship of them ! We will
also take the liberty to deny altogether that of the witty
Frenchman, that no man is a Hero to his valet-de-
chambre. Or if so, it is not the Hero's blame, but the
Valet's : that his soul, namely, is a mean *valet*-soul !
He expects his Hero to advance in royal stage-trappings,
with measured step, trains borne behind him, trumpets
sounding before him. It should stand rather, No man
can be a *Grand-Monarque* to his valet-de-chambre. Strip
your Louis Quatorze of his king-gear, and there *is* left
nothing but a poor forked radish with a head fantastically carved ;—admirable to no valet. The Valet does
not know a Hero when he sees him ! Alas, no : it
requires a kind of *Hero* to do that ;—and one of the
world's wants, in *this* as in other senses, is for the most
part want of such.

On the whole, shall we not say, that Boswell's admiration was well bestowed; that he could have found no
soul in all England so worthy of bending down before?
Shall we not say, of this great mournful Johnson too, that
he guided his difficult confused existence wisely; led it
well, like a right-valiant man? That waste chaos of
Authorship by trade; that waste chaos of Scepticism
in religion and politics, in life-theory and life-practice;
in his poverty, in his dust and dimness, with the sick
body and the rusty coat : he made it do for him, like
a brave man. Not wholly without a loadstar in the
Eternal; he had still a loadstar, as the brave all need
to have : with his eye set on that, he would change
his course for nothing in these confused vortices of the
lower sea of Time. 'To the Spirit of Lies, bearing
death and hunger, he would in no wise strike his flag.'
Brave old Samuel : *ultimus Romanorum!*

Of Rousseau and his Heroism I cannot say so much.
He is not what I call a strong man. A morbid, excitable, spasmodic man; at best, intense rather than strong.
He had not ' the talent of Silence,' an invaluable talent;
which few Frenchmen, or indeed men of any sort in these
times, excel in ! The suffering man ought really ' to
consume his own smoke ;' there is no good in emitting
smoke till you have made it into *fire*,—which, in the

metaphorical sense too, all smoke is capable of becoming! Rousseau has not depth or width, not calm force for difficulty; the first characteristic of true greatness. A fundamental mistake to call vehemence and rigidity strength! A man is not strong who takes convulsion-fits; though six men cannot hold him then. He that can walk under the heaviest weight without staggering, he is the strong man. We need forever, especially in these loud-shrieking days, to remind ourselves of that. A man who cannot *hold his peace*, till the time come for speaking and acting, is no right man.

Poor Rousseau's face is to me expressive of him. A high but narrow contracted intensity in it: bony brows; deep, straight-set eyes, in which there is something bewildered-looking,—bewildered, peering with lynx-eagerness. A face full of misery, even ignoble misery, and also of the antagonism against that; something mean, plebeian there, redeemed only by *intensity*: the face of what is called a Fanatic,—a sadly *contracted* Hero! We name him here because, with all his drawbacks, and they are many, he has the first and chief characteristic of a Hero: he is heartily *in earnest*. In earnest, if ever man was; as none of these French Philosophes were. Nay, one would say, of an earnestness too great for his otherwise sensitive, rather feeble nature; and which indeed in the end drove him into the strangest incoherences, almost delirations. There had come, at last, to be a kind of madness in him: his Ideas *possessed* him like demons; hurried him so about, drove him over steep places!—

The fault and misery of Rousseau was what we easily name by a single word *Egoism;* which is indeed the source and summary of all faults and miseries whatsoever. He had not perfected himself into victory over mere Desire; a mean hunger, in many sorts, was still the motive principle of him. I am afraid he was a very vain man; hungry for the praises of men. You remember Genlis's experience of him. She took Jean Jacques to the Theatre; he bargaining for a strict incognito,—" *He* would not be seen there for the world!" The curtain did happen nevertheless to be drawn aside: the Pit recognised Jean Jacques, but took no great notice of him! He expressed the bitterest indignation; gloomed all evening, spake no other than surly words. The glib Countess remained entirely convinced that his anger was not at being seen, but at not being applauded when seen. How the whole nature of the man is poisoned; nothing but suspicion, self-isolation, fierce moody ways! He could not live with anybody. A man of some rank from the country, who visited him often, and used to sit with him, expressing all reverence and affection for him, comes one day, finds Jean Jacques full of the sourest unintelligible humour. "Monsieur," said Jean Jacques, with flaming eyes, "I know why you come here. You come to see what a poor life I lead; how little is in my poor pot that is boiling there. Well, look into the pot! There is half a pound of meat, one carrot and three onions; that is all: go and tell the whole world that, if you like, Monsieur!"—A man of this sort was far gone. The whole world got itself supplied with anecdotes for light laughter, for a certain theatrical interest, from these perversions and contortions of poor Jean Jacques. Alas, to him they were not laughing or theatrical; too real to him! The contortions of a dying gladiator: the crowded amphitheatre looks-on with entertainment; but the gladiator is in agonies and dying.

And yet this Rousseau, as we say, with his passionate appeals to Mothers, with his *Contrat-social*, with his celebrations of Nature, even of savage life in Nature, did once more touch upon Reality, struggle towards Reality; was doing the function of a Prophet to his Time. As *he* could, and as the Time could! Strangely through all that defacement, degradation and almost madness, there is in the inmost heart of poor Rousseau a spark of real heavenly fire. Once more, out of the element of that withered mocking Philosophism, Scepticism and Persiflage, there has arisen in that man the ineradicable feeling and knowledge that this Life of ours is *true;* not a Scepticism, Theorem, or Persiflage, but a Fact, an awful Reality. Nature had made that revelation to him; had ordered him to speak it out. He got it spoken out; if not well and clearly, then ill and dimly,—as clearly as he could. Nay what are all errors and perversities of his, even those stealings of ribbons, aimless confused miseries and vagabondisms, if we will interpret them kindly, but the blinkard dazzlements and staggerings to and fro of a man sent on an errand he is too weak for, by a path he cannot yet find? Men are led by strange ways. One should have tolerance for a man, hope of him; leave him to try yet what he will do. While life lasts, hope lasts for every man.

Of Rousseau's literary talents, greatly celebrated still among his countrymen, I do not say much. His Books, like himself, are what I call unhealthy; not the good sort of Books. There is a sensuality in Rousseau. Combined with such an intellectual gift as his, it makes pictures of a certain gorgeous attractiveness : but they are not genuinely poetical. Not white sunlight: something *operatic;* a kind of rosepink, artificial bedizenment. It is frequent, or rather it is universal, among the French since his time. Madame de Staël has something of it; St. Pierre; and down onwards to the present astonishing convulsionary 'Literature of Desperation,' it is everywhere abundant. That same *rosepink* is not the right hue. Look at a Shakspeare, at a Goethe, even at a Walter Scott! He who has once seen into this, has seen the difference of the True from the Sham-True, and will discriminate them ever afterwards.

We had to observe in Johnson how much good a Prophet, under all disadvantages and disorganisations, can accomplish for the world. In Rousseau we are called to look rather at the fearful amount of evil which, under such disorganisation, may accompany the good. Historically it is a most pregnant spectacle, that of Rousseau. Banished into Paris garrets, in the gloomy company of his own Thoughts and Necessities there; driven from post to pillar; fretted, exasperated till the heart of him went mad, he had grown to feel deeply that the world was not his friend nor the world's law. It was expedient, if anyway possible, that such a man should *not* have been set in flat hostility with the world. He could be cooped into garrets, laughed at as a maniac, left to starve like a wild beast in his cage;—but he could not be hindered from setting the world on fire. The French Revolution found its Evangelist in Rousseau.

His semi-delirious speculations on the miseries of civilised life, the preferability of the savage to the civilised, and suchlike, helped well to produce a whole delirium in France generally. True, you may well ask, What could the world, the governors of the world, do with such a man? Difficult to say what the governors of the world could do with him! What he could do with them is unhappily clear enough,—*guillotine* a great many of them! Enough now of Rousseau.

It was a curious phenomenon, in the withered, unbelieving, secondhand Eighteenth Century, that of a Hero starting up, among the artificial pasteboard figures and productions, in the guise of a Robert Burns. Like a little well in the rocky desert places,—like a sudden splendour of Heaven in the artificial Vauxhall! People knew not what to make of it. They took it for a piece of the Vauxhall fire-work; alas, it *let* itself be so taken, though struggling half-blindly, as in bitterness of death, against that! Perhaps no man had such a false reception from his fellow-men. Once more a very wasteful life-drama was enacted under the sun.

The tragedy of Burns's life is known to all of you. Surely we may say, if discrepancy between place held and place merited constitute perverseness of lot for a man, no lot could be more perverse than Burns's. Among those secondhand acting-figures, *mimes* for most part, of the Eighteenth Century, once more a giant Original man; one of those men who reach down to the perennial Deeps, who take rank with the Heroic among men: and he was born in a poor Ayrshire hut. The largest soul of all the British lands came among us in the shape of a hard-handed Scottish Peasant.

His Father, a poor toiling man, tried various things; did not succeed in any; was involved in continual difficulties. The Steward, Factor as the Scotch call him, used to send letters and threatenings, Burns says, 'which threw us all into tears.' The brave, hard-toiling, hard-suffering Father, his brave heroine of a wife; and those children, of whom Robert was one! In this Earth, so wide otherwise, no shelter for *them*. The letters 'threw us all into tears:' figure it. The brave Father, I say always;—a *silent* Hero and Poet; without whom the son had never been a speaking one! Burns's Schoolmaster came afterwards to London, learnt what good society was; but declares that in no meeting of men did he ever enjoy better discourse than at the hearth of this peasant. And his poor ' seven acres of nursery-ground,'—not that, nor the miserable patch of clay-farm, nor anything he tried to get a living by, would prosper with him; he had a sore unequal battle all his days. But he stood to it valiantly; a wise, faithful, unconquerable man;—swallowing-down how many sore sufferings daily into silence; fighting like an unseen Hero,—nobody publishing newspaper paragraphs about his nobleness; voting pieces of plate to him! However, he was not lost: nothing is lost. Robert is there; the outcome of him,—and indeed of many generations of such as him.

This Burns appears under every disadvantage: uninstructed, poor, born only to hard manual toil; and writing, when it came to that, in a rustic special dialect, known only to a small province of the country he lived in. Had he written, even what he did write, in the general language of England, I doubt not he had already become universally recognised as being, or capable to be, one of our greatest men. That he should have tempted so many to penetrate through the rough husk of that dialect of his, is proof that there lay something far from common within it. He has gained a certain recognition, and is continuing to do so over all quarters of our wide Saxon world: wheresoever a Saxon dialect is spoken, it begins to be understood, by personal inspection of this and the other, that one of the most considerable Saxon men of the Eighteenth century was an Ayrshire Peasant named Robert Burns. Yes, I will say, here too was a piece of the right Saxon stuff: strong as the Harz-rock, rooted in the depths of the world;—rock, yet with wells of living softness in it! A wild impetuous whirlwind of passion and faculty slumbered quiet there; such heavenly *melody* dwelling in the heart of it. A noble rough genuineness; homely, rustic, honest; true simplicity of strength: with its

lightning-fire, with its soft dewy pity;—like the old
Norse Thor, the Peasant-god !—

Burns's Brother Gilbert, a man of much sense and
worth, has told me that Robert, in his young days, in
spite of their hardship, was usually the gayest of
speech; a fellow of infinite frolic, laughter, sense and
heart; far pleasanter to hear there, stript cutting peats
in the bog, or suchlike, than he ever afterwards knew
him. I can well believe it. This basis of mirth (' *fond
gaillard*,' as old Marquis Mirabeau calls it), a primal-
element of sunshine and joyfulness, coupled with his
other deep and earnest qualities, is one of the most
attractive characteristics of Burns. A large fund of
Hope dwells in him; spite of his tragical history, he
is not a mourning man. He shakes his sorrows gallantly
aside; bounds forth victorious over them. It is as
the lion shaking ' dew-drops from his mane;' as the
swift-bounding horse, that *laughs* at the shaking of the
spear.—But indeed, Hope, Mirth, of the sort like
Burns's, are they not the outcome properly of warm
generous affection,—such as is the beginning of all to
every man?

You would think it strange if I called Burns the most
gifted British soul we had in all that century of his :
and yet I believe the day is coming when there will be
little danger in saying so. His writings, all that he
did under such obstructions, are only a poor fragment
of him. Professor Stewart remarked very justly, what
indeed is true of all Poets good for much, that his
poetry was not any particular faculty; but the general
result of a naturally vigorous original mind expressing
itself in that way. Burns's gifts, expressed in conversation, are the theme of all that ever heard him. All
kinds of gifts : from the gracefulest utterances of courtesy,
to the highest fire of passionate speech; loud floods of
mirth, soft wailings of affection, laconic emphasis, clear
piercing insight; all was in him. Witty duchesses celebrate him as a man whose speech ' led them off their feet.'
This is beautiful : but still more beautiful that which
Mr. Lockhart has recorded, which I have more than
once alluded to, How the waiters and ostlers at inns

would get out of bed, and come crowding to hear this man speak! Waiters and ostlers :—they too were men, and here was a man! I have heard much about his speech; but one of the best things I ever heard of it was, last year, from a venerable gentleman long familiar with him. That it was speech distinguished by always *having something in it.* " He spoke rather little than much," this old man told me; " sat rather silent in those early days, as in the company of persons above him; and always when he did speak, it was to throw new light on the matter." I know not why any one should ever speak otherwise!—But if we look at his general force of soul, his healthy *robustness* everyway, the rugged down-rightness, penetration, generous valour and manfulness that was in him,—where shall we readily find a better-gifted man?

Among the great men of the Eighteenth Century, I sometimes feel as if Burns might be found to resemble Mirabeau more than any other. They differ widely in vesture; yet look at them intrinsically. There is the same burly thick-necked strength of body as of soul;— built, in both cases, on what the old Marquis calls a *fond gaillard.* By nature, by course of breeding, indeed by nation, Mirabeau has much more of bluster; a noisy, forward, unresting man. But the characteristic of Mirabeau too is veracity and sense, power of true *insight,* superiority of vision. The thing that he says is worth remembering. It is a flash of insight into some object or other : so do both these men speak. The same raging passions; capable too in both of manifesting themselves as the tenderest noble affections. Wit, wild laughter, energy, directness, sincerity : these were in both. The types of the two men are not dissimilar. Burns too could have governed, debated in National Assemblies; politicised, as few could. Alas, the courage which had to exhibit itself in capture of smuggling schooners in the Solway Frith; in keeping *silence* over so much, where no good speech, but only inarticulate rage was possible : this might have bellowed forth Ushers de Brézé and the like; and made itself visible to all men, in managing of kingdoms, in ruling of great ever-memorable epochs! But they said to

him reprovingly, his Official Superiors said, and wrote :
' You are to work, not think.' Of your *thinking*-
faculty, the greatest in this land, we have no need ; you
are to gauge beer there ; for that only are *you* wanted.
Very notable ;—and worth mentioning, though we know
what is to be said and answered ! As if Thought,
Power of Thinking, were not, at all times, in all places
and situations of the world, precisely the thing that
was wanted.   The fatal man, is he not always the
*un*thinking man, the man who cannot think and *see ;*
but only grope, and hallucinate, and *mis*see the nature
of the thing he works with?   He missees it, mis*takes*
it as we say ; takes it for one thing, and it *is* another
thing,—and leaves him standing like a Futility there !
He is the fatal man ; unutterably fatal, put in the high
places of men.—" Why complain of this ?" say some :
" Strength is mournfully denied its arena ; that was
true from of old."   Doubtless ; and the worse for the
arena, answer I !   *Complaining* profits little ; stating
of the truth may profit.   That a Europe, with its
French Revolution just breaking out, finds no need of
a Burns except for gauging beer,—is a thing I, for
one, cannot *rejoice* at !—

Once more we have to say here, that the chief quality
of Burns is the *sincerity* of him.   So in his Poetry, so
in his Life.   The Song he sings is not of fantastical-
ities ; it is of a thing felt, really there ; the prime merit
of this, as of all in him, and of his Life generally, is
truth.   The Life of Burns is what we may call a great
tragic sincerity.   A sort of savage sincerity,—not cruel,
far from that ; but wild, wrestling naked with the truth
of things.   In that sense, there is something of the
savage in all great men.

Hero-worship,—Odin, Burns?   Well ; these Men of
Letters too were not without a kind of Hero-worship :
but what a strange condition has that got into now !
The waiters and ostlers of Scotch inns, prying about
the door, eager to catch any word that fell from Burns,
were doing unconscious reverence to the Heroic.   Johnson had his Boswell for worshipper.   Rousseau had
worshippers enough ; princes calling on him in his mean
garret ; the great, the beautiful doing reverence to the

poor moonstruck man. For himself a most portentous
contradiction; the two ends of his life not to be brought
into harmony. He sits at the tables of grandees; and
has to copy music for his own living. He cannot even
get his music copied. " By dint of dining out," says
he, " I run the risk of dying by starvation at home."
For his worshippers too a most questionable thing ! If
doing Hero-worship well or badly be the test of vital
wellbeing or illbeing to a generation, can we say that
these generations are very first-rate?—And yet our
heroic Men of Letters do teach, govern, are kings,
priests, or what you like to call them; intrinsically
there is no preventing it by any means whatever. The
world *has* to obey him who thinks and sees in the
world. The world can alter the manner of that; can
either have it as blessed continuous summer sunshine,
or as unblessed black thunder and tornado,—with unspeakable difference of profit for the world ! The
manner of it is very alterable; the matter and fact of
it is not alterable by any power under the sky. Light;
or, failing that, lightning: the world can take its
choice. Not whether we call an Odin god, prophet,
priest, or what we call him; but whether we believe
the word he tells us : there it all lies. If it be a true
word, we shall have to believe it; believing it, we shall
have to do it. What *name* or welcome we give him or
it, is a point that concerns ourselves mainly. *It*, the
new Truth, new deeper revealing of the Secret of this
Universe, is verily of the nature of a message from on
high; and must and will have itself obeyed.—

My last remark is on that notablest phasis of Burns's
history,—his visit to Edinburgh. Often it seems to me
as if his demeanour there were the highest proof he
gave of what a fund of worth and genuine manhood
was in him. If we think of it, few heavier burdens
could be laid on the strength of a man. So sudden;
all common *Lionism*, which ruins innumerable men,
was as nothing to this. It is as if Napoleon had been
made a King of, not gradually, but at once from the
Artillery Lieutenancy in the Regiment La Fère. Burns,
still only in his twenty-seventh year, is no longer even
a ploughman; he is flying to the West Indies to escape

disgrace and a jail.   This month he is a ruined peasant, his wages seven pounds a year, and these gone from him : next month he is in the blaze of rank and beauty, handing down jewelled Duchesses to dinner; the cynosure of all eyes!   Adversity is sometimes hard upon a man; but for one man who can stand prosperity, there are a hundred that will stand adversity.   I admire much the way in which Burns met all this.   Perhaps no man one could point out, was ever so sorely tried, and so little forgot himself.   Tranquil, unastonished; not abashed, not inflated, neither awkwardness nor affectation :   he feels that *he* there is the man Robert Burns ; that the ' rank is but the guinea-stamp;' that the celebrity is but the candle-light, which will show *what* man, not in the least make him a better or other man !   Alas, it may readily, unless he look to it, make him a *worse* man ; a wretched inflated wind-bag,— inflated till he *burst* and become a *dead* lion; for whom, as some one has said, ' there is no resurrection of the body;' worse than a living dog !—Burns is admirable here.

And yet, alas, as I have observed elsewhere, these Lion-hunters were the ruin and death of Burns.   It was they that rendered it impossible for him to live !   They gathered round him in his Farm; hindered his in- dustry ;   no place was remote enough from them.   He could not get his Lionism forgotten, honestly as he was disposed to do so.   He falls into discontents, into miseries, faults;   the world getting ever more desolate for him;   health, character, peace of mind all gone;— solitary enough now.   It is tragical to think of !   These men came but to *see* him;   it was out of no sympathy with him, nor no hatred to him.   They came to get a little amusement :   they got their amusement;—and the Hero's life went for it !

Richter says, in the Island of Sumatra, there is a kind of ' Light-chafers,' large Fire-flies, which people stick upon spits, and illuminate the ways with at night. Persons of condition can thus travel with a pleasant radiance, which they much admire.   Great honour to the Fire-flies !   But— !—

LECTURE VI

THE HERO AS KING.   CROMWELL, NAPOLEON : MODERN
REVOLUTIONISM.

[Friday, 22nd May 1840]

WE come now to the last form of Heroism; that
which we call Kingship.   The Commander over men;
he to whose will our wills are to be subordinated, and
loyally surrender themselves, and find their welfare in
doing so, may be reckoned the most important of Great
Men.   He is practically the summary for us of *all* the
various figures of Heroism; Priest, Teacher, whatsoever of earthly or of spiritual dignity we can fancy to
reside in a man, embodies itself here, to *command* over
us, to furnish us with constant practical teaching, to
tell us for the day and hour what we are to *do*.   He is
called *Rex*, Regulator, *Roi:* our own name is still
better; King, *Könning*, which means *Can*-ning, Able-
man.

Numerous considerations, pointing towards deep,
questionable, and indeed unfathomable regions, present
themselves here : on the most of which we must
resolutely for the present forbear to speak at all.   As
Burke said that perhaps fair *Trial by Jury* was the Soul
of Government, and that all legislation, administration,
parliamentary debating, and the rest of it, went on, in
' order to bring twelve impartial men into a jury-box;'
—so, by much stronger reason, may I say here, that the
finding of your *Ableman* and getting him invested with
the *symbols of ability*, with dignity, worship (*worth*-
ship), royalty, kinghood, or whatever we call it, so that
he may actually have room to guide according to his
faculty of doing it,—is the business, well or ill accomplished, of all social procedure whatsoever in this world !
Hustings-speeches, Parliamentary motions, Reform
Bills, French Revolutions, all mean at heart this; or
else nothing.   Find in any country the Ablest Man that
exists there; raise *him* to the supreme place, and loyally

reverence him : you have a perfect government for that country ; no ballot-box, parliamentary eloquence, voting, constitution-building, or other machinery whatsoever can improve it a whit. It is in the perfect state : an ideal country. The Ablest Man ; he means also the truest-hearted, justest, the Noblest Man : what he *tells us to do* must be precisely the wisest, fittest, that we could anywhere or anyhow learn ;—the thing which it will in all ways behove us, with right loyal thankfulness, and nothing doubting, to do ! Our *doing* and life were then, so far as government could regulate it, well regulated ; that were the ideal of constitutions.

Alas, we know very well that Ideals can never be completely embodied in practice. Ideals must ever lie a very great way off ; and we will right thankfully content ourselves with any not intolerable approximation thereto ! Let no man, as Schiller says, too querulously ' measure by a scale of perfection the meagre product of reality ' in this poor world of ours. We will esteem him no wise man ; we will esteem him a sickly, discontented, foolish man. And yet, on the other hand, it is never to be forgotten that Ideals do exist ; that if they be not approximated to at all, the whole matter goes to wreck ! Infallibly. No bricklayer builds a wall *perfectly* perpendicular, mathematically this is not possible ; a certain degree of perpendicularity suffices him ; and he, like a good bricklayer, who must have done with his job, leaves it so. And yet if he sway *too much* from the perpendicular ; above all, if he throw plummet and level quite away from him, and pile brick on brick heedless, just as it comes to hand— ! Such bricklayer, I think, is in a bad way. *He* has forgotten himself : but the Law of Gravitation does not forget to act on him ; he and his wall rush-down into confused welter of ruin !—

This is the history of all rebellions, French Revolutions, social explosions in ancient or modern times. You have put the too *Un*able man at the head of affairs ! The too ignoble, unvaliant, fatuous man. You have forgotten that there is any rule, or natural necessity whatever, of putting the Able Man there. Brick must lie on brick as it may and can. Unable Simulacrum of

Ability, *quack*, in a word, must adjust himself with quack, in all manner of administration of human things; —which accordingly lie unadministered, fermenting into unmeasured masses of failure, of indigent misery: in the outward, and in the inward or spiritual, miserable millions stretch-out the hand for their due supply, and it is not there. The ' law of gravitation ' acts; Nature's laws do none of them forget to act. The miserable millions burst-forth into Sansculottism, or some other sort of madness; bricks and bricklayers lie as a fatal chaos!—

Much sorry stuff, written some hundred years ago or more, about the ' Divine right of Kings,' moulders unread now in the Public Libraries of this country. Far be it from us to disturb the calm process by which it is disappearing harmlessly from the earth, in those repositories! At the same time, not to let the immense rubbish go without leaving us, as it ought, some soul of it behind—I will say that it did mean something; something true, which it is important for us and all men to keep in mind. To assert that in whatever man you chose to lay hold of (by this or the other plan of clutching at him); and clapt a round piece of metal on the head of, and called King,—there straightway came to reside a divine virtue, so that *he* became a kind of God, and a Divinity inspired him with faculty and right to rule over you to all lengths: this,—what can we do with this but leave it to rot silently in the Public Libraries? But I will say withal, and that is what these Divine-right men meant, That in Kings, and in all human Authorities, and relations that men god-created can form among each other, there is verily either a Divine Right or else a Diabolic Wrong; one or the other of these two! For it is false altogether, what the last Sceptical Century taught us, that this world is a steamengine. There is a God in this world; and a God's-sanction, or else the violation of such, does look-out from all ruling and obedience, from all moral acts of men. There is no act more moral between men than that of rule and obedience. Woe to him that claims obedience when it is not due; woe to him that refuses it when it is! God's law is in that, I say, however the Parchment-laws may run : there is a Divine Right or else a Diabolic Wrong at the heart of every claim that one man makes upon another.

It can do none of us harm to reflect on this : in all the relations of life it will concern us ; in Loyalty and Royalty, the highest of these. I esteem the modern error, That all goes by self-interest and the checking and balancing of greedy knaveries, and that, in short, there is nothing divine whatever in the association of men, a still more despicable error, natural as it is to an unbelieving century, than that of a ' divine right ' in people *called* Kings. I say, Find me the true *Könning*, King, or Able-man, and he *has* a divine right over me. That we knew in some tolerable measure how to find him, and that all men were ready to acknowledge his divine right when found : this is precisely the healing which a sick world is every-where, in these ages, seeking after ! The true King, as guide of the practical, has ever something of the Pontiff in him,—guide of the spiritual, from which all practice has its rise. This too is a true saying, That the *King* is head of the Church.—But we will leave the Polemic stuff of a dead century to lie quiet on its bookshelves.

Certainly it is a fearful business, that of having your Ableman to *seek*, and not knowing in what manner to proceed about it ! That is the world's sad predicament in these times of ours. They are times of Revolution, and have long been. The bricklayer with his bricks, no longer heedful of plummet or the law of gravitation, have toppled, tumbled, and it all welters as we see ! But the beginning of it was not the French Revolution ; that is rather the *end*, we can hope. It were truer to say, the *beginning* was three centuries farther back : in the Reformation of Luther. That the thing which still called itself Christian Church had become a Falsehood, and brazenly went about pretending to pardon men's sins for metallic coined money, and to do much else which in the everlasting truth of Nature it did *not* now do : here lay the vital malady. The inward being wrong, all outward went ever more and more wrong. Belief died away ; all was Doubt, Disbelief. The builder

cast away his plummet; said to himself, " What is
gravitation? Brick lies on brick there!" Alas, does
it not still sound strange to many of us, the assertion
that there *is* a God's truth in the business of god-created
men; that all is not a kind of grimace, an ' expediency,'
diplomacy, one knows not what!—

From that first necessary assertion of Luther's, " You,
self-styled *Papa*, you are no Father in God at all; you
are—a Chimera, whom I know not how to name in
polite language!"—from that onwards to the shout
which rose round Camille Desmoulins in the Palais-Royal,
" *Aux armes!*" when the people had burst-up against
all manner of Chimeras,—I find a natural historical
sequence. That shout too, so frightful, half-infernal,
was a great matter. Once more the voice of awakened
nations; starting confusedly, as out of nightmare, as
out of death-sleep, into some dim feeling that Life was
real; that God's-world was not an expediency and
diplomacy! Infernal;—yes, since they would not have
it otherwise. Infernal, since not celestial or terrestrial!
—Hollowness, insincerity *has* to cease;—sincerity of
some sort has to begin. Cost what it may, reigns of
terror, horrors of French Revolution or what else, we
have to return to truth. Here is a Truth, as I said:
a Truth clad in hell-fire, since they would not but have
it so!—

A common theory among considerable parties of men
in England and elsewhere used to be, that the French
Nation had, in those days, as it were gone *mad;* that
the French Revolution was a general act of insanity,
a temporary conversion of France and large sections
of the world into a kind of Bedlam. The Event had
risen and raged; but was a madness and nonentity,—
gone now happily into the region of Dreams and the
Picturesque!—To such comfortable philosophers, the
Three Days of July 1830 must have been a surprising
phenomenon. Here is the French Nation risen again,
in musketry and death-struggle, out shooting and being
shot, to make that same mad French Revolution good!
The sons and grandsons of those men, it would seem,
persist in the enterprise: they do not disown it; they
will have it made good; will have themselves shot, if

it be not made good! To philosophers who had made-up their life-system on that 'madness' quietus, no phenomenon could be more alarming. Poor Niebuhr, they say, the Prussian Professor and Historian, fell broken-hearted in consequence; sickened, if we can believe it, and died of the Three Days! It was surely not a very heroic death;—little better than Racine's, dying because Louis Fourteenth looked sternly on him once. The world had stood some considerable shocks, in its time; might have been expected to survive the Three Days too, and be found turning on its axis after even them! The Three Days told all mortals that the old French Revolution, mad as it might look, was not a transitory ebullition of Bedlam, but a genuine product of this Earth where we all live; that it was verily a Fact, and that the world in general would do well everywhere to regard it as such.

Truly, without the French Revolution, one would not know what to make of an age like this at all. We will hail the French Revolution, as shipwrecked mariners might the sternest rock, in a world otherwise all of baseless sea and waves. A true Apocalypse, though a terrible one, to this false withered artificial time; testifying once more that Nature is *preter*natural; if not divine, then diabolic; that Semblance is not reality; that it has to become reality, or the world will take-fire under it,—burn *it* into what it is, namely Nothing! Plausibility has ended; empty Routine has ended; much has ended. This, as with a Trump of Doom, has been proclaimed to all men. They are the wisest who will learn it soonest. Long confused generations before it be learned; peace impossible till it be! The earnest man, surrounded, as ever, with a world of inconsistencies, can await patiently, patiently strive to do *his* work, in the midst of that. Sentence of Death is written down in Heaven against all that; sentence of Death is now proclaimed on the Earth against it: this he with his eyes may see. And surely, I should say, considering the other side of the matter, what enormous difficulties lie there, and how fast, fearfully fast, in all countries, the inexorable demand for solution of them is pressing on,—he may easily find other work to do than labouring in the Sansculottic province at this time of day !

To me, in these circumstances, that of ' Hero-wor-ship ' becomes a fact inexpressibly precious; the most solacing fact one sees in the world at present. There is an everlasting hope in it for the management of the world. Had all traditions, arrangements, creeds, societies that men ever instituted, sunk away, this would remain. The certainty of Heroes being sent us; our faculty, our necessity, to reverence Heroes when sent: it shines like a polestar through smoke-clouds, dust-clouds, and all manner of down-rushing and con-flagration.

Hero-worship would have sounded very strange to those workers and fighters in the French Revolution. Not reverence for Great Men; not any hope or belief, or even wish, that Great Men could again appear in the world ! Nature, turned into a ' Machine,' was as if effete now; could not any longer produce Great Men : —I can tell her, she may give-up the trade altogether, then; we cannot do without Great Men !—But neither have I any quarrel with that of ' Liberty and Equality;' with the faith that, wise great men being impossible, a level immensity of foolish small men would suffice. It was a natural faith then and there. " Liberty and Equality; no Authority needed any longer. Hero-worship, rerevence for *such* Authorities, has proved false, is itself a falsehood; no more of it ! We have had such *forgeries*, we will now trust nothing. So many base plated coins passing in the market, the belief has now become common that no gold any longer exists,—and even that we can do very well without gold !" I find this, among other things, in that uni-versal cry of Liberty and Equality; and find it very natural, as matters then stood.

And yet surely it is but the *transition* from false to true. Considered as the whole truth, it is false alto-gether;—the product of entire sceptical blindness, as yet only *struggling* to see. Hero-worship exists for-ever, and everywhere: not Loyalty alone; it extends from divine adoration down to the lowest practical regions of life. ' Bending before men,' if it is not to

be a mere empty grimace, better dispensed with than
practised, is Hero-worship,—a recognition that there
does dwell in that presence of our brother something
divine; that every created man, as Novalis said, is a
'revelation in the Flesh.' They were Poets too, that
devised all those graceful courtesies which make life
noble! Courtesy is not a falsehood or grimace; it
need not be such. And Loyalty, religious Worship
itself, are still possible; nay still inevitable.

May we not say, moreover, while so many of our
late Heroes have worked rather as revolutionary men,
that nevertheless every Great Man, every genuine man,
is by the nature of him a son of Order, not of Disorder?
It is a tragical position for a true man to work in revolutions. He seems an anarchist; and indeed a painful
element of anarchy does encumber him at every step,—
him to whose whole soul anarchy is hostile, hateful.
His mission is Order; every man's is. He is here to
make what was disorderly, chaotic, into a thing ruled,
regular. He is the missionary of Order. Is not all
work of man in this world a *making of Order?* The
carpenter finds rough trees : shapes them, constrains
them into square fitness, into purpose and use. We
are all born enemies of Disorder : it is tragical for us
all to be concerned in image-breaking and down-pulling; for the Great Man, *more* a man than we, it is
doubly tragical.

Thus too all human things, maddest French Sans-
culottisms, do and must work towards Order. I say,
there is not a *man* in them, raging in the thickest of
the madness, but is impelled withal, at all moments,
towards Order. His very life means that; Disorder is
dissolution, death. No chaos but it seeks a *centre* to
revolve round. While man is man, some Cromwell or
Napoleon is the necessary finish of a Sansculottism.—
Curious : in those days when Hero-worship was the
most incredible thing to every one, how it does come-
out nevertheless, and assert itself practically, in a way
which all have to credit. Divine *right*, take it on the
great scale, is found to mean divine *might* withal!
While old false Formulas are getting trampled everywhere into destruction, new genuine Substances unex-

430 On Heroes, Hero-Worship

is what we have now to look at.

pectedly unfold themselves indestructible. In rebellious ages, when Kingship itself seems dead and abolished, Cromwell, Napoleon step-forth again as Kings. The history of these men is what we have now to look at, as our last phasis of Heroism. The old ages are brought back to us; the manner in which Kings were made, and Kingship itself first took rise, is again exhibited in the history of these Two.

We have had many civil-wars in England; wars of Red and White Roses, wars of Simon de Montfort; wars enough, which are not very memorable. But that war of the Puritans has a significance which belongs to no one of the others. Trusting to your candour, which will suggest on the other side what I have not room to say, I will call it a section once more of that great universal war which alone makes-up the true History of the World,—the war of Belief against Unbelief! The struggle of men intent on the real essence of things, against men intent on the semblances and forms of things. The Puritans, to many, seem mere savage Iconoclasts, fierce destroyers of Forms; but it were more just to call them haters of *untrue* Forms. I hope we know how to respect Laud and his King as well as them. Poor Laud seems to me to have been weak and ill-starred, not dishonest; an unfortunate Pedant rather than anything worse. His 'Dreams' and superstitions, at which they laugh so, have an affectionate, lovable kind of character. He is like a College-Tutor, whose whole world is forms, College-rules; whose notion is that these are the life and safety of the world. He is placed suddenly, with that unalterable luckless notion of his, at the head not of a College but of a Nation, to regulate the most complex deep-reaching interests of men. He thinks they ought to go by the old decent regulations; nay that their salvation will lie in extending and improving these. Like a weak man, he drives with spasmodic vehemence towards his purpose; cramps himself to it, heeding no voice of prudence, no cry of pity: He will have his College-rules obeyed by his Collegians; that first; and till that, nothing. He is an ill-starred Pedant, as I said. He

would have it the world was a College of that kind,
and the world *was not* that. Alas, was not his doom
stern enough? Whatever wrongs he did, were they
not all frightfully avenged on him?

It is meritorious to insist on forms; Religion and all
else naturally clothes itself in forms. Everywhere the
formed world is the only habitable one. The naked
formlessness of Puritanism is not the thing I praise
in the Puritans; it is the thing I pity,—praising only
the spirit which had rendered that inevitable! All substances clothe themselves in forms: but there are suitable true forms, and then there are untrue unsuitable.
As the briefest definition, one might say, Forms which
grow round a substance, if we rightly understand that,
will correspond to the real nature and purport of it,
will be true, good; forms which are consciously *put*
round a substance, bad. I invite you to reflect on this.
It distinguishes true from false in Ceremonial Form,
earnest solemnity from empty pageant, in all human
things.

There must be a veracity, a natural spontaneity in
forms. In the commonest meeting of men, a person
making, what we call, ' set speeches,' is not he an
offence? In the mere drawing-room, whatsoever
courtesies you see to be grimaces, prompted by no
spontaneous reality within, are a thing you wish to get
away from. But suppose now it were some matter of
vital concernment, some transcendent matter (as Divine
Worship is), about which your whole soul, struck dumb
with its excess of feeling, knew not how to *form* itself
into utterance at all, and preferred formless silence to
any utterance there possible,—what should we say of
a man coming forward to represent or utter it for you
in the way of upholsterer-mummery? Such a man,—
let him depart swiftly, if he love himself! You have
lost your only son; are mute, struck down, without
even tears: an importunate man importunately offers
to celebrate Funeral Games for him in the manner of
the Greeks! Such mummery is not only not to be
accepted,—it is hateful, unendurable. It is what the
old Prophets called ' Idolatry,' worshipping of hollow
shows; what all earnest men do and will reject. We

can partly understand what those poor Puritans meant.
Laud dedicating that St. Catherine Creed's Church, in
the manner we have it described; with his multiplied
ceremonial bowings, gesticulations, exclamations :
surely it is rather the rigorous formal *Pedant*, intent on
his ' College-rules,' than the earnest Prophet, intent on
the essence of the matter !

Puritanism found *such* forms insupportable; trampled
on such forms;—we have to excuse it for saying, No
form at all rather than such ! It stood preaching in its
bare pulpit, with nothing but the Bible in its hand.
Nay, a man preaching from his earnest *soul* into the
earnest *souls* of men : is not this virtually the essence
of all Churches whatsoever? The nakedest, savagest
reality, I say, is preferable to any semblance, however
dignified. Besides, it will clothe itself with *due* semblance by and by, if it be real. No fear of that; actually
no fear at all. Given the living *man*, there will be
found *clothes* for him; he will find himself clothes. But
the suit-of-clothes pretending that *it* is both clothes and
man— !—We cannot ' fight the French ' by three-
hundred-thousand red uniforms; there must be *men* in
the inside of them ! Semblance, I assert, must actually
not divorce itself from Reality. If Semblance do,—why
then there must be men found to rebel against Semblance, for it has become a lie ! These two Antagon-
sms at war here, in the case of Laud and the Puritans,
are as old nearly as the world. They went to fierce
battle over England in that age; and fought-out their
confused controversy to a certain length, with many
results for all of us.

In the age which directly followed that of the Puritans,
their cause or themselves were little likely to have justice
done them. Charles Second and his Rochesters were
not the kind of men you would set to judge what the
worth or meaning of such men might have been. That
there could be any faith or truth in the life of a man,
was what these poor Rochesters, and the age they
ushered-in, had forgotten. Puritanism was hung on
gibbets,—like the bones of the leading Puritans. Its
work nevertheless went on accomplishing itself. All

true work of a man, hang the author of it on what gibbet
you like, must and will accomplish itself. We have our
Habeas-Corpus, our free Representation of the People;
acknowledgment, wide as the world, that all men are,
or else must, shall, and will become, what we call *free*
men;—men with their life grounded on reality and
justice, not on tradition, which has become unjust and
a chimera ! This in part and much besides this, was
the work of the Puritans.

And indeed, as these things became gradually manifest, the character of the Puritans began to clear itself.
Their memories were, one after another, taken *down*
from the gibbet; nay a certain portion of them are now,
in these days, as good as canonised. Eliot, Hampden,
Pym, nay Ludlow, Hutchinson, Vane himself, are admitted to be a kind of Heroes; political Conscript
Fathers, to whom in no small degree we owe what
makes us a free England : it would not be safe for anybody to designate these men as wicked now. Few
Puritans of note but find their apologists somewhere,
and have a certain reverence paid them by earnest men.
One Puritan, I think, and almost he alone, our poor
Cromwell, seems to hang yet on the gibbet, and find
no hearty apologist anywhere. Him neither saint nor
sinner will acquit of great wickedness. A man of
ability, infinite talent, courage, and so forth : but he
betrayed the Cause. Selfish ambition, dishonesty,
duplicity ; a fierce, coarse, hypocritical *Tartufe;* turning all that noble Struggle for constitutional Liberty
into a sorry farce played for his own benefit : this and
worse is the character they give of Cromwell. And then
there come contrasts with Washington and others;
above all, with these noble Pyms and Hampdens, whose
noble work he stole for himself, and ruined into a futility
and deformity.

This view of Cromwell seems to me the not unnatural
product of a century like the Eighteenth. As we said of
the Valet, so of the Sceptic : He does not know a Hero
when he sees him ! The Valet expected purple mantles,
gilt sceptres, body-guards and flourishes of trumpets :
the Sceptic of the Eighteenth century looks for regulated
respectable Formulas, ' Principles,' or what else he

may call them; a style of speech and conduct which
has got to seem 'respectable,' which can plead for itself
in a handsome articulate manner, and gain the suffrages
of an enlightened sceptical Eighteenth century! It is,
at bottom, the same thing that both the Valet and he
expect: the garnitures of some *acknowledged* royalty,
which *then* they will acknowledge! The King coming
to them in the rugged *un*formulistic state shall be no
King.

For my own share, far be it from me to say or insinuate a word of disparagement against such characters as
Hampden, Eliot, Pym; whom I believe to have been
right worthy and useful men. I have read diligently
what books and documents about them I could come
at;—with the honestest wish to admire, to love and
worship them like Heroes; but I am sorry to say,
if the real truth must be told, with very indifferent success! At bottom, I found that it would not do. They
are very noble men, these; step along in their stately
way, with their measured euphemisms, philosophies,
parliamentary eloquences, Ship-moneys, *Monarchies of
Man;* a most constitutional, unblamable, dignified set
of men. But the heart remains cold before them; the
fancy alone endeavours to get-up some worship of them.
What man's heart does, in reality, break-forth into any
fire of brotherly love for these men? They are become
dreadfully dull men! One breaks-down often enough
in the constitutional eloquence of the admirable Pym,
with his 'seventhly and lastly.' You find that it may
be the admirablest thing in the world, but that it is
heavy,—heavy as lead, barren as brick-clay; that, in a
word, for you there is little or nothing now surviving
there! One leaves all these Nobilities standing in their
niches of honour: the rugged out-cast Cromwell, he is
the man of them all in whom one still finds human stuff.
The great savage *Baresark:* he could write no euphemistic *Monarchy of Man;* did not speak, did not work
with glib regularity; had no straight story to tell for
himself anywhere. But he stood bare, not cased in
euphemistic coat-of-mail; he grappled like a giant, face
to face, heart to heart, with the naked truth of things!
That, after all, is the sort of man for one. I plead

guilty to valuing such a man beyond all other sorts of
men. Smooth-shaven Respectabilities not a few one
finds, that are not good for much. Small thanks to a
man for keeping his hands clean, who would not touch
the work but with gloves on !

Neither, on the whole, does this constitutional tolerance of the Eighteenth century for the other happier
Puritans seem to be a very great matter. One might
say, it is but a piece of Formulism and Scepticism, like
the rest. They tell us, It was a sorrowful thing to consider that the foundation of our English Liberties should
have been laid by 'Superstition.' These Puritans came
forward with Calvinistic incredible Creeds, Anti-Laud-
isms, Westminster Confessions; demanding, chiefly of
all, that they should have liberty to *worship* in their own
way. Liberty to *tax* themselves : that was the thing they
should have demanded ! It was Superstition, Fanaticism,
disgraceful Ignorance of Constitutional Philosophy to
insist on the other thing !—Liberty to *tax* oneself ? Not
to pay-out money from your pocket except on reason
shown ? No century, I think, but a rather barren one
would have fixed on that as the first right of man ! I
should say, on the contrary, A just man will generally
have better cause than *money* in what shape soever,
before deciding to revolt against his Government. Ours
is a most confused world; in which a good man will be
thankful to see any kind of Government maintain itself
in a not insupportable manner; and here in England,
to this hour, if he is not ready to pay a great many taxes
which *he* can see very small reason in, it will not go
well with him, I think ! He must try some other climate
than this. Taxgatherer ? Money ? He will say :
" Take my money, since you *can,* and it is so desirable
to you; take it,—and take yourself away with it; and
leave me alone to my work here. *I* am still here; can
still work, after all the money you have taken from
me !" But if they come to him, and say, " Acknowledge a Lie; pretend to say you are worshipping God,
when you are not doing it : believe not the thing that
you find true, but the thing that I find, or pretend to
find true !" He will answer : " No; by God's help,
no ! You may take my purse; but I cannot have my

moral Self annihilated. The purse is any Highway-man's who might meet me with a loaded pistol : but the Self is mine and God my Maker's ; it is not yours ; and I will resist you to the death, and revolt against you, and, on the whole, front all manner of extremities, accusations and confusions, in defence of that !''—

Really, it seems to me the one reason which could justify revolting, this of the Puritans. It has been the soul of all just revolts among men. Not *Hunger* alone produced even the French Revolution : no, but the feeling of the insupportable all-pervading *Falsehood* which had now embodied itself in Hunger, in universal material Scarcity and Nonentity, and thereby become *indisputably* false in the eyes of all ! We will leave the Eighteenth century with its ' liberty to tax itself.' We will not astonish ourselves that the meaning of such men as the Puritans remained dim to it. To men who believe in no reality at all, how shall a *real* human soul, the intensest of all realities, as it were the Voice of this world's Maker still speaking to *us*,—be intelligible? What it cannot reduce into constitutional doctrines relative to ' taxing,' or other the like material interest, gross, palpable to the sense, such a century will needs reject as an amorphous heap of rubbish. Hampdens, Pyms, and Ship-money will be the theme of much constitutional eloquence, striving to be fervid ;—which will glitter, if not as fire does, then as *ice* does : and the irreducible Cromwell will remain a chaotic mass of ' madness,' ' hypocrisy,' and much else.

From of old, I will confess, this theory of Cromwell's falsity has been incredible to me. Nay I cannot believe the like, of any Great Man whatever. Multitudes of Great Men figure in History as false selfish men ; but if we will consider it, they are but *figures* for us, unintelligible shadows ; we do not see into them as men that could have existed at all. A superficial unbelieving generation only, with no eye but for the surfaces and semblances of things, could form such notions of Great Men. Can a great soul be possible without a *conscience* in it, the essence of all *real* souls, great or small?— No, we cannot figure Cromwell as a Falsity and Fatuity ;

the longer I study him and his career, I believe this the less. Why should we? There is no evidence of it. Is it not strange that, after all the mountains of calumny this man has been subject to, after being represented as the very prince of liars, who never, or hardly ever, spoke truth, but always some cunning counterfeit of truth, there should not yet have been one falsehood brought clearly home to him? A prince of liars, and no lie spoken by him. Not one that I could yet get sight of. It is like Pococke asking Grotius, Where is your *proof* of Mahomet's Pigeon? No proof!—Let us leave all these calumnious chimeras, as chimeras ought to be left. They are not portraits of the man; they are distracted phantasms of him, the joint product of hatred and darkness.

Looking at the man's life with our own eyes, it seems to me, a very different hypothesis suggests itself. What little we know of his earlier obscure years, distorted as it has come down to us, does it not all betoken an earnest, affectionate, sincere kind of man? His nervous melancholic temperament indicates rather a seriousness *too* deep for him. Of those stories of ' Spectres;' of the white Spectre in broad daylight, predicting that he should be King of England, we are not bound to believe much;—probably no more than of the other black Spectre, or Devil in person, to whom the Officer *saw* him sell himself before Worcester Fight! But the mournful, over-sensitive, hypochondriac humour of Oliver, in his young years, is otherwise indisputably known. The Huntingdon Physician told Sir Philip Warwick himself, He had often been sent for at midnight; Mr. Cromwell was full of hypochondria, thought himself near dying, and " had fancies about the Town-cross." These things are significant. Such an excitable deep-feeling nature, in that rugged stubborn strength of his, is not the symptom of falsehood; it is the symptom and promise of quite other than falsehood!

The young Oliver is sent to study Law; falls, or is said to have fallen, for a little period, into some of the dissipations of youth; but if so, speedily repents, abandons all this : not much above twenty, he is married, settled as an altogether grave and quiet man. ' He

pays-back what money he had won at gambling,' says
the story;—he does not think any gain of that kind
could be really *his*. It is very interesting, very natural,
this ' conversion,' as they well name it; this awakening of a great true soul from the worldly slough, to see
into the awful *truth* of things;—to see that time and its
shows all rested on Eternity, and this poor Earth of
ours was the threshold either of Heaven or of Hell !
Oliver's life at St Ives or Ely, as a sober industrious
Farmer, is it not altogether as that of a true and devout
man? He has renounced the world and its ways; *its*
prizes are not the thing that can enrich him. He tills
the earth; he reads his Bible; daily assembles his
servants round him to worship God. He comforts persecuted ministers, is fond of preachers; nay can himself
preach,—exhorts his neighbours to be wise, to redeem
the time. In all this what ' hypocrisy,' ' ambition,'
' cant,' or other falsity? The man's hopes, I do believe,
were fixed on the other Higher World; his aim to get
well *thither*, by walking well through his humble course
in *this* world. He courts no notice : what could notice
here do for him? ' Ever in his great Taskmaster's
eye.'

It is striking, too, how he comes-out once into public
view; he, since no other is willing to come : in resist-
ance to a public grievance. I mean, in that matter of
the Bedford Fens. No one else will go to law with
Authority; therefore he will. That matter once settled,
he returns back into obscurity, to his Bible and his
Plough. ' Gain influence '? His influence is the most
legitimate; derived from personal knowledge of him,
as a just, religious, reasonable and determined man.
In this way he has lived till past forty; old age is now
in view of him, and the earnest portal of Death and
Eternity; it was at this point that he suddenly became
' ambitious '! I do not interpret his Parliamentary
mission in that way !

His successes in Parliament, his successes through
the war, are honest successes of a brave man; who
has more resolution in the heart of him, more light in
the head of him than other men. His prayers to God;
his spoken thanks to the God of Victory, who had pre-

served him safe, and carried him forward so far, through the furious clash of a world all set in conflict, through desperate-looking envelopments at Dunbar; through the death-hail of so many battles; mercy after mercy; to the ' crowning mercy ' of Worcester Fight: all this is good and genuine for a deep-hearted Calvinistic Cromwell. Only to vain unbelieving Cavaliers, worshipping not God but their own ' lovelocks,' frivolities and formalities, living quite apart from contemplations of God, living *without* God in the world, need it seem hypocritical.

Nor will his participation in the King's death involve him in condemnation with us. It is a stern business killing of a King ! But if you once go to war with him, it lies *there;* this and all else lies there. Once at war, you have made wager of battle with him: it is he to die, or else you. Reconciliation is problematic; may be possible, or, far more likely, is impossible. It is now pretty generally admitted that the Parliament, having vanquished Charles First, had no way of making any tenable arrangement with him. The large Presbyterian party, apprehensive now of the Independents, were most anxious to do so; anxious indeed as for their own existence; but it could not be. The unhappy Charles, in those final Hampton-Court negotiations, shows himself as a man fatally incapable of being dealt with. A man who, once for all, could not and would not *understand :*—whose thought did not in any measure represent to him the real fact of the matter; nay worse, whose *word* did not at all represent his thought. We may say this of him without cruelty, with deep pity rather : but it is true and undeniable. Forsaken there of all but the *name* of Kingship, he still, finding himself treated with outward respect as a King, fancied that he might play-off party against party, and smuggle himself into his old power by deceiving both. Alas, they both *discovered* that he was deceiving them. A man whose *word* will not inform you at all what he means or will do, is not a man you can bargain with. You must get out of that man's way, or put him out of yours ! The Presbyterians, in their despair, were still for believing Charles, though found false, unbelievable again and again. Not so Cromwell: " For all our fighting," says he, "we are to have a little bit of paper?" No!—

In fact, everywhere we have to note the decisive practical *eye* of this man; how he drives towards the practical and practicable; has a genuine insight into what *is* fact. Such an intellect, I maintain, does not belong to a false man : the false man sees false shows, plausibilities, expediences : the true man is needed to discern even practical truth. Cromwell's advice about the Parliament's Army, early in the contest, How they were to dismiss their city-tapsters, flimsy riotous persons, and choose substantial yeomen, whose heart was in the work, to be soldiers for them : this is advice by a man who *saw*. Fact answers, if you see into Fact. Cromwell's *Ironsides* were the embodiment of this insight of his; men fearing God; and without any other fear. No more conclusively genuine set of fighters ever trod the soil of England, or of any other land.

Neither will we blame greatly that word of Cromwell's to them; which was so blamed : " If the King should meet me in battle, I would kill the King." Why not? These words were spoken to men who stood as before a Higher than Kings. They had set more than their own lives on the cast. The Parliament may call it, in official language, a fighting ' *for* the King;' but we, for our share, cannot understand that. To us it is no dilettante work, no sleek officiality; it is sheer rough death and earnest. They have brought it to the calling-forth of *War;* horrid internecine fight, man grappling with man in fire-eyed rage,—the *infernal* element in man called forth, to try it by that ! *Do* that therefore; since that is the thing to be done.—The successes of Cromwell seem to me a very natural thing ! Since he was not shot in battle, they were an inevitable thing. That such a man, with the eye to see, with the heart to dare, should advance, from post to post, from victory to victory, till the Huntingdon Farmer became, by whatever name you might call him, the acknowledged Strongest Man in England, virtually the King of England, requires no magic to explain it !—

Truly it is a sad thing for a people, as for a man, to fall into Scepticism, into dilettantism, insincerity;

not to know a Sincerity when they see it. For this world, and for all worlds, what curse is so fatal? The heart lying dead, the eye cannot see. What intellect remains is merely the *vulpine* intellect. That a true *King* be sent them is of small use; they do not know him when sent. They say scornfully, Is this your King? The Hero wastes his heroic faculty in bootless contradiction from the unworthy; and can accomplish little. For himself he does accomplish a heroic life, which is much, which is all; but for the world he accomplishes comparatively nothing. The wild rude Sincerity, direct from Nature, is not glib in answering from the witness-box; in your small-debt *pie-powder* court, he is scouted as a counterfeit. The vulpine intellect 'detects' him. For being a man worth any thousand men, the response, your Knox, your Cromwell gets, is an argument for two centuries, whether he was a man at all. God's greatest gift to this Earth is sneeringly flung away. The miraculous talisman is a paltry plated coin, not fit to pass in the shops as a common guinea.

Lamentable this! I say, this must be remedied. Till this be remedied in some measure, there is nothing remedied. 'Detect quacks'? Yes do, for Heaven's sake; but know withal the men that are to be trusted! Till we know that, what is all our knowledge; how shall we even so much as 'detect'? For the vulpine sharpness, which considers itself to be knowledge, and 'detects' in that fashion, is far mistaken. Dupes indeed are many: but, of all *dupes,* there is none so fatally situated as he who lives in undue terror of being duped. The world does exist; the world has truth in it or it would not exist! First recognise what is true, we shall *then* discern what is false; and properly never till then.

'Know the men that are to be trusted:' alas, this is yet, in these days, very far from us. The sincere alone can recognise sincerity. Not a Hero only is needed, but a world fit for him; a world not of *Valets;* —the Hero comes almost in vain to it otherwise! Yes, it is far from us: but it must come; thank God, it is visibly coming. Till it do come, what have we? Ballot-boxes, suffrages, French Revolutions:—if we are as

Valets, and do not know the Hero when we see him,
what good are all these? A heroic Cromwell comes;
and for a hundred-and-fifty years he cannot have a vote
from us. Why, the insincere, unbelieving world is the
natural property of the Quack, and of the Father of
quacks and quackeries! Misery, confusion, unveracity
are alone possible there. By ballot-boxes we alter the
figure of our Quack; but the substance of him continues. The Valet-World *has* to be governed by the
Sham-Hero, by the King merely *dressed* in King-gear.
It is his; he is its! In brief, one of two things: We
shall either learn to know a Hero, a true Governor and
Captain, somewhat better, when we see him; or else
go on to be forever governed by the Unheroic;—had we
ballot-boxes clattering at every street-corner, there were
no remedy in these.

Poor Cromwell,—great Cromwell! The inarticulate
Prophet; Prophet who could not *speak*. Rude, confused, struggling to utter himself, with his savage
depth, with his wild sincerity; and he looked so strange,
among the elegant Euphemisms, dainty little Falk-
lands, didactic Chillingworths, diplomatic Clarendons!
Consider him. An outer hull of chaotic confusion,
visions of the Devil, nervous dreams, almost semi-mad-
ness; and yet such a clear determinate man's-energy
working in the heart of that. A kind of chaotic man.
The ray as of pure starlight and fire, working in such
an element of boundless hypochondria, *un*formed black
of darkness! And yet withal this hypochondria, what
was it but the very greatness of the man? The depth
and tenderness of his wild affections: the quantity of
sympathy he had with things,—the quantity of insight
he would yet get into the heart of things, the mastery
he would yet get over things: this was his hypochondria. The man's misery, as man's misery always does,
came of his greatness. Samuel Johnson too is that
kind of man. Sorrow-stricken, half-distracted; the
wide element of mournful *black* enveloping him,—wide
as the world. It is the character of a prophetic man;
a man with his whole soul *seeing*, and struggling to see.

On this ground, too, I explain to myself Cromwell's
reputed confusion of speech. To himself the internal

meaning was sun-clear; but the material with which he was to clothe it in utterance was not there. He had *lived* silent; a great unnamed sea of Thought round him all his days; and in his way of life little call to attempt *naming* or uttering that. With his sharp power of vision, resolute power of action, I doubt not he could have learned to write Books withal, and speak fluently enough :—he did harder things than writing of Books. This kind of man is precisely he who is fit for doing manfully all things you will set him on doing. Intellect is not speaking and logicising; it is seeing and ascertaining. Virtue, *Vir-tus*, manhood, *hero*-hood, is not fair-spoken immaculate regularity; it is first of all, what the Germans well name it, *Tugend* (*Taugend*, *dow*-ing or *Dough*-tiness), Courage and the Faculty to *do*. This basis of the matter Cromwell had in him.

One understands moreover how, though he could not speak in Parliament, he might *preach*, rhapsodic preaching; above all, how he might be great in extempore prayer. These are the free outpouring utterances of what is in the heart : method is not required in them; warmth, depth, sincerity are all that is required. Cromwell's habit of prayer is a notable feature of him. All his great enterprises were commenced with prayer. In dark inextricable-looking difficulties, his Officers and he used to assemble, and pray alternately, for hours, for days, till some definite resolution rose among them, some ' door of hope,' as they would name it, disclosed itself. Consider that. In tears, in fervent prayers, and cries to the great God, to have pity on them, to make His light shine before them. They, armed Soldiers of Christ, as they felt themselves to be; a little band of Christian Brothers, who had drawn the sword against a great black devouring world not Christian, but Mammonish, Devilish,—they cried to God in their straits, in their extreme need, not to forsake the Cause that was His. The light which now rose upon them,—how could a human soul, by any means at all, get better light? Was not the purpose so formed like to be precisely the best, wisest, the one to be followed without hesitation any more? To them it was as the

shining of Heaven's own Splendour in the waste-howl-
ing darkness; the Pillar of Fire by night, that was
to guide them on their desolate perilous way. *Was* it
not such? Can a man's soul, to this hour, get guidance by any other method than intrinsically by that
same,—devout prostration of the earnest struggling
soul before the Highest, the Giver of all Light; be such
prayer a spoken, articulate, or be it a voiceless, inarticulate one? There is no other method. 'Hypocrisy'? One begins to be weary of all that. They
who call it so, have no right to speak on such matters.
They never formed a purpose, what one can call a purpose. They went about balancing expediences, plausibilities; gathering votes, advices; they never were
alone with the *truth* of a thing at all.—Cromwell's
prayers were likely to be 'eloquent,' and much more
than that. His was the heart of a man who *could*
pray.

But indeed his actual Speeches, I apprehend, were
not nearly so ineloquent, incondite, as they look. We
find he was, what all speakers aim to be, an impressive
speaker, even in Parliament; one who, from the first,
had weight. With that rude passionate voice of his,
he was always understood to *mean* something, and men
wished to know what. He disregarded eloquence, nay
despised and disliked it; spoke always without pre-
meditation of the words he was to use. The Reporters,
too, in those days seem to have been singularly candid;
and to have given the Printer precisely what they found
on their own notepaper. And withal, what a strange
proof is it of Cromwell's being the premeditative ever-
calculating hypocrite, acting a play before the world,
That to the last he took no more charge of his
Speeches! How came he not to study his words a
little, before flinging them out to the public? If the
words were true words, they could be left to shift for
themselves.

But with regard to Cromwell's 'lying,' we will make
one remark. This, I suppose, or something like this,
to have been the nature of it. All parties found themselves deceived in him; each party understood him to
be meaning *this*, heard him even say so, and behold he

turns-out to have been meaning *that!* He was, cry they, the chief of liars. But now, intrinsically, is not all this the inevitable fortune, not of a false man in such times, but simply of a superior man? Such a man must have *reticences* in him. If he walk wearing his heart upon his sleeve for daws to peck at, his journey will not extend far! There is no use for any man's taking-up his abode in a house built of glass. A man always is to be himself the judge how much of his mind he will show to other men; even to those he would have work along with him. There are impertinent inquiries made: your rule is, to leave the inquirer *un*informed on that matter; not, if you can help it, *mis*informed; but precisely as dark as he was! This, could one hit the right phrase of response, is what the wise and faithful man would aim to answer in such a case.

Cromwell, no doubt of it, spoke often in the dialect of small subaltern parties; uttered to them a *part* of his mind. Each little party thought him all its own. Hence their rage, one and all, to find him not of their party, but of his own party! Was it his blame? At all seasons of his history he must have felt, among such people, how, if he explained to them the deeper insight he had, they must either have shuddered aghast at it, or believing it, their own little compact hypothesis must have gone wholly to wreck. They could not have worked in his province any more; nay perhaps they could not now have worked in their own province. It is the inevitable position of a great man among small men. Small men, most active, useful, are to be seen everywhere, whose whole activity depends on some conviction which to you is palpably a limited one; imperfect, what we call an *error*. But would it be a kindness always, is it a duty always or often, to disturb them in that? Many a man, doing loud work in the world, stands only on some thin traditionality, conventionality; to him indubitable, to you incredible: break that beneath him, he sinks to endless depths! " I might have my hand full of truth," said Fontenelle, " and open only my little finger."

And if this be the fact even in matters of doctrine,

how much more in all departments of practice! He
that cannot withal *keep his mind to himself* cannot
practise any considerable thing whatever. And we call
it ' dissimulation,' all this? What would you think of
calling the general of an army a dissembler because he
did not tell every corporal and private soldier, who
pleased to put the question, what his thoughts were
about everything?—Cromwell, I should rather say,
managed all this in a manner we must admire for its
perfection. An endless vortex of such questioning ' cor-
porals ' rolled confusedly round him through his whole
course; whom he did answer. It must have been as a
great true-seeing man that he managed this too. Not
one proved falsehood, as I said; not one! Of what
man that ever wound himself through such a coil of
things will you say so much?—

But in fact there are two errors, widely prevalent,
which pervert to the very basis our judgments formed
about such men as Cromwell; about their ' ambition,'
' falsity,' and such-like. The first is what I might call
substituting the *goal* of their career for the course and
starting point of it. The vulgar Historian of a Cromwell fancies that he had determined on being Protector
of England, at the time when he was ploughing the
marsh lands of Cambridgeshire. His career lay all
mapped-out : a program of the whole drama; which he
then step by step dramatically unfolded, with all manner
of cunning, deceptive dramaturgy, as he went on,— the
hollow, scheming Ὑποκριτής, or Play-actor that he was!
This is a radical perversion; all but universal in such
cases. And think for an instant how different the fact
is! How much does one of us foresee of his own life?
Short way ahead of us it is all dim; an *un*wound skein
of possibilities, of apprehensions, attemptabilities,
vague-looming hopes. This Cromwell had *not* his life
lying all in that fashion of Program, which he needed
then, with that unfathomable cunning of his, only to
enact dramatically, scene after scene! Not so. We
see it so; but to him it was in no measure so. What
absurdities would fall-away of themselves, were this
one undeniable fact kept honestly in view by History!

Historians indeed will tell you that they do keep it in view;—but look whether such is practically the fact! Vulgar History, as in this Cromwell's case, omits it altogether; even the best kinds of History only remember it now and then. To remember it duly with rigorous perfection, as in the fact it *stood*, requires indeed a rare faculty; rare, nay impossible. A very Shakspeare for faculty; or more than Shakspeare; who could *enact* a brother-man's biography, see with the brother-man's eyes at all points of his course what things *he* saw; in short, *know* his course and him, as few ' Historians ' are like to do. Half or more of all the thick-plied perversions which distort our image of Cromwell, will disappear, if we honestly so much as try to represent them so; in sequence, as they *were;* not in the lump, as they are thrown-down before us.

But a second error, which I think the generality commit, refers to this same ' ambition ' itself. We exaggerate the ambition of Great Men; we mistake what the nature of it is. Great Men are not ambitious in that sense; he is a small poor man that is ambitious so. Examine the man who lives in misery because he does not shine above other men; who goes about producing himself, pruriently anxious about his gifts and claims; struggling to force everybody, as it were begging everybody for God's sake, to acknowledge him a great man, and set him over the heads of men ! Such a creature is among the wretchedest sights seen under this sun. A *great* man? A poor morbid prurient empty man; fitter for the ward of a hospital, than for a throne among men. I advise you to keep-out of his way. He cannot walk on quiet paths; unless you will look at him, wonder at him, write paragraphs about him, he cannot live. It is the *emptiness* of the man, not his greatness. Because there is nothing in himself, he hungers and thirsts that you would find something in him. In good truth, I believe no great man, not so much as a genuine man who had health and real substance in him of whatever magnitude, was ever much tormented in this way.

Your Cromwell, what good could it do him to be ' noticed ' by noisy crowds of people? God his Maker

already noticed him. He, Cromwell, was already there; no notice would make *him* other than he already was. Till his hair was grown gray; and Life from the downhill slope was all seen to be limited, not infinite but finite, and all a measurable matter *how* it went,— he had been content to plough the ground, and read his Bible. He in his old days could not support it any longer, without selling himself to Falsehood, that he might ride in gilt carriages to Whitehall, and have clerks with bundles of papers haunting him, " Decide this, decide that," which in utmost sorrow of heart no man can perfectly decide! What could gilt carriages do for this man? From of old, was there not in his life a weight of meaning, a terror and a splendour as of Heaven itself? His existence there as man set him beyond the need of gilding. Death, Judgment and Eternity : these already lay as the background of what-soever he thought or did. All his life lay begirt as in a sea of nameless Thoughts, which no speech of a mortal could name. God's Word, as the Puritan prophets of that time had read it : this was great, and all else was little to him. To call such a man ' ambitious,' to figure him as the prurient windbag described above, seems to me the poorest solecism. Such a man will say : " Keep your gilt carriages and huzzaing mobs, keep your red-tape clerks, your influentialities, your important busi-nesses. Leave me alone, leave me alone; there is *too much of life* in me already !" Old Samuel Johnson, the greatest soul in England in his day, was not ambitious. ' Corsica Boswell ' flaunted at public shows with printed ribbons round his hat; but the great old Samuel stayed at home. The world-wide soul wrapt-up in its thoughts, in its sorrows;—what could paradings, and ribbons in the hat, do for it?

Ah yes, I will say again: The great *silent* men ! Looking round on the noisy inanity of the world, words with little meaning, actions with little worth, one loves to reflect on the great Empire of *Silence*. The noble silent men, scattered here and there, each in his depart-ment; silently thinking, silently working; whom no Morning Newspaper makes mention of ! They are the salt of the Earth. A country that has none or few of

these is in a bad way. Like a forest which had no *roots;* which had all turned into leaves and boughs;—which must soon wither and be no forest. Woe for us if we had nothing but what we can *show*, or speak. Silence, the great Empire of Silence : higher than the stars ; deeper than the Kingdoms of Death ! It alone is great; all else is small.—I hope we English will long maintain our *grand talent pour le silence*. Let others that cannot do without standing on barrel-heads, to spout, and be seen of all the market-place, cultivate speech exclusively,—become a most green forest without roots ! Solomon says, There is a time to speak; but also a time to keep silence. Of some great silent Samuel, not urged to writing, as old Samuel Johnson says he was, by *want of money*, and nothing other, one might ask, "Why do not you too get up and speak; promulgate your system, found your sect?" "Truly," he will answer, "I am *continent* of my thought hitherto; happily I have yet had the ability to keep it in me, no compulsion strong enough to speak it. My 'system' is not for promulgation first of all; it is for serving myself to live by. That is the great purpose of it to me. And then the 'honour'? Alas, yes;—but as Cato said of the statue : So many statues in that Forum of yours, may it not be better if they ask, Where is Cato's statue?"——

But, now, by way of counterpoise to this of Silence, let me say that there are two kinds of ambition; one wholly blamable, the other laudable and inevitable. Nature has provided that the great silent Samuel shall not be silent too long. The selfish wish to shine over others, let it be accounted altogether poor and miserable. 'Seekest thou great things, seek them not :' this is most true. And yet, I say, there is an irrepressible tendency in every man to develop himself according to the magnitude which Nature has made him of ; to speak-out, to act-out, what Nature has laid in him. This is proper, fit, inevitable; nay it is a duty, and even the summary of duties for a man. The meaning of life here on earth might be defined as consisting in this : To unfold your *self*, to work what thing you have the faculty for. It is a necessity for the human being, the first law of our existence. Coleridge beautifully remarks that the infant learns to *speak* by this necessity it feels.—We will say therefore : To decide about ambition, whether it is bad or not, you have two things to take into view. Not the coveting of the place alone, but the fitness of the man for the place withal : that is the question. Perhaps the place was *his;* perhaps he had a natural right, and even obligation, to seek the place ! Mirabeau's ambition to be Prime Minister, how shall we blame it, if he were ' the only man in France that could have done any good there '? Hopefuler perhaps had he not so clearly *felt* how much good he could do ! But a poor Necker, who could do no good, and had even felt that he could do none, yet sitting broken-hearted because they had flung him out, and he was now quit of it, well might Gibbon mourn over him.—Nature, I say, has provided amply that the silent great man shall strive to speak withal; *too* amply, rather !

Fancy, for example, you had revealed to the brave old Samuel Johnson, in his shrouded-up existence, that it was possible for him to do priceless divine work for his country and the whole world. That the perfect Heavenly Law might be made law on this earth; that the prayer he prayed daily, ' Thy kingdom come,' was at length to be fulfilled ! If you had convinced his judgment of this; that it was possible, practicable; that he the mournful silent Samuel was called to take a part in it ! Would not the whole soul of the man have flamed up into a divine clearness, into noble utterance and determination to act; casting all sorrows and misgivings under his feet, counting all affliction and contradiction small,—the whole dark element of his existence blazing into articulate radiance of light and lightning? It were a true ambition this ! And think now how it actually was with Cromwell. From of old, the sufferings of God's Church, true zealous preachers of the truth flung into dungeons, whipt, set on pillories, their ears cropt off, God's Gospel-cause trodden under foot of the unworthy : all this had lain heavy on his soul. Long years he had looked upon it, in silence, in prayer; seeing no remedy on Earth; trusting well that a remedy in Heaven's goodness would come,—that such a course was false, unjust, and could not last forever. And now behold the dawn of it; after twelve years silent waiting, all England stirs itself; there is to be once more a Parliament, the Right will get a voice for itself : inexpressible well-grounded hope has come again into the Earth. Was not such a Parliament worth being a member of? Cromwell threw down his ploughs and hastened thither.

He spoke there,—rugged bursts of earnestness, of a self-seen truth, where we get a glimpse of them. He worked there; he fought and strove, like a strong true giant of a man, through cannon-tumult and all else,— on and on, till the Cause *triumphed*, its once so formidable enemies all swept from before it, and the dawn of hope had become clear light of victory and certainty. That *he* stood there as the strongest soul of England, the undisputed Hero of all England,—what of this? It was possible that the law of Christ's Gospel could now establish itself in the world! The Theocracy which John Knox in his pulpit might dream of as a ' devout imagination,' this practical man, experienced in the whole chaos of most rough practice, dared to consider as capable of being *realised*. Those that were highest in Christ's Church, the devoutest wisest men, were to rule the land : in some considerable degree, it might be so and should be so. Was it not *true*, God's truth? And if *true,* was it not then the very thing to do? The strongest practical intellect in England dared to answer, Yes! This I call a noble true purpose; is it not, in its own dialect, the noblest that could enter into the heart of Statesman or man? For a Knox to take it up was something; but for a Cromwell, with his great sound sense and experience of what our world *was*,— History, I think, shows it only this once in such a degree. I account it the culminating point of Protestantism; the most heroic phasis that ' Faith in the Bible ' was appointed to exhibit here below. Fancy it : that it were made manifest to one of us, how we could make the Right supremely victorious over Wrong, and all that we had longed and prayed for, as the highest good to England and all lands, an attainable fact !

Well, I must say, the *vulpine* intellect, with its knowingness, its alertness and expertness in 'detecting hypocrites,' seems to me a rather sorry business. We have had one such Statesman in England; one man, that I can get sight of, who ever had in the heart of him any such purpose at all. One man, in the course of fifteen hundred years; and this was his welcome. He had adherents by the hundred or the ten; opponents by the million. Had England rallied all round him,— why, then, England might have been a *Christian* land! As it is, vulpine knowingness sits yet at its hopeless problem, 'Given a world of Knaves, to educe an Honesty from their united action;'—how cumbrous a problem, you may see in Chancery Law-Courts, and some other places! Till at length, by Heaven's just anger, but also by Heaven's great grace, the matter begins to stagnate; and this problem is becoming to all men a *palpably* hopeless one.—

But with regard to Cromwell and his purposes : Hume and a multitude following him, come upon me here with an admission that Cromwell *was* sincere at first; a sincere 'Fanatic' at first, but gradually became a 'Hypocrite' as things opened round him. This of the Fanatic-Hypocrite is Hume's theory of it; extensively applied since,—to Mahomet and many others. Think of it seriously, you will find something in it; not much, not all, very far from all. Sincere hero hearts do not sink in this miserable manner. The Sun flings forth impurities, gets balefully incrusted with spots; but it does not quench itself, and become no Sun at all, but a mass of Darkness! I will venture to say that such never befell a great, deep Cromwell; I think, never. Nature's own lion-hearted Son! Antæus-like, his strength is got by *touching the Earth*, his Mother; lift him up from the Earth, lift him up into Hypocrisy, In- anity, his strength is gone. We will not assert that Cromwell was an immaculate man; that he fell into no faults, no insincerities among the rest. He was no dilettante professor of 'perfections,' 'immaculate con- ducts.' He was a rugged Orson, rending his rough way through actual true *work*,—doubtless with many a *fall* therein. Insincerities, faults, very many faults

daily and hourly : it was too well known to him ; known
to God and him ! The Sun was dimmed many a time ;
but the Sun had not himself grown a Dimness. Cromwell's last words, as he lay waiting for death, are those
of a Christian heroic man. Broken prayers to God, that
He would judge him and this Cause, He since man
could not, in justice yet in pity. They are most touching words. He breathed out his wild great soul, its
toils and sins all ended now, into the presence of his
Maker, in this manner.

I, for one, will not call the man a Hypocrite ! Hypocrite, mummer, the life of him a mere theatricality ;
empty barren quack, hungry for the shouts of mobs?
The man had made obscurity do very well for him till
his head was gray ; and now he *was*, there as he stood
recognised unblamed, the virtual King of England.
Cannot a man do without King's Coaches and Cloaks?
Is it such a blessedness to have clerks forever pestering
you with bundles of papers in red tape? A simple
Diocletian prefers planting of cabbages ; a George
Washington, no very immeasurable man, does the like.
One would say, it is what any genuine man could do ;
and would do. The instant his real work were out in
the matter of Kingship,—away with it !

Let us remark, meanwhile, how indispensable everywhere a *King* is, in all movements of men. It is
strikingly shown, in this very War, what becomes of
men when they cannot find a Chief Man, and their
enemies can. The Scotch Nation was all but unanimous
in Puritanism ; zealous and of one mind about it, as
in this English end of the Island was far from being
the case. But there was no great Cromwell among
them ; poor tremulous, hesitating, diplomatic Argyles
and suchlike ; none of them had a heart true enough
for the truth, or durst commit himself to the truth.
They had no leader ; and the scattered Cavalier party
in that country had one : Montrose, the noblest of all
the Cavaliers ; an accomplished, gallant-hearted,
splendid man ; what one may call the Hero-Cavalier.
Well, look at it ; on the one hand subjects without a
King ; on the other a King without subjects ! The
subjects without King can do nothing ; the subjectless

King can do something. This Montrose, with a handful of Irish or Highland savages, few of them so much as guns in their hands, dashes at the drilled Puritan armies like a wild whirlwind; sweeps them, time after time, some five times over, from the field before him. He was at one period, for a short while, master of all Scotland. One man; but he was a man: a million zealous men, but *without* the one; they against him were powerless! Perhaps of all the persons in that Puritan struggle, from first to last, the single indispensable one was verily Cromwell. To see and dare, and decide; to be a fixed pillar in the welter of uncertainty;—a King among them, whether they called him so or not.

Precisely here, however, lies the rub for Cromwell. His other proceedings have all found advocates, and stand generally justified; but this dismissal of the Rump Parliament and assumption of the Protectorship, is what no one can pardon him. He had fairly grown to be King in England; Chief Man of the victorious party in England: but it seems he could not do without the King's Cloak, and sold himself to perdition in order to get it. Let us see a little how this was.

England, Scotland, Ireland, all lying now subdued at the feet of the Puritan Parliament, the practical question arose, What was to be done with it? How will you govern these Nations, which Providence in a wondrous way has given-up to your disposal? Clearly those hundred surviving members of the Long Parliament, who sit there as supreme authority, cannot continue for ever to sit. What *is* to be done?—It was a question which theoretical constitution-builders may find easy to answer; but to Cromwell, looking there into the real practical facts of it, there could be none more complicated. He asked of the Parliament, What it was they would decide upon? It was for the Parliament to say. Yet the Soldiers too, however contrary to Formula, they who had purchased this victory with their blood, it seemed to them that they also should have something to say in it! We will not "For all our fighting have nothing but a little piece of paper."

We understand that the Law of God's Gospel, to which He through us has given the victory, shall establish itself, or try to establish itself, in this land!

For three years, Cromwell says, this question had been sounded in the ears of the Parliament. They could make no answer; nothing but talk, talk. Perhaps it lies in the nature of parliamentary bodies; perhaps no Parliament could in such case make any answer but even that of talk, talk! Nevertheless the question must and shall be answered. You sixty men there, becoming fast odious, even despicable, to the whole nation, whom the nation already calls Rump Parliament, *you* cannot continue to sit there: who or what then is to follow? 'Free Parliament,' right of Election, Constitutional Formulas of one sort or the other,—the thing is a hungry Fact coming on us, which we must answer or be devoured by it! And who are you that prate of Constitutional Formulas, rights of Parliament? You have had to kill your King, to make Pride's Purges, to expel and banish by the law of the stronger whosoever would not let your Cause prosper: there are but fifty or three-score of you left there, debating in these days. Tell us what we shall do; not in the way of Formula, but of practicable Fact!

How they did finally answer, remains obscure to this day. The diligent Godwin himself admits that he cannot make it out. The likeliest is, that this poor Parliament still would not, and indeed could not dissolve and disperse; that when it came to the point of actually dispersing, they again, for the tenth or twentieth time, adjourned it,—and Cromwell's patience failed him. But we will take the favourablest hypothesis ever started for the Parliament; the favourablest, though I believe it is not the true one, but too favourable.

According to this version: At the uttermost crisis, when Cromwell and his Officers were met on the one hand, and the fifty or sixty Rump Members on the other, it was suddenly told Cromwell that the Rump in its despair *was* answering in a very singular way; that in their splenetic envious despair, to keep-out the army at least, these men were hurrying through the

House a kind of Reform Bill,—Parliament to be chosen
by the whole of England; equable electoral division
into districts; free suffrage, and the rest of it! A
very questionable, or indeed for *them* an unquestionable thing. Reform Bill, free suffrage of Englishmen?
Why, the Royalists themselves, silenced indeed but
not exterminated, perhaps out*number* us; the great
numerical majority of England was always indifferent
to our Cause, merely looked at it and submitted to it.
It is in weight and force, not by counting of heads, that
we are the majority! And now with your Formulas
and Reform Bills, the whole matter, sorely won by our
swords, shall again launch itself to sea; become a mere
hope, and likelihood, *small* even as a likelihood? And
it is not a likelihood; it is a certainty, which we have
won, by God's strength and our own right hands, and
do now hold *here*. Cromwell walked down to these
refractory Members; interrupted them in that rapid
speed of their Reform Bill;—ordered them to begone,
and talk there no more.—Can we not forgive him? Can
we not understand him? John Milton, who looked on
it all near at hand, could applaud him. The Reality
had swept the Formulas away before it. I fancy, most
men who were realities in England might see into the
necessity of that.

The strong daring man, therefore, has set all manner
of Formulas and logical superficialities against him;
has dared appeal to the genuine fact of this England,
Whether it will support him or not? It is curious to
see how he struggles to govern in some constitutional
way; find some Parliament to support him; but cannot. His first Parliament, the one they call Barebones's
Parliament, is, so to speak, a *Convocation of the
Notables*. From all quarters of England the leading
Ministers and chief Puritan Officials nominate the men
most distinguished by religious reputation, influence and
attachment to the true Cause: these are assembled to
shape-out a plan. They sanctioned what was past;
shaped as they could what was to come. They were
scornfully called *Barebones's Parliament*, the man's
name, it seems, was not *Barebones*, but Barbone,—a
good enough man. Nor was it a jest, their work; it

was a most serious reality,—a trial on the part of these Puritan Notables how far the Law of Christ could become the Law of this England. There were men of sense among them, men of some quality; men of deep piety I suppose the most of them were. They failed, it seems, and broke down, endeavouring to reform the Court of Chancery! They dissolved themselves, as incompetent; delivered-up their power again into the hands of the Lord-General Cromwell, to do with it what he liked and could.

What *will* he do with it? The Lord-General Cromwell, ' Commander-in Chief of all the Forces raised and to be raised;' he hereby sees himself, at this unexampled juncture, as it were the one available Authority left in England, nothing between England and utter Anarchy but him alone. Such is the undeniable Fact of his position and England's, there and then. What will he do with it? After deliberation, he decides that he will *accept* it; will formally, with public solemnity, say and vow before God and men, " Yes, the Fact is so, and I will do the best I can with it!" Protectorship, Instrument of Government,—these are the external forms of the thing; worked-out and sanctioned as they could in the circumstances be, by the Judges, by the leading Official people, ' Council of Officers and Persons of interest in the Nation :' and as for the thing itself, undeniably enough, at the pass matters had now come to, there *was* no alternative but Anarchy or that. Puritan England might accept it or not; but Puritan England was, in real truth, saved from suicide thereby ! —I believe the Puritan People did, in an inarticulate, grumbling, yet on the whole grateful and real way, accept this anomalous act of Oliver's; at least, he and they together made it good, and always better to the last. But in their Parliamentary *articulate* way, they had their difficulties, and never knew fully what to say to it !—

Oliver's second Parliament, properly his *first* regular Parliament, chosen by the rule laid-down in the Instrument of Government, did assemble, and worked;—but got, before long, into bottomless questions as to the Protector's *right*, as to ' usurpation,' and so forth; and

had at the earliest legal day to be dismissed. Cromwell's concluding Speech to these men is a remarkable
one. So likewise to his third Parliament, in similar
rebuke for their pedantries and obstinacies. Most rude,
chaotic, all these Speeches are; but most earnest-look-
ing. You would say, it was a sincere helpless man;
not used to *speak* the great inorganic thought of him,
but to act it rather ! A helplessness of utterance, in
such bursting fulness of meaning. He talks much about
' births of Providence :' All these changes, so many
victories and events, were not forethoughts, and
theatrical contrivances of men, of *me* or of men; it
is blind blasphemers that will persist in calling them so !
He insists with a heavy sulphurous wrathful emphasis
on this. As he well might. As if a Cromwell in that
dark huge game he had been playing, the world wholly
thrown into chaos round him, had *foreseen* it all, and
played it all off like a precontrived puppetshow by wood
and wire ! These things were foreseen by no man, he
says; no man could tell what a day would bring forth :
they were ' births of Providence,' God's finger guided
us on, and we came at last to clear height of victory,
God's Cause triumphant in these Nations; and you
as a Parliament could assemble together, and say in
what manner all this could be *organised*, reduced into
rational feasibility among the affairs of men. You were
to help with your wise counsel in doing that. " You
have had such an opportunity as no Parliament in
England ever had." Christ's Law, the Right and
True, was to be in some measure made the Law of this
land. In place of that, you have got into your idle
pedantries, constitutionalities, bottomless cavillings and
questionings about written laws for *my* coming here;—
and would send the whole matter into Chaos again,
because I have no Notary's parchment, but only God's
voice from the battle-whirlwind, for being President
among you ! That opportunity is gone; and we know
not when it will return. You have had your constitutional Logic; and Mammon's Law, not Christ's Law,
rules yet in this land. " God be judge between you
and me !" These are his final words to them : Take
you your constitution-formulas in your hand; and I

my *in*formal struggles, purposes, realities and acts; and " God be judge between you and me !"—

We said above what shapeless, involved chaotic things the printed Speeches of Cromwell are. *Wilfully* ambiguous, unintelligible, say the most : a hypocrite shrouding himself in confused Jesuitic jargon ! To me they do not seem so. I will say rather, they afforded the first glimpses I could ever get into the reality of this Cromwell, nay into the possibility of him. Try to believe that he means something, search lovingly what that may be : you will find a real *speech* lying imprisoned in these broken rude tortuous utterances ; a meaning in the great heart of this inarticulate man ! You will, for the first time, begin to see that he was a man ; not an enigmatic chimera, unintelligible to you, incredible to you. The Histories and Biographies written of this Cromwell, written in shallow sceptical generations that could not know or conceive of a deep believing man, are far more *obscure* than Cromwell's Speeches. You look through them only into the infinite vague of Black and the Inane. ' Heats and Jealousies,' says Lord Clarendon himself : ' heats and jealousies,' mere crabbed whims, theories and crochets ; these induced slow sober quiet Englishmen to lay down their ploughs and work ; and fly into red fury of confused war against the best-conditioned of Kings ! *Try* if you can find that true. Scepticism writing about Belief may have great gifts ; but it is really *ultra vires* there. It is Blindness laying-down the Laws of Optics.—

Cromwell's third Parliament split on the same rock as his second. Ever the constitutional Formula : How came *you* there? Show us some Notary parchment ! Blind pedants :—" Why, surely the same power which makes you a Parliament, that, and something more, made me a Protector !" If my Protectorship is nothing, what in the name of wonder is your Parliamenteership, a reflex and creation of that?—

Parliaments having failed, there remained nothing but the way of Despotism. Military Dictators, each with his district, to *coerce* the Royalists and other gainsayers, to govern them, if not by act of Parliament, then by the sword. Formula shall *not* carry it, while

the Reality is here! I will go on, protecting oppressed
Protestants abroad, appointing just judges, wise
managers, at home, cherishing true Gospel ministers;
doing the best I can to make England a Christian England, greater than old Rome, the Queen of Protestant
Christianity; I, since you will not help me; I while
God leaves me life!—Why did he not give it up; retire
into obscurity again, since the Law would not acknowledge him? cry several. That is where they mistake.
For him there was no giving of it up! Prime Ministers
have governed countries, Pitt, Pombal, Choiseul; and
their word was a law while it held: but this Prime
Minister was one that *could not get resigned*. Let him
once resign, Charles Stuart and the Cavaliers waited
to kill him; to kill the Cause *and* him. Once embarked,
there is no retreat, no return. This Prime Minister
could *retire* nowhither except into his tomb.

One is sorry for Cromwell in his old days. His
complaint is incessant of the heavy burden Providence
has laid on him. Heavy; which he must bear till
death. Old Colonel Hutchinson, as his wife relates it,
Hutchinson, his old battle-mate, coming to see him on
some indispensable business, much against his will,—
Cromwell 'follows him to the door,' in a most fraternal,
domestic, conciliatory style; begs that he would be
reconciled to him, his old brother in arms; says how
much it grieves him to be misunderstood, deserted by
true fellow-soldiers, dear to him from of old: the rigorous
Hutchinson, cased in his republican formula, sullenly
goes his way.—And the man's head now white; his
strong arm growing weary with its long work! I think
always too of his poor Mother, now very old, living in
that Palace of his; a right brave woman: as indeed
they lived all an honest God-fearing Household there:
if she heard a shot go off, she thought it was her son
killed. He had to come to her at least once a day,
that she might see with her own eyes that he was yet
living. The poor old Mother!——What had this man
gained; what had he gained? He had a life of sore
strife and toil, to his last day. Fame, ambition, place in
History? His dead body was hung in chains; his
'place in History,'—place in History forsooth!—has

been a place of ignominy, accusation, blackness and disgrace; and here, this day, who knows if it is not rash
in me to be among the first that ever ventured to pronounce him not a knave and a liar, but a genuinely
honest man! Peace to him. Did he not, in spite of
all, accomplish much for us? *We* walk smoothly over
his great rough heroic life; step-over his body sunk
in the ditch there. We need not *spurn* it, as we step
on it!—Let the Hero rest. It was not to *men's* judgment that he appealed; nor have men judged him very
well.

Precisely a century and a year after this of Puritanism had got itself hushed-up into decent composure,
and its results made smooth in 1688, there broke-out a
far deeper explosion, much more difficult to hush-up,
known to all mortals, and like to be long known, by
the name of French Revolution. It is properly the third
and final act of Protestantism; the explosive confused
return of Mankind to Reality and Fact, now that they
were perishing of Semblance and Sham. We call our
English Puritanism the second act: "Well then, the
Bible is true; let us go by the Bible!" "In Church,"
said Luther; "In Church and State," said Cromwell,
"let us go by what actually *is* God's Truth." Men
have to return to reality; they cannot live on semblance.
The French Revolution, or third act, we may well call
the final one; for lower than that savage *Sansculottism*
men cannot go. They stand there on the nakedest
haggard Fact, undeniable in all seasons and circumstances; and may and must begin again confidently to
build-up from that. The French explosion, like the
English one, got its King,—who had no Notary parchment to show for himself. We have still to glance for
a moment at Napoleon, our second modern King.

Napoleon does by no means seem to me so great a
man as Cromwell. His enormous victories which
reached over all Europe, while Cromwell abode mainly
in our little England, are but as the high *stilts* on which
the man is seen standing; the stature of the man is
not altered thereby. I find in him no such *sincerity* as
in Cromwell; only a far inferior sort. No silent walk-

ing, through long years, with the Awful Unnamable of this Universe; ' walking with God,' as he called it; and faith and strength in that alone : *latent* thought and valour, content to lie latent, then burst out as in blaze of Heaven's lightning ! Napoleon lived in an age when God was no longer believed; the meaning of all Silence, Latency, was thought to be Nonentity : he had to begin not out of the Puritan Bible, but out of poor Sceptical *Encyclopédies*. This was the length the man carried it. Meritorious to get so far. His compact, prompt, everyway articulate character is in itself perhaps small, compared with our great chaotic inarticulate Cromwell's. Instead of ' *dumb* Prophet struggling to speak,' we have a portentous mixture of the Quack withal! Hume's notion of the Fanatic-Hypocrite, with such truth as it has, will apply much better to Napoleon than it did to Cromwell, to Mahomet or the like,—where indeed taken strictly it has hardly any truth at all. An element of blamable ambition shows itself, from the first, in this man; gets the victory over him at last, and involves him and his work in ruin.

' False as a bulletin ' became a proverb in Napoleon's time. He makes what excuse he could for it : that it was necessary to mislead the enemy, to keep up his own men's courage, and so forth. On the whole, there are no excuses. A man in no case has liberty to tell lies. It had been, in the long-run, *better* for Napoleon too if he had not told any. In fact, if a man have any purpose reaching beyond the hour and day, meant to be found extant *next* day, what good can it ever be to promulgate lies? The lies are found-out; ruinous penalty is exacted for them. No man will believe the liar next time even when he speaks truth, when it is of the last importance that he be believed. The old cry of wolf!—A Lie is *no*-thing; you cannot of nothing make something; you make *nothing* at last, and lose your labour into the bargain.

Yet Napoleon *had* a sincerity; we are to distinguish between what is superficial and what is fundamental in insincerity. Across these outer manœuverings and quackeries of his, which were many and most blamable, let us discern withal that the man had a certain instinctive ineradicable feeling for reality; and did base himself upon fact, so long as he had any basis. He has an instinct of Nature better than his culture was. His *savans*, Bourrienne tells us, in that voyage to Egypt were one evening busily occupied arguing that there could be no God. They had proved it, to their satisfaction, by all manner of logic. Napoleon looking up into the stars, answers, " Very ingenious, Messieurs : but *who made* all that?" The Atheistic logic runs-off from him like water; the great Fact stares him in the face : " Who made all that?" So too in Practice : he, as every man that can be great, or have victory in this world, sees, through all entanglements, the practical heart of the matter; drives straight towards that. When the steward of his Tuileries Palace was exhibiting the new upholstery, with praises, and demonstration how glorious it was, and how cheap withal, Napoleon, making little answer, asked for a pair of scissors, clipt one of the gold tassels from a window-curtain, put it in his pocket, and walked on. Some days afterwards, he produced it at the right moment, to the horror of his upholstery functionary; it was not gold but tinsel ! In Saint Helena, it is notable how he still, to his last days, insists on the practical, the real. " Why talk and complain; above all, why quarrel with one another? There is no *result* in it; it comes to nothing that one can *do*. Say nothing, if one can do nothing !" He speaks often so, to his poor discontented followers ; he is like a piece of silent strength in the middle of their morbid querulousness there.

And accordingly was there not what we can call a *faith* in him, genuine so far as it went? That this new enormous Democracy asserting itself here in the French Revolution is an insuppressible Fact, which the whole world, with its old forces and institutions cannot put down; this was a true insight of his, and took his conscience and enthusiasm along with it,—a *faith*. And did he not interpret the dim purport of it well? ' *La carrière ouverte aux talens,* The implements to him who can handle them :' this actually is the truth, and even the whole truth; it includes whatever the French

Revolution, or any Revolution, could mean. Napoleon,
in his first period, was a true Democrat. And yet by
the nature of him, fostered too by his military trade, he
knew that Democracy, if it were a true thing at all,
could not be an anarchy : the man had a heart-hatred
for anarchy. On that Twentieth of June (1792), Bourrienne and he sat in a coffee-house, as the mob rolled
by : Napoleon expresses the deepest contempt for
persons in authority that they do not restrain this rabble.
On the Tenth of August he wonders why there is no
man to command these poor Swiss ; they would conquer
if there were. Such a faith in Democracy, yet hatred
of Anarchy, it is that carries Napoleon through all his
great work. Through his brilliant Italian Campaigns,
onwards to the Peace of Leoben, one would say, his
inspiration is : ' Triumph to the French Revolution ;
assertion of it against these Austrian Simulacra that
pretend to call it a Simulacrum !' Withal, however, he
feels, and has a right to feel, how necessary a strong
Authority is ; how the Revolution cannot prosper or
last without such. To bridle-in that great devouring,
self-devouring French Revolution ; to *tame* it, so that
its intrinsic purpose can be made good, that it may
become *organic*, and be able to live among other organ-
isms and *formed* things, not as a wasting destruction
alone : is not this still what he partly aimed at, as the
true purport of his life ; nay what he actually managed
to do ? Through Wagrams, Austerlitzes ; triumph after
triumph,—he triumphed so far. There was an eye to
see in this man, a soul to dare and do. He rose naturally
to be the King. All men saw that he *was* such. The
common soldiers used to say on the march : " These
babbling *Avocats*, up at Paris ; all talk and no work !
What wonder it runs all wrong ? We shall have to go
and put our *Petit Caporal* there !" They went, and
put him there ; they and France at large. Chief-con-
sulship, Emperorship, victory over Europe ;—till the
poor Lieutenant of *La Fère*, not unnaturally, might
seem to himself the greatest of all men that had been
in the world for some ages.

But at this point, I think, the fatal charlatan-element
got the upper hand. He apostatised from his old Faith

in Facts : took to believing in Semblances; strove to connect himself with Austrian Dynasties, Popedoms, with the old false Feudalities which he once saw clearly to be false;—considered that *he* would found "his Dynasty" and so forth; that the enormous French Revolution meant only that ! The man was 'given-up to strong delusion, that he should believe a lie;' a fearful but most sure thing. He did not know true from false now when he looked at them,—the fearfulest penalty a man pays for yielding to untruth of heart. *Self* and false ambition had now become his god : *self*-deception once yielded to, *all* other deceptions follow naturally more and more. What a paltry patch-work of theatrical paper-mantles, tinsel and mummery, had this man wrapt his own great reality in, thinking to make it more real thereby ! His hollow Pope's-*Concordat*, pretending to be a re-establishment of Catholicism, felt by himself to be the method of extirpating it, "*la vaccine de la religion:*" his ceremonial Coronations, consecrations by the old Italian Chimera in Notre-Dame, —"wanting nothing to complete the pomp of it," as Augereau said, "nothing but the half-million of men who had died to put an end to all that "! Cromwell's Inauguration was by the Sword and Bible; what we must call a genuinely *true* one. Sword and Bible were borne before him, without any chimera : were not these the *real* emblems of Puritanism; its true decoration and insignia? It had used them both in a very real manner, and pretended to stand by them now ! But this poor Napoleon mistook : he believed too much in the *Dupeability* of men; saw no fact deeper in men than Hunger and this ! He was mistaken. Like a man that should build upon cloud; his house and he fall down in confused wreck, and depart out of the world.

Alas, in all of us this charlatan-element exists; and *might* be developed, were the temptation strong enough. 'Lead us not into temptation '! But it is fatal, I say, that it *be* developed. The thing into which it enters as a cognisable ingredient is doomed to be altogether transitory; and, however huge it may *look*, is in itself small. Napoleon's working, accordingly, what was it with all the noise it made? A flash as of gunpowder wide-spread; a blazing-up as of dry heath. For an hour the whole Universe seems wrapt in smoke and flame; but only for an hour. It goes out: the Universe with its old mountains and streams, its stars above and kind soil beneath, is still there.

The Duke of Weimar told his friends always, To be of courage; this Napoleonism was *unjust*, a falsehood, and could not last. It is true doctrine. The heavier this Napoleon trampled on the world, holding it tyrannously down, the fiercer would the world's recoil against him be, one day. Injustice pays itself with frightful compound-interest. I am not sure but he had better have lost his best park of artillery, or had his best regiment drowned in the sea, than shot that poor German Bookseller, Palm! It was a palpable tyrannous murderous injustice, which no man, let him paint an inch thick, could make-out to be other. It burnt deep into the hearts of men, it and the like of it; suppressed fire flashed in the eyes of men, as they thought of it,— waiting their day! Which day *came:* Germany rose round him.—What Napoleon *did* will in the long-run amount to what he did *justly;* what Nature with her laws will sanction. To what of reality was in him; to that and nothing more. The rest was all smoke and waste. *La carrière ouverte aux talens:* that great true Message, which has yet to articulate and fulfil itself everywhere, he left in a most inarticulate state. He was a great *ébauche*, a rude-draught never completed; as indeed what great man is other? Left in *too* rude a state, alas!

His notions of the world, as he expresses them there at St. Helena, are almost tragical to consider. He seems to feel the most unaffected surprise that it has all gone so; that he is flung-out on the rock here, and the World is still moving on its axis. France is great, and all-great; and at bottom, he is France. England itself, he says, is by Nature only an appendage of France; "another Isle of Oleron to France." So it was *by Nature*, by Napoleon-Nature; and yet look how in fact,—HERE AM I! He cannot understand it: inconceivable that the reality has not corresponded to his program of it; that France was not all-great, that he was not France. 'Strong delusion,' that he should believe the thing to be which *is* not! The compact, clear-seeing, decisive Italian nature of him, strong, genuine, which he once had, has enveloped itself, half-dissolved itself, in a turbid atmosphere of French fanfaronade. The world was not disposed to be trodden-down underfoot; to be bound into masses, and built together, as *he* liked, for a pedestal to France and him: the world had quite other purposes in view! Napoleon's astonishment is extreme. But alas, what help now? He had gone that way of his; and Nature also had gone her way. Having once parted with Reality, he tumbles helpless in Vacuity; no rescue for him. He had to sink there, mournfully as man seldom did; and break his great heart, and die,—this poor Napoleon: a great implement too soon wasted, till it was useless: our last Great Man!

Our last, in a double sense. For here finally these wide roamings of ours through so many times and places, in search and study of Heroes, are to terminate. I am sorry for it: there was pleasure for me in this business, if also much pain. It is a great subject, and a most grave and wide one, this which, not to be too grave about it, I have named *Hero-worship*. It enters deeply, as I think, into the secret of Mankind's ways and vitalest interests in this world, and is well worth explaining at present. With six months, instead of six days, we might have done better. I promised to break-ground on it; I know not whether I have even managed to do that. I have had to tear it up in the rudest manner in order to get into it at all. Often enough, with these abrupt utterances thrown-out isolated, un-explained, has your tolerance been put to the trial. Tolerance, patient candour, all-hoping favour and kind-ness, which I will not speak of at present. The accom-plished and distinguished, the beautiful, the wise, some-thing of what is best in England, have listened patiently to my rude words. With many feelings, I heartily thank you all; and say, Good be with you all!

INDEX

THE END

EVERYMAN'S LIBRARY was founded in 1906, and for all the changes and chances in the book world during its long life the series stands strong to-day as the most comprehensive, inexpensive collection of books of classic measure. It is, indeed, still what its publisher intended it to be. J. M. Dent conceived it as a library arranged to cover the whole field of English literature, including translations of the ancient classics and outstanding foreign works; a series to make widely available those great books which appeal, as he says in his Memoirs, 'to every kind of reader: the worker, the student, the cultured man, the child, the man, and the woman.' The aim and scope of the series was crystallized in the title *Everyman's Library*, a title which has justified itself by the worldwide sales, totalling in 1958 some forty-five millions.

There were, of course, other popular series of reprints already in being in 1906, but none on the scale proposed for *Everyman*. One hundred and fifty-five volumes were published in three batches in the Library's first year; they comprised a balanced selection from many branches of literature and set the standard on which the Library has been built up. By early 1915 the 733rd volume had been issued; and, in spite of the interruptions of two world wars and their aftermath, the total had reached 980 by the end of the Second World War. The founder-publisher aimed at a library of a thousand volumes, and that goal was achieved at the jubilee of the Library in 1956.

A rough and ready pointer to the representative character of the Library is the number of volumes in each of the broad classifications into which the Library is divided—Biography has some 80 volumes; the Greek and Latin classics, about 40; Essays and Belles-lettres, 100; Fiction, 300; History, 80; Poetry and Drama, 100; Romance, 30; Science, 25; Religion and Philosophy, 60; Travel and Topography, 45. (The reference section is now being published separately as Everyman's Reference Library, and the Young People's Section is in the process of transference to our Children's Illustrated Classics Series.) Most of these volumes are in print now; some absent ones are works which changing taste has ruled out; but the classified sections of the Library are maintained in the original proportions, and to-day there are available in the Library the works of some five hundred authors of all times and all lands, the honoured names that stand for great literature. Moreover, many 'temporarily out of print' volumes are now being reinstated.

In March 1953 a fresh development of the Library began:

new volumes and all new issues of established volumes in *Everyman's Library* began to be produced in the larger size of crown octavo. The larger volumes have new title-pages, bindings, and wrappers, and the text pages have generous margins. Three hundred and forty volumes in this improved format have been issued in the first five years of its inauguration.

Editorially the Library is under constant survey; all volumes are re-examined and brought up to date, with new introductions, annotations, and additional matter wherever desirable; often a completely new translation or newly edited text is substituted when transferring an old volume to the new format, such as the new editions of *Pepys's Diary*, *Caesar's War Commentaries*, *The Anglo-Saxon Chronicle*, and the *Canterbury Tales*. New titles are still added: Manzoni's *Betrothed*, Aristotle's *Metaphysics*, Conrad's *Nostromo*, Jerome's *Three Men in a Boat* are all recent accessions.

The new larger volumes are in keeping with the reader's own collection in his home, for which the Library is planned, and they are also in the suitable size for the shelves of all public, institutional, university, and school libraries. Many important works in *Everyman's Library* are unobtainable in any other edition, while over 250 are *unobtainable in any other reprint series*, and they are as essential to the comprehensiveness of the Library as are the masterpieces of fiction, some of which are in one *Everyman* volume of anything up to 800 or 900 pages. The new *Everyman's Library* in crown octavo is published at four prices (except in the U.S.A.), according to the length and nature of the work. Volumes at the lowest price are in red wrapper, marked * in catalogues; the second price in blue wrapper †; the third price in green wrapper §; the highest price in yellow wrapper ‡.

This development entails no break in the continuity of the Library; there are at this writing some two hundred and eighty volumes in the original format, and they will be obtainable in the old size and at the old price until they are reissued in the new. At intervals the Publishers issue a prospectus of the volumes to be issued in the larger format during the next few months: this will be sent free to all applicants. A descriptive catalogue of all volumes is also freely available, the annotations giving the year of birth and death of the author, the date of first publication of the work, and a brief description, or details of the contents, of the last revised *Everyman's Library* edition.

J. M. DENT & SONS LTD.